PRENTICE HALL LITERATURE

PENGUIN EDITION

Teaching Resources

Unit 2
Short Stories

Grade Ten

PEARSON

Prentice Hall

Upper Saddle River, New Jersey
Boston, Massachusetts

D1229519

PEARSON

Prentice
Hall

ISBN 0-13-134205-3

1 2 3 4 5 6 7 8 9 10   09 08 07 06 05

Contents

iii

Part 2 Draw Conclusions

"The Garden of Stubborn Cats" by Italo Calvino

"Like the Sun" by R. K. Narayan

"The Censors" by Luisa Valenzuela

Vocabulary Warm-up Word Lists

Study these words from "The Threads of Time." Then apply your knowledge to the activities that follow.

Word List A

acquired [uh KWYRD] *v.* gained
  She lived in London for so long that she <u>acquired</u> a British accent.

alterations [awl tuh RAY shuhnz] *n.* changes
  After some small <u>alterations</u>, I was able to wear my mother's vintage dress.

arrival [uh RY vuhl] *n.* the act of coming to a place
  We are eagerly awaiting the <u>arrival</u> of spring.

evolved [ee VAHLVD] *v.* changed gradually over time
  Although they disliked each other at first, a friendship slowly <u>evolved</u>.

melancholy [MEL uhn kah lee] *adj.* gloomy; sad
  That song is so sad that it always makes me feel <u>melancholy</u>.

random [RAN duhm] *adj.* without careful choice; accidental
  I made a <u>random</u> choice, grabbing the first shirt I found in my closet.

transfer [TRANS fer] *v.* to send or move from one place to another
  We are going to help <u>transfer</u> books from the old library to the new one.

warp [WAWRP] *n.* bend; twist
  This board has a <u>warp</u> in it, so we can't use it in the bookshelf.

Word List B

beset [bee SET] *v.* attacked from all sides
  They were so <u>beset</u> by mosquitoes that they decided to eat indoors.

contradicting [kahn truh DIK ting] *v.* saying the opposite
  My annoying brother is always <u>contradicting</u> everything I say.

hazardous [HA zer dus] *adj.* risky; dangerous
  Riding in a car without a safety belt is <u>hazardous</u>.

overseeing [oh ver SEE ing] *v.* supervising; watching
  After his promotion, my uncle began <u>overseeing</u> the entire department.

perplexed [per PLEKST] *adj.* confused; uncertain
  The detective felt <u>perplexed</u> because she could not solve the mystery.

somber [SAHM ber] *adj.* serious; solemn
  His silly joke seemed out of place at the <u>somber</u> business meeting.

valid [VAL id] *adj.* justified; acceptable
  My new driver's license will be <u>valid</u> for eight years.

violate [VY uh layt] *v.* to break
  If you <u>violate</u> any of the pool rules, you will be asked to leave.

from "**The Threads of Time**" by C. J. Cherryh
Vocabulary Warm-up Exercises

Exercise A *Fill in each blank in the paragraph below with an appropriate word from Word List A. Use each word only once.*

Surfboards have [1] _____ quite a bit over the last fifty years. I

[2] _____ my first surf board when I was twelve. It was made of poor

quality wood. In just a few days, the board developed a big [3] _____.

The bump made it impossible to ride, but I refused to feel [4] _____

about it. Instead, I asked my father to help me make a few [5] _____.

We took careful measurements and reshaped the board. Everything we did was care-

fully planned—nothing was [6] _____. The remodeled board was great! I

rode it for many years. Finally, I bought a new fiberglass board from a catalog. I awaited

its [7] _____ every day. I decided to [8] _____ a decal

from my old board to my new one so I would always remember my first board.

Exercise B *Revise each sentence so that the underlined vocabulary word is used in a logical way. Be sure to keep the vocabulary word in your revision.*

Example: A fair player will always <u>violate</u> the rules of the game.
A fair player will never <u>violate</u> the rules of the game.

1. You are lucky if you are <u>beset</u> by problems.

   _____

2. A stand-up comic loves it when the mood of the audience is <u>somber</u>.

   _____

3. If the coupon is <u>valid</u>, the grocery store will refuse to accept it.

   _____

4. Nodding your head up and down is a nonverbal way of <u>contradicting</u> what someone
   is saying.

   _____

5. If someone is <u>overseeing</u> a project, he or she follows orders from the project boss.

   _____

6. Reading a book and talking on the phone are two very <u>hazardous</u> activities.

   _____

7. If the plot of a movie is easy to follow, the audience will probably be <u>perplexed</u>.

   _____

from **"The Threads of Time"** by C. J. Cherryh
Reading Warm-up A

Read the following passage. Pay special attention to the underlined words. Then, read it again, and complete the activities. Use a separate sheet of paper for your written answers.

In our world, time moves in one direction: forward. Many writers, however, have wondered what might happen if we could <u>transfer</u> ourselves forward or backward in time. Many early stories of time travel describe people who travel back in time by accident. Mark Twain's *A Connecticut Yankee in King Arthur's Court* is one example. In this novel, a modern man adjusts after his surprising <u>arrival</u> in medieval times.

Most critics agree, however, that the genre of time-travel fiction truly began with *The Time Machine*. In this 1896 novel by H. G. Wells, a character called the Time Traveller uses a machine to travel into the future. One important reason that this novel is considered a landmark in this field is that the Time Traveller carefully selects the time to which he travels. In most earlier tales, characters travel to a <u>random</u> time. They do not control the situation.

The genre of time-travel fiction has <u>evolved</u> a great deal since 1896. Authors like Robert Heinlein have written stories about how time travel could create impossible situations. A character might meet himself. <u>Alterations</u> in the past could lead to enormous changes in the future. What would happen if a man accidentally killed his grandmother when she was a young girl? How could the man ever be born and exist?

Some time-travel fiction describes shifts in time called a time <u>warp</u>, in which the flow of time bends or changes shape. A character entering a time warp might be brought into the future or the past.

For some writers, time travel suggests dangerous possibilities. Characters who travel in time might become disconnected from their own lives. Unable to return to their families, they might develop strong feelings of <u>melancholy</u> and sadness.

Regardless of the point of view, it is clear that many readers have <u>acquired</u> a taste for reading about characters who break out of the here and now. Time still marches on, and so will time-travel fiction.

1. Underline the words that tell where we might <u>transfer</u> ourselves. Then, describe what it might be like to *transfer* to a new school.

2. Circle the words that tell the modern man's place of <u>arrival</u>. Then, describe an *arrival* of one of your relatives or friends.

3. Circle the words that mean the opposite of <u>random</u>. Then, describe a *random* choice you might make.

4. Underline the words that tell what has <u>evolved</u>. Then, tell what *evolved* means.

5. Circle a word that is a synonym for <u>alterations</u>. Then, describe some *alterations* you would like to make at home or at school.

6. Underline the words that describe a <u>warp</u>. Explain how you can tell if a shelf has a *warp* in it.

7. Circle a word that is close in meaning to <u>melancholy</u>. Then, describe a place that might make people feel *melancholy*.

8. Underline the words that describe something people have <u>acquired</u>. Then, tell about something you have *acquired* this year.

from "The Threads of Time" by C. J. Cherryh
Reading Warm-up B

Read the following passage. Pay special attention to the underlined words. Then, read it again, and complete the activities. Use a separate sheet of paper for your written answers.

Do we live in the only possible universe? Some science-fiction writers suggest that there could be many other worlds that exist at the same time as ours. These other worlds are often called *parallel* or *alternate universes*.

Some writers create alternate universes that are comically upside-down. Rules that are <u>valid</u> in our world are nonsense in these strange worlds. A famous example is found in Lewis Carroll's *Alice's Adventures in Wonderland*. After falling down a rabbit hole, Alice is <u>beset</u> by weird characters and events. Characters in Wonderland are constantly <u>contradicting</u> the logic of our world. At a trial, the Queen of Hearts demands that the jury announce the sentence before the verdict.

Many other science-fiction writers create alternate universes that are much less humorous and more <u>somber</u> in tone. In the trilogy *His Dark Materials*, Philip Pullman describes how characters learn to move in and out of a number of parallel worlds, including our own. Characters are naturally <u>perplexed</u> when they enter a new world because they know nothing about the history or culture there.

Some writers use the word *multiverse* to describe all of the universes that exist. There may or may not be an intelligent life form <u>overseeing</u> what happens in every universe, watching and perhaps guiding events and actions. Often, writers suggest that interaction between universes can have <u>hazardous</u> results, leading to severe problems. In *The Gods Themselves*, Isaac Asimov imagines that scientists discover another universe. The results of this contact with another universe are unpredictable and nearly disastrous.

Another kind of alternate universe is a fictional past. For example, a writer might invent a medieval world in which electricity was discovered. Although events like this <u>violate</u> the truth as we know it, some people think they could be true in an alternate universe.

1. Circle a word that has a meaning opposite to <u>valid</u>. Then, describe one way you can decide if a statement is *valid*.

2. Underline the words that tell what Alice is <u>beset</u> by. Then, tell what *beset* means.

3. Underline the words that tell what the characters are <u>contradicting</u>. Then, describe a time when you were *contradicting* someone else.

4. Circle a word that has an opposite meaning to <u>somber</u>. Then, describe somewhere you have been where the mood was *somber*.

5. Underline the words that tell why characters are <u>perplexed</u>. Then, tell about a time when you felt *perplexed*.

6. Underline the words that tell what a life form might be <u>overseeing</u>. Then, tell what *overseeing* means.

7. Circle the words that tell why the results are <u>hazardous</u>. Then, describe one activity that is *hazardous*.

8. Underline the words that tell what imaginary events <u>violate</u>. Then, tell what *violate* means.

C. J. Cherryh
Listening and Viewing

Segment 1: Meet C. J. Cherryh
- In addition to writing, C. J. Cherryh keeps busy with many other activities. What hobbies and interests does C. J. Cherryh explore? How do you think her willingness to explore new activities affects her writing?

_____

_____

_____

_____

Segment 2: The Short Story
- According to C. J. Cherryh, what is the difference between fantasy and science-fiction stories? Why do you think a short story is an effective way of writing science-fiction and fantasy stories?

_____

_____

_____

_____

Segment 3: The Writing Process
- What does C. J. Cherryh mean by her motto "write garbage but edit brilliantly"? Do you agree with her that revising is the most "magical" step in the writing process? Explain why you agree or disagree.

_____

_____

_____

_____

Segment 4: The Rewards of Writing
- Why do you think students should read science-fiction stories? Why is it important for writers to write for readers of the future as well as for readers of today?

_____

_____

_____

_____

Learning About Short Stories

A **short story** is a brief work of fiction. The following chart shows the key elements of a short story.

Element	Definition
Plot	The events that make up the action: introduction, rising action, climax, and falling action.
Conflict	External conflict: a struggle between two characters, a character and a group, or a character and a force Internal conflict: a struggle within the mind of a character
Character	An individual who participates in the action Direct characterization: developed through statements about a character's personality, habits, goals, values, or beliefs Indirect characterization: developed through a character's words, thoughts, actions, and interaction
Setting	The time and place of the action
Theme	The central message or insight about life in a story Stated theme: expressed directly by the author Implied theme: suggested indirectly through characters' experiences or events and setting

DIRECTIONS: *Read each item. Write which of the following it describes—internal conflict, external conflict, direct characterization, indirect characterization, setting, stated theme, or implied theme.*

1. Julian was painfully shy. _____
2. "I refuse to babysit Taisha tonight!" Frida told her mother. _____
3. The house was cold and gloomy in the winter wind. _____
4. Be careful what you wish for; you just might get it. _____
5. People looked through Bobby as if he did not exist. _____
6. Mindy worried about whether to invite Luisa. _____
7. It had been a hundred years since the last war. _____
8. "Carmen can dish it out, but she sure cannot take it," Sammy said. _____
9. "The wind is too strong!" I shouted. "I cannot control the boat!" _____
10. At last, summer had come. We had two whole months of freedom. _____

Name _____   Date _____

from "The Threads of Time" by C. J. Cherryh
Model Selection: Short Story

A **short story** is a brief work of fiction. It includes a series of events called the **plot.** The plot centers on conflict. An **external conflict** is a conflict between characters, between an individual and a group, or between a character and a force. An **internal conflict** occurs within a character's mind. The conflict develops to a **climax** and is then sorted out in a **resolution.**

The **characters** in a short story are the individuals who participate in the plot. Writers reveal **character development** through **direct characterization,** or statements about the characters, and **indirection characterization,** a character's words, thoughts, and actions. The story's **setting** is the time and place in which it occurs. Its **theme** is the central message or insight about life it provides. The theme can be **stated** or **implied.**

A. DIRECTIONS: *"The Threads of Time" is a short story. Use the following chart to list details of its conflicts, climax, resolution, characters, and setting.*

Element	Details
Conflict	
Climax	
Resolution	
Character	
Setting	

B. DIRECTIONS: *Most short stories contain a **theme,** a message about life. A theme can be **stated,** or expressed directly by the author. It can also be **implied,** or suggested indirectly by events, setting, or experiences of the characters. What is the theme of "The Threads of Time"? Is it stated or implied? Support your answer with details from the story.*

_____

_____

_____

_____

_____

_____

_____

_____

from "The Threads of Time" by C.J. Cherryh
Selection Test A

Critical Thinking *Identify the letter of the choice that best answers the question.*

____ 1. Which is the BEST definition of a short story?
   A. a work that has a plot
   B. writing with settings and characters
   C. a brief work of fiction
   D. writing that tells a true story

____ 2. What is the climax of a plot?
   A. when the events are resolved
   B. the high point of the action
   C. when the characters are introduced
   D. the most suspenseful events

____ 3. Which of the following is an example of direct characterization?
   A. a character's interaction with another character
   B. a statement about a character's family
   C. a character's conversation with another character
   D. a statement about a character's personality

____ 4. Which of the following defines the theme of a short story?
   A. a generalization about the meaning of events
   B. a summary of what happens in a story
   C. a description of the setting and characters
   D. a restatement of the story's climax

____ 5. Which of the following is an example of a setting?
   A. a fifteen-year-old girl and her brother
   B. a fight between two close friends
   C. the North Carolina shore in 1951
   D. a raging, uncontrolled fire in a pet store

Critical Reading

____ 6. Who is the main character of "The Threads of Time"?
   A. Gates
   B. Harrh
   C. Mhreihrrinn
   D. Alhir

_____ 7. What does Harrh decide he wants to do in "The Threads of Time"?
    A. go back to the First Gate
    B. stop time-traveling
    C. find the End of Time
    D. change the past

_____ 8. Why do the qhal in "The Threads of Time" not go beyond the End of Time?
    A. They are afraid to move on.
    B. They are physically unable.
    C. They are forbidden to move on.
    D. They are paid not to go farther.

_____ 9. What is Harrh's job in "The Threads of Time"?
    A. He is a time-mender.
    B. He is a Gate-builder.
    C. He is an intelligence-collector.
    D. He is a time-tamperer.

_____ 10. What is the setting of "The Threads of Time"?
    A. in the United States in the future
    B. in Europe in the distant past
    C. on a space ship far in the future
    D. on another planet in another time

_____ 11. What happens to the qhal in "The Threads of Time" who backtime too close to their own time period?
    A. They get caught in time-loops.
    B. They die a painful death.
    C. They disappear from sight.
    D. They live their lives backward.

_____ 12. How does the Now affect Harrh in "The Threads of Time"?
    A. It disgusts him.
    B. It annoys him.
    C. It terrifies him.
    D. It thrills him.

_____ 13. Why does Alhir visit Harrh in "The Threads of Time"?

    A. to warn him that someone wants to kill him

    B. to escape from a number of enemies

    C. to warn him about a time-travel accident

    D. to try to change what happened in the past

_____ 14. What happens in the climax of "The Threads of Time"?

    A. Alhir says that the potsherd has disappeared.

    B. Harrh dies a difficult and painful death.

    C. Harrh and Alhir argue terribly.

    D. Harrh stops traveling through time.

_____ 15. Why does Harrh's memory start to change?

    A. He has grown old.

    B. Alhir has harmed him.

    C. He is unwell.

    D. The past has changed.

Essay

16. The author of "The Threads of Time" chose to make her characters a race called *qhal*. Why do you think she did not make them human? What characteristics do they share with humans? Support your answer with at least two details from the story.

17. What message, or theme, is the author implying about science in "The Threads of Time"? Write a brief analysis of the theme. Support your analysis with at least two details from the story.

Name _____ Date _____

from "The Threads of Time" by C.J. Cherryh
Selection Test B

Critical Thinking *Identify the letter of the choice that best completes the statement or answers the question.*

____ 1. Which is the BEST definition of a short story's plot?
   A. a progression of fictional events
   B. a series of true events
   C. a group of events with a climax
   D. a climax and a resolution

____ 2. Which is NOT an example of external conflict?
   A. a struggle between two characters
   B. a struggle between an individual and a group
   C. a struggle between a character and a force
   D. a struggle within a character's mind

____ 3. Which statement is always true about a short story?
   A. It is read in one sitting.
   B. It has only one character.
   C. It is a work of fiction.
   D. It is set in the present.

____ 4. Which of the following is NOT an example of indirect characterization?
   A. a character's words
   B. a characer's actions
   C. a character's interaction with other characters
   D. an author's statement about a character

____ 5. Which of the following is an example of a theme?
   A. A fireworks factory explodes during the day.
   B. A boy realizes that family matters more than anything.
   C. Two best friends try out for the same part in a play.
   D. An old and abandoned house stands in an empty field.

____ 6. Which of these statements includes details about setting?
   A. A new student in school wants desperately to make friends.
   B. You can get satisfaction from trying, even if you do not succeed.
   C. The Great Depression had put half of the town out of work.
   D. Nobody has seen the twins since they came over for lunch.

Critical Reading

____ 7. How might the Gates be "killing the qhal" in "The Threads of Time"?
   A. They destroy any qhal who time-travels.
   B. They are allowing the qhal to destroy time.
   C. They physically weaken the qhal by their existence.
   D. They allow diseases from the past to survive.

_____ 8. Which of the following is a theme of "The Threads of Time"?
  A. There is no place like home and appreciating one's family.
  B. Those who do not learn from history are condemned to repeat it.
  C. A lack of understanding of science can cause destruction.
  D. Love can overcome all barriers—even the hurdles of time.

_____ 9. At the end of "The Threads of Time," what are Harrh's dreams?
  A. other people's fantasies and dreams
  B. memories of nonexistent events
  C. events that will happen in the future
  D. warnings from the long-gone past

_____ 10. Where is the main conflict in "The Threads of Time"?
  A. between Harrh and Alhir
  B. between Harrh and his wife
  C. between Harrh and time
  D. between time-menders and the Gates

_____ 11. Why does Harrh's memory fade in "The Threads of Time"?
  A. because he has grown old and weary, and he is unwell
  B. because he has time-traveled too often for too many years
  C. because the events that formed his memories did not happen
  D. because he has been given a drug to destroy his memory

_____ 12. In "The Threads of Time," why does Alhir leave Harrh's house?
  A. He is very sick.
  B. He no longer exists.
  C. He is afraid of Harrh.
  D. Harrh tells him to go.

_____ 13. In "The Threads of Time," what is implied by the disappearance of the potsherd?
  A. The world is ending.
  B. Morurir has been destroyed.
  C. Harrh is in danger.
  D. Time has warped.

_____ 14. When does Harrh feel fear in "The Threads of Time"?
  A. when he forgets the potsherd
  B. when his wife dies
  C. when his children disappear
  D. when a man in the Council dies

_____ 15. What does Harrh's decision to stop working reveal about his character in "The Threads of Time"?
  A. He is lazy and unwilling to work.
  B. He feels guilty about what he does.
  C. He loves his home and family.
  D. He is angry at his co-workers.

_____ 16. In "The Threads of Time," what is beginning to happen in Harrh's time as he sits at breakfast?
   A. He is getting ill.
   B. Time is falling apart.
   C. His family is dying.
   D. A war is starting.

_____ 17. When is Now in "The Threads of Time"?
   A. at the End of Time
   B. 390 years after the First Gate
   C. 1,003 years after the First Gate
   D. 5,045 years after the First Gate

_____ 18. What do time-menders in "The Threads of Time" do?
   A. They severely punish backtimers.
   B. They regulate the flow of time.
   C. They make needed changes to reality.
   D. They make rules about time travel.

_____ 19. What does the End of Time teach Harrh in "The Threads of Time"?
   A. that he will live forever
   B. that he is a mortal being
   C. that the world will end soon
   D. that the universe is infinite

_____ 20. What happens at the End of Time in "The Threads of Time"?
   A. The qhal gather, too fearful to move on.
   B. The qhal all die and disappear from sight.
   C. The qhal go back to a time before their births.
   D. The Gates all disappear, leaving the qhal to stay.

Essay

21. The qhal have a sense of both longing and fear about going beyond the End of Time in "The Threads of Time." Why do you think they feel this way? Explain your answer using at least two details from the story.

22. As the plot of "The Threads of Time" progresses, Agent Harrh loses his memory of his wife, his home, and finally himself. Why do you think this experience of forgetfulness happens? Refer to at least two events in the story to support your answer.

23. The author of "The Threads of Time" refers to the "paradox" of backtiming. What is this paradox, and how does it work? Use at least two details from the story in your explanation.

Unit 2: Short Stories
Part 1 Concept Map

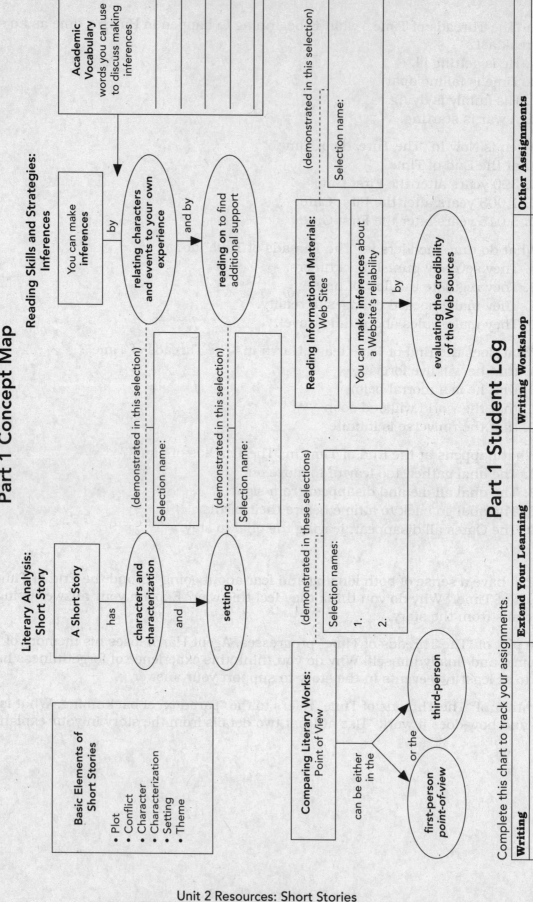

Academic Vocabulary words you can use to discuss making inferences

_____
_____
_____

Reading Skills and Strategies: Inferences

You can make inferences → by → relating characters and events to your own experience → and by → reading on to find additional support

(demonstrated in this selection)
Selection name:

(demonstrated in this selection)
Selection name:

Reading Informational Materials: Web Sites

You can make inferences about a Website's reliability → by → evaluating the credibility of the Web sources

(demonstrated in this selection)
Selection name:

Literary Analysis: Short Story

A Short Story → has → characters and characterization → and → setting

Basic Elements of Short Stories
- Plot
- Conflict
- Character
- Characterization
- Setting
- Theme

Comparing Literary Works: Point of View

can be either in the → third-person
or the → first-person point-of-view

(demonstrated in these selections)
Selection names:
1.
2.

Part 1 Student Log

Complete this chart to track your assignments.

Writing	Extend Your Learning	Writing Workshop	Other Assignments

Unit 2: Short Stories
Part 1 Diagnostic Test 3

MULTIPLE CHOICE

Read the selections. Then answer the questions that follow.

For his descriptions of hell in *The Inferno,* Dante depended greatly on ancient Greek mythology. For the ancient Greeks, all the dead—both good and evil—went to a rather vaguely imagined, shadowy land called simply "the underworld." The spirits of the dead, or "shades" as the Greeks called them, were ruled by Hades, the brother of Zeus, king of the gods.

In Greek myth, there are nine rivers in the underworld, the most famous of which are Acheron, Lethe, and Styx. In *The Inferno,* Dante and his guide Virgil are borne across the Acheron by the grim ferryman Charon, whose mother was Nyx, goddess of night. The Greeks believed that if Charon were not paid for his services, he would refuse to row, so they placed a coin in the mouth of everyone who died. The money allowed that soul to enter the underworld.

Lethe was the underworld river of forgetfulness, or oblivion. The Greeks believed that all who drank from this river would lose memory of their past existence. The river Styx was important because the gods swore a sacred oath near its edge. If any betrayed such an oath, that god would suffer exile from divine society for nine years.

1. According to Greek mythology, what is the underworld?
   - A. a place people go when they die
   - B. a land of shadows
   - C. the world of spirits
   - D. the inferno

2. Who rules the shades?
   - A. king of the gods
   - B. Zeus
   - C. Charon
   - D. Hades

3. Which of the following best describes Acheron, Lethe, and Styx?
   - A. gods of the underworld
   - B. rivers of the underworld
   - C. characters from Greek mythology
   - D. guides for the spirits of the dead

4. In Greek mythology, who was Charon?
   - A. the god who ruled the spirits of the dead in the underworld
   - B. the god who guarded the entrance to the underworld
   - C. the ferryman who was also the god of the night
   - D. the ferryman who rowed people across the river to the underworld

5. Which of the following best describes how Charon was paid for his services?
   - A. The shades gave Charon gold coins to ferry them across the river.
   - B. People placed a coin in the mouth of those who died.
   - C. The living buried gold coins along with the body of the deceased.
   - D. The shades promised to perform a service in return for Charon's service.

6. What would happen if Charon were not paid for his services?
   - A. He would refuse to ferry souls to the underworld.
   - B. He would plunge the souls into the inferno.
   - C. He would leave the souls on the banks of a river.
   - D. He would send the souls into the land of the shadows.

7. How did the shades who passed into the underworld lose the memory of their past life?
   - A. The goddess Nyx put them to sleep.
   - B. They were ferried across the river.
   - C. They drank from the river Lethe.
   - D. Charon wiped their memories away.

8. What happened to gods who betrayed their most sacred oath?
   - A. Their immortality was taken away.
   - B. They were sent to the underworld.
   - C. They were punished in the inferno.
   - D. They were exiled for nine years.

Read the selections. Then answer the questions that follow.

The American Bald Eagle, the Liberty Bell, and the Stars and Stripes are popular symbols of the United States. Each symbol reflects beliefs and values associated with the United States.

The majestic American Bald Eagle is often depicted with arrows in one claw and an olive branch in the other, symbolizing power and independence in war and peace. In 1789, the American Bald Eagle was declared the U.S. national bird, giving it special protection. Its population began to dwindle, however, due to the use of pesticides. Fortunately, environmentalists encouraged passage of regulations eliminating the pesticides that caused the damage, and as a result, the eagle is no longer an endangered species.

The Liberty Bell was cast in England in 1752 for the Philadelphia State House. The bell cracked after it arrived, but it was repaired and rung at the signing of the Declaration of Independence in 1776. Because the bell is linked to that moment in history, it symbolizes freedom's triumph.

The Stars and Stripes are the most recognizable symbol of the United States. Flying the flag shows pride in the United States. Because so many died defending it, reverence is expected when handling the flag, and a code of conduct applies to all flag ceremonies.

9. What is the purpose of the symbols that represent the United States?
   - A. to help people understand history
   - B. to reflect beliefs and values
   - C. to illustrate patriotism
   - D. for individuals and groups to display

10. Why is the American Bald Eagle an important symbol?
   - A. It is a majestic bird.
   - B. It is the national bird.
   - C. It symbolizes war and peace.
   - D. It was once endangered.

11. Which of the following best explains the symbolism of the arrows and olive branch often depicted in the eagle's claws?
   - A. the importance of liberty
   - B. strength and honor
   - C. war and peace
   - D. pride and strength

12. Why was the Liberty Bell originally cast?

A. to be installed in the Philadelphia State House

B. to celebrate the Declaration of Independence

C. to symbolize the victory of freedom over tyranny

D. to be a symbol of the history of the United States

13. Which of the following best explains why the Liberty Bell symbolizes freedom?

A. It was cast in England for the Philadelphia State House.

B. It was cast especially for the signing of the Declaration of Independence.

C. Even though it was cracked, it was still able to ring.

D. It was rung at the signing of the Declaration of Independence.

14. Why is the Stars and Stripes the most recognizable symbol of the United States?

A. It is seen and displayed in many places.

B. It shows pride in the United States.

C. There is a code of conduct surrounding it.

D. It is treated with reverence.

15. Which is the best reason for treating the flag with reverence?

A. It is a symbol of the United States.

B. It has a code of conduct surrounding it.

C. Many people have died defending it.

D. It is the object of many ceremonies.

Vocabulary Warm-up Word Lists

Study these words from "A Visit to Grandmother." Then, complete the activities.

Word List A

absence [AB suhns] *n.* state of being away or not present
   Did you notice the <u>absence</u> of green in that painting?

additional [uh DISH uh nuhl] *adj.* extra; other; further
   I would like an <u>additional</u> slice of pizza, please.

discussion [dis KUSH uhn] *n.* talk among people about a subject
   The class had a <u>discussion</u> about endangered species.

engaging [en GAYJ ing] *adj.* charming in a way that holds the attention
   His speech was so <u>engaging</u> we could not stop listening.

swapped [SWAPT] *v.* traded; exchanged
   My sister <u>swapped</u> her comic book for a necklace.

injured [IN juhrd] *v.* hurt; harmed
   The swimmer's foot was <u>injured</u> when he kicked the pool wall.

reunion [ree YOON yuhn] *n.* a coming together of people who have been separated
   The long-lost cousins had a tearful <u>reunion</u>.

ventured [VEN cherd] *v.* took a risk
   The research team <u>ventured</u> deep into the dark cave system.

Word List B

diplomas [di PLOH muhz] *n.* documents given to show graduation or certification
   We all received our high school <u>diplomas</u> at the graduation.

exception [ek SEP shuhn] *n.* a case to which a rule does not apply
   The penguin is an <u>exception</u> to the rule that birds can fly.

meager [MEE guhr] *adj.* lacking in quality or quantity
   We had almost no food at home, so I ate only a <u>meager</u> snack.

particularly [pahr TI kyuh luhr lee] *adj.* unusually; especially
   Dinner was <u>particularly</u> tasty last night.

potentially [poh TEN shuh lee] *adv.* possibly; able to happen
   Football is <u>potentially</u> very exciting, though it is sometimes dull.

suspicion [suh SPISH uhn] *n.* act of thinking something is wrong without proof; doubt; mistrust
   Paul could not prove his <u>suspicion</u> that Leo took the poster.

timidly [TIM id lee] *adv.* shyly; easily frightened
   The shy dancer moved very <u>timidly</u> to the music.

uncertainty [uhn SER tuhn tee] *n.* state of being not sure of something; doubt
   The speaker showed her <u>uncertainty</u> by shuffling her feet.

"A Visit to Grandmother" by William Melvin Kelley
Vocabulary Warm-up Exercises

Exercise A *Fill in each blank in the paragraph below with an appropriate word from Word List A. Use each word only once.*

Simon's fascinating ideas made him a truly [1] _____ hiking partner. He could start a fascinating [2] _____ about almost any topic. At the end of a long hike, we decided to hike around one [3] _____ hill. I was walking ahead, but then we [4] _____ places and Simon took the lead. We had already [5] _____ more than five miles on a rough, rocky trail. Suddenly, Simon slipped and [6] _____ his ankle badly. I had to go back for help. I felt his [7] _____ strongly and missed his friendly chatter. It took me about three hours to come back with a doctor, but at our [8] _____, we both felt as if we had been apart for days.

Exercise B *Revise each sentence so that the underlined vocabulary word is used in a logical way. Be sure to keep the vocabulary word in your revision.*

Example: We received our <u>diplomas</u> from a hardware store.
We received our <u>diplomas</u> from a community college.

1. The case is still unsolved because the detective's <u>suspicion</u> turned out to be true.

   _____

2. You could see Mai's <u>uncertainty</u> because she walked firmly to the door.

   _____

3. A <u>particularly</u> interesting story is one that is probably very predictable.

   _____

4. Our picnic was rather <u>meager</u> so we were all stuffed and lazy afterward.

   _____

5. She had acted in many plays, so she performed <u>timidly</u> onstage.

   _____

6. Someone who is an <u>exception</u> will always blend in with the crowd.

   _____

7. Rainbows are a <u>potentially</u> useful source of energy for electricity.

   _____

"A Visit to Grandmother" by William Melvin Kelley
Reading Warm-up A

Read the following passage. Pay special attention to the underlined words. Then, read it again, and complete the activities. Use a separate sheet of paper for your written answers.

What could be more fun than a family <u>reunion</u>—a big, friendly gathering of relatives? While many reunions are indeed happy occasions, others become sour opportunities to reheat old arguments and start new ones. Some careful planning can help prevent this kind of disaster.

First, you need to decide what kind of reunion you want to have. Will your event include just a meal, or will there be <u>additional</u> activities, such as a talent show, games, or crafts for the kids? Where and when will you meet? Organize a planning committee to help. Make a list of questions and issues prior to the committee's first meeting. An organized list will help keep the group's <u>discussion</u> on track and keep the conversation focused.

If the invitation list leaves someone out, feelings can be <u>injured</u>. Make a clear decision about which branches of the family you will invite. Try to invite everyone in those branches. Don't leave out people because you think they won't want to come—let them decide for themselves.

At the reunion itself, ask several family members to act as a welcoming committee. Remember that many of the participants may have <u>ventured</u> long, tiring distances to come to the event. If possible, make the schedule flexible to allow everyone time to relax after traveling.

Few family reunions are complete. There are always some relatives who cannot attend. Their <u>absence</u> does not have to prevent their participation. Ask those who cannot attend to send letters to be read aloud or videos to be played for the group. You might also arrange for a surprise telephone call from an absent loved one.

An effective way to make your reunion <u>engaging</u> is to make time for storytelling. Many family members, especially older relatives, can tell fascinating and often amusing stories about your family's history. You might also suggest that guests bring photographs to share and trade. After everyone has <u>swapped</u> stories and exchanged photographs, you will all know a lot more about your family's rich past.

1. Underline the words that describe a <u>reunion</u>. Then, tell who might come to a family *reunion*.

2. Circle the words that describe three <u>additional</u> activities. Then, tell what *additional* means.

3. Circle a synonym for <u>discussion</u>. Describe a *discussion* you could have with your family.

4. Underline the words that tell why feelings might be <u>injured</u>. Then, write what *injured* means.

5. Circle the word that tells who <u>ventured</u> long distances to come to the event. Write a sentence about a time in which you *ventured* a great distance.

6. Underline the words that give the reasons for <u>absence</u>. Then, tell what *absence* means.

7. Underline the words that tell how to make a reunion <u>engaging</u>. Describe an event that you would find *engaging*.

8. Circle the synonym for <u>swapped</u>. Then, tell something that could be *swapped* by children.

"A Visit to Grandmother" by William Melvin Kelley
Reading Warm-up B

Read the following passage. Pay special attention to the underlined words. Then, read it again, and complete the activities. Use a separate sheet of paper for your written answers.

Slaves in the United States were not allowed to read or be educated. Slave owners enforced these rules due to their suspicion that learning would lead to disobedience and rebellion. When slavery was abolished, many freed slaves eagerly sought the education that had been denied them.

At first, the number of educational opportunities was meager. Few existing schools would accept former slaves as students. This was a period of great uncertainty. No one could predict the effects of this enormous change to society's structure. In just a few years, however, new schools were founded to educate African Americans. Schools like Fisk University would make a particularly important change in the history of education in the United States.

Three men founded Fisk School in 1866 in Nashville, Tennessee. . . . but, all the students worked hard and stayed focused on their potentially better future. Just one year later, the school was incorporated as Fisk University. It was dedicated to "the highest standards, not of Negro education, but of American education at its best."

With an increasing student enrollment, Fisk University needed new facilities. Instead of timidly asking for contributions, the university boldly launched a new method of raising funds. A student choir called the Jubilee Singers began touring the United States in 1971. They raised more than $50,000 for campus construction.

Fisk University continued to expand, awarding diplomas to graduating students, many of whom went on to become teachers or professors themselves. Indeed, many graduates of Fisk University have dedicated their lives to enriching the educational and civil possibilities for all citizens of the United States. W.E.B. DuBois graduated from the university in 1888 and went on to become a prominent leader and scholar. He taught at Atlanta University and helped to found the National Association for the Advancement of Colored People (NAACP). Far from being an exception, DuBois is a standard of the dedicated, passionate Fisk University graduate.

1. Underline the words that describe the suspicion of the slave owners. Then, tell what *suspicion* means.

2. Underline the sentence that tells why educational opportunities were meager. Then, tell what *meager* means.

3. Underline the words that describe why it was a period of uncertainty. Then, describe another period of *uncertainty*.

4. Describe another *particularly* important time in U.S. history.

5. Circle the words that describe what was potentially possible for the entry class. Then, tell what *potentially* means.

6. Circle the antonym for timidly. Then, tell what *timidly* means.

7. Circle the words that tell who received diplomas. Write about another school that awards *diplomas*.

8. Circle the word that is an antonym for exception. Then describe someone who is an *exception* in your school or community.

"A Visit to Grandmother" by William Melvin Kelley
Literary Analysis: Characterization

Characters are the people, animals, or objects who perform the actions and experience the events of a story. An author reveals the personalities of characters in a story by using **direct** or **indirect characterization.** With direct characterization, an author makes direct statements about a character. With indirect characterization, the author reveals a character's traits through his or her **dialogue,** actions, thoughts, and appearance and through what other people in the story think of the character.

Think about the information you learn about characters and how you learn it. Think also about **character development**—changes the character undergoes through the course of the story or new information that the author reveals about the character.

A. DIRECTIONS: *Complete this chart with examples from the story of direct and indirect characterization of each character listed. If there is no example of either direct or indirect characterization, explain why you think the author chose not to use that form of characterization.*

Character	Examples of Direct Characterization	Examples of Indirect Characterization
Example: GL	GL is said to be part con man, part practical joker, and part Don Juan.	He is wearing brown and white two-tone shoes with very pointed toes and a white summer suit. His smile is innocent and open, like a five-year-old's.
1. Charles		
2. Chig		
3. Mama		

B. DIRECTIONS: *In a brief essay, indicate whether direct or indirect characterization makes you feel you know a character better. Explain your answer.*

_____

_____

_____

_____

"A Visit to Grandmother" by William Melvin Kelley

Reading: Relate Characters and Events to Your Own Experiences to Make Inferences

An **inference** is something you figure out about information that is not directly stated in a story. One way to make inferences is to **relate characters and events to your own experiences.** For example, when Rose offers to make dinner, Mama says, "You can do the cooking if you promise it ain't because you think I can't." By thinking about a strong aging person in your own family, you might be able to infer that Mama is very proud and wants people to understand that she is not feeble. Or you might think about a time when you were hurt or sick and hated having to rely on others to take care of you. Personal observations and experiences such as these can help you to better understand characters in literature.

DIRECTIONS: *Complete the following chart with personal experiences you can relate to each passage and an inference you are able to make based on your experiences. If you do not have a personal experience you can directly relate to the passage, make an educated guess based on observations of people you know.*

Passage From Story	Personal Experience Related to Passage	Inference
1. But when he had bent to kiss the old lady's black face, something new and almost ugly had come into his eyes: fear, uncertainty, sadness, and perhaps even hatred.		
2. Aunt Rose, over Chig's weak protest, was spooning mashed potatoes onto his plate.		
3. Chig turned to his father and found his face completely blank, without even trace of a smile or a laugh.		
4. He [GL] stood in the doorway, smiling broadly, an engaging, open, friendly smile, the innocent smile of a five-year-old.		

Name _____ Date _____

"A Visit to Grandmother" by William Melvin Kelley
Vocabulary Builder

Word List

indulgence	grimacing	trace

A. DIRECTIONS: *Match each word in the left column with its definition in the right column. Write the letter of the definition on the line next to the word it defines.*

___ 1. indulgence

___ 2. grimacing

___ 3. trace

A. making a twisted or distorted facial expression

B. a tiny amount

C. leniency; readiness to forgive

B. DIRECTIONS: *Create two different sentences for each of the Word List words. You may use different forms of the vocabulary word for your second sentence. Write sentences that reveal the meaning of the words through context clues.*

Examples for the word *ventured*: A. Though the shadows in the dark yard scared me, I <u>ventured</u> out to try to find my dog.

B. I couldn't believe that my timid little puppy would <u>venture</u> out of the house so late.

1. A. _____

_____

B. _____

_____

2. A. _____

_____

B. _____

_____

3. A. _____

_____

B. _____

_____

Name _____ Date _____

"A Visit to Grandmother" by William Melvin Kelley

Support for Writing a Retelling

For your retelling, use the following story map to list the main events of "A Visit to Grandmother."

The Main Conflict or Problem:

Event 1:	Event 2:	Event 3:

Event 4:	Event 5:	Event 6:

The Resolution or Solution to the Problem:

The Ending:

Now, use this story map to help you retell the story from Mama's point of view and then from GL's viewpoint.

"A Visit to Grandmother" by William Melvin Kelley
Support for Extend Your Learning

Listening and Speaking

Use the following chart to help you and your partner organize your overview of "A Visit to Grandmother." List the major characters in the first column. Write examples of each character's speech in the second column. In the third column, identify social and regional factors that affect each character's speech.

Character	Example of Speech	Social and Regional Factors

Research and Technology

On the following lines, list and evaluate the sources you find for your research on the Great Migration. Use your notes to write your report on the accuracy and reliability of the sources. Attach a separate sheet of paper if you need more space.

Source 1: _____

_____

Source 2: _____

_____

Source 3: _____

_____

Source 4: _____

_____

"A Visit to Grandmother" by William Melvin Kelley
Enrichment: Connecting to the Performing Arts Through Storytelling

Storytelling is the art of sharing an experience with an audience. As with any other art form, it requires special tools and the skills to use these tools effectively. The storyteller's tools are language and his or her own voice and body. Whether they are performing on stage or sharing an experience at a family party, great storytellers are able to use words, voice, and body language to create vivid pictures in the minds of their listeners.

A. DIRECTIONS: *Answer the following questions.*

1. What specific elements do you think are important in the art of storytelling?

   _____

   _____

   _____

2. What story does Chig's grandmother share in "A Visit to Grandmother"? How do people react to her story?

   _____

   _____

   _____

3. What elements of effective storytelling can be found in Chig's grandmother's tale? What specific details does she use to make the story visual for her audience? At what moments in the story is her own, unique perspective most noticeable?

   _____

   _____

   _____

   _____

   _____

B. *Practice your skills as a storyteller. First, take a few moments to think about an experience you would like to share with your classmates. Your story can be humorous, frightening, sad, or exciting. Then, practice telling your story. You may practice with a partner if you wish so that you can give each other suggestions and feedback. Use specific, interesting details to make the story come alive for your audience. Practice changing the level of loudness and softness in your voice at appropriate moments. Then, decide where to use movement and hand gestures to emphasize parts of your story. When everyone has finished rehearsing, gather in a circle with your classmates and share your stories. After each story is told, discuss which elements of good storytelling were used by the performer.*

"A Visit to Grandmother" by William Melvin Kelley
Selection Test A

Critical Reading *Identify the letter of the choice that best answers the question.*

____ 1. What reason does Charles give for driving south in "A Visit to Grandmother"?
   A. He needs to take Chig's brother and sister to camp.
   B. He wants to go see his brother GL and GL's wife Rose.
   C. He wants to go to Nashville to attend his college class reunion.
   D. He is taking Chig to see his old college in case he decides to go there.

____ 2. In "A Visit to Grandmother," Chig's father talks most about which family member?
   A. Aunt Rose
   B. his brother GL
   C. Mae
   D. Uncle Hiram

____ 3. Charles says that he left home when he was fifteen because he wanted to attend school. What was probably the real reason why Charles left home?
   A. He thought nobody in his family loved him.
   B. He had a terrible fight with his brother Hiram.
   C. Mama sent Charles away so she could spend all her time with GL.
   D. He wanted to get a college degree to show he was better than GL.

____ 4. Chig notices that his father gets an ugly look on his face when he hugs Mama. What can you infer about how Charles feels about Mama?
   A. He is frightened of Mama's rage.
   B. He feels respect and love for Mama.
   C. He is angry at Mama about something.
   D. He feels ashamed of himself around Mama.

____ 5. What is the best way to describe GL's character in "A Visit to Grandmother"?
   A. friendly and intelligent
   B. lazy and stupid
   C. sincere and pessimistic
   D. charming and irresponsible

____ 6. For Charles, what does the story of GL and the horse represent?
   A. his mother's preference for GL
   B. GL's ignorance about horses
   C. his mother's stubborn pride
   D. GL's friendly personality

____ 7. Which of the following lines from "A Visit to Grandmother" is an example of direct characterization?

A. "Doctor Charles Dunford cared about people."

B. "She let him go, and fell back into her chair, grabbing the arms."

C. "When Uncle Hiram and Mae, his wife, came they sat down to eat."

D. "They sat in silence for awhile and then heard a key in the front door."

____ 8. Which of the following lines from the story is an example of indirect characterization?

A. "The old lady had not heard him; only Chig had heard."

B. "She smiled. She had all her teeth, but they were too perfect to be her own."

C. "They had been met at the door by Aunt Rose, GL's wife, and ushered into the living room."

D. "Tears now traveled down the lines in her face, but when she spoke, her voice was clear."

____ 9. Why does Mama say she spent more time with GL than with Charles in "A Visit to Grandmother"?

A. She liked GL better because he had good hair and looked almost white.

B. She thought Charles did not love her and did not want to spend time with her.

C. She worried less about Charles because he was smarter and more mature than GL.

D. She enjoyed being with GL more than being with Charles because she always had fun with him.

____ 10. Which of the following might help you to infer that Chig was very upset by his father's tears?

A. knowing that Charles cries about many things

B. knowing that Chig's mother is not a nervous woman

C. thinking about how Mama paid more attention to GL than to Charles

D. thinking about how you might feel if you saw your own father crying

____ 11. At the end of "A Visit to Grandmother," the author describes GL's smile as the innocent smile of a five-year-old. Why does the author compare GL to a five-year-old?

A. to reveal that Charles is in fact older than GL

B. to show that GL is not mature and not very smart

C. to make it clear that Charles is wrong to be jealous of GL

D. to imply that GL is very attractive and does not show his age

___ 12. What lesson about life can be learned from "A Visit to Grandmother"?
   A. Brothers should forgive one another's faults.
   B. Grandchildren should not visit their grandparents.
   C. The pain of family misunderstandings can last a lifetime.
   D. Parents and adult children should not argue for the grandchildren's sake.

Vocabulary and Grammar

___ 13. A teacher decides not to punish a child for breaking a school rule. What is this an example of?
   A. manipulation
   B. respect
   C. indulgence
   D. consequences

___ 14. A grimace is a twisted facial expression showing disgust or pain. Which of the following activities would most likely result in a person grimacing?
   A. watching a movie from a seat in the middle of the theater
   B. trying to lift something that is extremely heavy
   C. winning a championship tennis game
   D. getting a new job that pays well

___ 15. In which of the following sentences is the principal verb part in its past form?
   A. GL is smiling broadly at the end of the story.
   B. Chig's father resented his mother's preference for GL.
   C. Charles will be angry at his family for many more years.
   D. Mama rides with GL in a buggy behind a crazy horse.

Essay

16. In an essay, discuss the techniques William Melvin Kelley uses to characterize Mama. Describe at least three of her traits and how you as a reader learn about these traits (direct or indirect characterization). Use details from "A Visit to Grandmother" to support your character description.

17. In an essay, describe Mama's approach to raising her ten children. Then, tell whether or not you think her approach was a good one. Use examples from "A Visit to Grandmother" and from real life to explain your opinion.

"A Visit to Grandmother" by William Melvin Kelley
Selection Test B

Critical Reading *Identify the letter of the choice that best answers the question.*

____ 1. Charles does not tell Chig right away about his plans to visit his family. What can you infer about his feelings concerning the visit?
A. Charles is not looking forward to the visit.
B. Charles wants the visit to be a surprise for Chig.
C. Charles thinks Chig will be reluctant to go.
D. Charles did not think he would have time to visit.

____ 2. What detail is explained by the following passage from the selection?

Ten days before in New York, Chig's father had decided suddenly he wanted to go to Nashville to attend his college class reunion, twenty years out . . . Chig was seventeen, had nothing to do that summer, and his father asked if he would like to go along.

A. The reason why Chig's father moved to New York when he was an adult.
B. The reason why Chig's father thinks of GL as a practical joker.
C. The reason why Chig and his father were traveling near Grandmother's home.
D. The reason Chig's father wanted to go to his college reunion.

____ 3. What reason does Charles give for leaving home when he was fifteen?
A. He had met Chig's mother and moved to Knoxville to marry her.
B. He thought his mother liked his brother GL better than him.
C. He wanted to go to school, but there was no Negro high school where he grew up.
D. He wanted to be a doctor, but his home town already had all the doctors it needed.

____ 4. Chig notices that his father gets an ugly look on his face when he hugs Mama. Later, Charles sits quietly while Chig does all the talking with Mama. Charles speaks only when he is spoken to. What can you infer from Charles's behavior?
A. He is frightened of Mama's rage.
B. He feels respect and love for Mama.
C. He is angry at Mama about something.
D. He is waiting for GL to arrive before he speaks.

____ 5. In "A Visit to Grandmother," why is it important to Mama for people to understand that she can do things for herself?
A. She is embarrassed by GL and his wife Rose.
B. She thinks everyone else does things the wrong way.
C. She is too proud to let people think that she is old and feeble.
D. She wants her children to leave her alone to enjoy her retirement.

____ 6. Which of the following lines is an example of direct characterization?
A. "He'll be here though; he ain't as young and footloose as he used to be."
B. "It took only a few words from him to make them relax, and even laugh. Doctor Charles Dunford cared about people."
C. "He had spoken of GL with the kind of indulgence he would have shown a cute, but ill-behaved and potentially dangerous, five-year-old."
D. "And Chig had a suspicion now that the reunion had been only an excuse to drive south, that his father had been heading to this house all the time."

____ 7. Which line from "A Visit to Grandmother" is an example of indirect characterization?
  A. "She smiled. She had all her teeth, but they were too perfect to be her own."
  B. "She was standing now, her back and shoulders straight."
  C. "Uncle Hiram was somewhat smaller than Chig's father; his short-cropped kinky hair was half gray, half black."
  D. "'They don't know nothing about old ladies. When I want help, I'll let you know.'"

____ 8. In "A Visit to Grandmother," Charles uses formal standard English at his mother's house because he
  A. respects and admires the family.
  B. wants Chig to be proud of him.
  C. has serious professional ambitions.
  D. sets himself apart from the family.

____ 9. What does Mrs. Dunford mean when she says, "GL could-a ended up swinging"?
  A. He could have wasted his life at parties.
  B. He might have lived a cheerful, carefree life.
  C. He could have been hanged as a criminal.
  D. He might have suffered emotional ups and downs.

____ 10. Which of the following quotations from the story explains why Charles's mother spent more time with GL than with Charles?
  A. "You was more growed up than GL when you was five and he was ten, and I tried to show you that by letting you do what you wanted to do."
  B. "That's not true, Mama. You know it."
  C. "I said that if I had done it, if I had done just exactly what GL did, you would have beaten me good for it, Mama."
  D. "Don't ask me how I did that; I reckon it was that I was a mother and my baby asked me to do something, is all."

____ 11. What do Charles's words and actions surrounding his mother's treatment of him as a child reveal about his character in "A Visit to Grandmother"?
  A. He is sensitive and full of anger.
  B. He is unable to express his feelings.
  C. He dislikes humorous stories.
  D. He thinks his mother is perfect.

____ 12. Which of the following might help you to infer that Chig was shocked, worried, and upset by his father's tears?
  A. knowing that Chig's mother is not a nervous woman
  B. knowing that Charles cries frequently about many things
  C. thinking about how Mama paid more attention to GL than to Charles
  D. thinking about how you might feel if you saw your own father crying

____ 13. Why does GL refer to Charles as a "rascal" at the end of "A Visit to Grandmother"?
  A. GL suspects Charles is dishonest.
  B. GL is fond of Charles.
  C. GL resents Charles's interference.
  D. GL thinks Charles is mischievous.

____ 14. What is the most important story in "A Visit to Grandmother"?
   A. a teenager's first meeting with his father's family
   B. a mother's reunion with her son
   C. a man's attempt to deal with a painful childhood.
   D. a horse's misbehavior and its results

____ 15. Which statement best expresses the theme or message of "A Visit to Grandmother"?
   A. Brothers should be tolerant and forgiving of one another's faults.
   B. The pain of family misunderstandings can last a lifetime.
   C. Parents and adult children should resolve conflicts for the grandchildren's sake.
   D. Adults often resume childhood roles when they visit their parents.

Vocabulary and Grammar

____ 16. If a parent decides not to punish a child for breaking a family rule, he or she is treating the child with
   A. manipulation.
   B. respect.
   C. indulgence.
   D. consequences.

____ 17. Which of the following situations would most likely result in a person grimacing?
   A. mailing a package from the nearest post office
   B. struggling to lift something that is extremely heavy
   C. winning a championship tennis game against an expert player
   D. getting a new job that pays well and provides valuable experience

____ 18. In which of the following sentences is the word *trace* used correctly?
   A. Aunt Rose heaped a trace of food on Chig's plate.
   B. There was not even a trace of a smile on Charles's face after Mama's story.
   C. Mama was filled with a trace of pride when she saw how well her grandson had turned out.
   D. Charles displayed a trace of anger when he jumped up and ran to his room.

____ 19. In which of the following sentences is the principal verb part in its present participle form?
   A. GL is smiling broadly at the end of the story.
   B. Charles had been angry at his family for years.
   C. Chig's father resented his mother's preference for GL.
   D. Mama was riding with GL in a buggy behind a crazy horse.

Essay

20. In an essay, identify the problem Charles has with his mother and his brother. Explain the specific misunderstanding between Charles and his mother that is at the root of the problem. What is Charles's attitude toward GL? What is the true reason for this attitude?

21. When Charles bends down to kiss his mother, Chig notices that "something new and almost ugly had come into his (Charles's) eyes: fear, uncertainty, sadness, and perhaps even hatred." In an essay, explain why Chig sees each of these things in his father's eyes. What is the purpose of his visit home? Why might his visit home cause him to feel these emotions?

Vocabulary Warm-up Word Lists

Study these words from "A Problem." Then apply your knowledge to the activities that follow.

Word List A

awaiting [uh WAY ting] *v.* waiting for; expecting
We are eagerly <u>awaiting</u> the results of the contest.

commit [kuh MIT] *v.* do something
You are likely to <u>commit</u> an error if you proofread too quickly.

disagreeable [dis uh GREE uh buhl] *adj.* unpleasant
The sour candy had a very <u>disagreeable</u> flavor.

guarantee [ga ruhn TEE] *v.* promise; pledge
Did the seller <u>guarantee</u> that the car is in working condition?

motives [MOH tivz] *n.* reasons for acting a certain way
The thief's <u>motives</u> were greed and laziness.

philosophy [fi LAHS uh fee] *n.* a set of underlying principles or concepts
The sports historian studied the <u>philosophy</u> of baseball.

signature [SIG nuh chuhr] *n.* a person's name signed by himself or herself
Please write your <u>signature</u> on this application form.

sufficiently [suh FISH uhnt lee] *adv.* enough; adequately
Are you <u>sufficiently</u> prepared for the quiz?

Word List B

asserted [uh SERT id] *v.* stated; declared; claimed
The mayor <u>asserted</u> that she would never raise taxes.

astray [uh STRAY] *adv.* off the right path
We were led <u>astray</u> by the confused tour guide.

blandly [BLAND lee] *adv.* dully; mildly; not harshly
I like spicy food, so I never cook <u>blandly</u>.

consequence [KAHN suh kwens] *n.* result of an action
One <u>consequence</u> of exercise is reduced blood pressure.

distinguished [dis TING gwisht] *adj.* celebrated; deserving of respect
His <u>distinguished</u> grandfather won many medals in the war.

emphatic [em FAT ik] *adj.* expressed with emphasis; forceful
He made the statement <u>emphatic</u> by pounding his fist.

indifferent [in DIF uhr uhnt] *adj.* showing no interest or preference
She was <u>indifferent</u> to the child's demands for attention.

initiated [i NISH ee ay tid] *v.* admitted into a group or secret
We <u>initiated</u> my sister into our secret club.

Name _____ Date _____

"A Problem" by Anton Chekhov
Vocabulary Warm-up Exercises

Exercise A *Fill in each blank in the paragraph below with an appropriate word from Word List A. Use each word only once.*

Although many students find standardized testing [1] _____, the

[2] _____, or principle, behind these tests is not to make life unpleasant.

Test writers try to [3] _____ that the tests will be fair. Of course, they also

write tough questions that encourage students to [4] _____ errors. One of

the [5] _____, or reasons, for using these tests is that they offer a conve-

nient way to compare students. However, experts advise students to relax because test

scores alone do not provide a [6] _____ complete picture of a student any

more than a student's [7] _____ shows everything about the student's

handwriting. Still, [8] _____ test results can make you nervous!

Exercise B *Decide whether each statement below is true or false. Explain your answers.*

1. Most baby food is <u>blandly</u> spiced.
   T / F _____

2. An experienced teacher can never lead a class <u>astray</u>.
   T / F _____

3. Ignorance is one <u>consequence</u> of laziness.
   T / F _____

4. An <u>emphatic</u> speaker is likely to put an audience to sleep.
   T / F _____

5. If an author <u>asserted</u> a fact in a published book, it must be true.
   T / F _____

6. Performers prefer a lively audience to an <u>indifferent</u> crowd.
   T / F _____

7. If you are <u>initiated</u> into a club, you probably have to follow its rules.
   T / F _____

8. Graduation speakers are often <u>distinguished</u> members of the community.
   T / F _____

Name _____ Date _____

"A Problem" by Anton Chekhov
Reading Warm-up A

Read the following passage. Pay special attention to the underlined words. Then, read it again, and complete the activities. Use a separate sheet of paper for your written answers.

Financial loans are a type of debt. The borrower receives money from a lender, such as a bank or a credit union. Borrowers sign a contract to <u>guarantee</u> that they will pay back the money. The loan is not provided free of charge—the lend charges a fee called interest.

People have many <u>motives</u> for borrowing money, from buying a car to starting a business. Regardless of the reasons for the loan, the application process is basically the same. The lender requires proof that the borrower is <u>sufficiently</u> reliable, so the forms must be satisfactorily filled out. This process can be time-consuming, but it does not have to be <u>disagreeable</u>. Borrowers should gather the information they need, take their time, and be sure to ask questions about unclear terms.

After the forms are complete, it will take time for the lender to review the application. Lenders carefully review all information, so borrowers should expect to spend some time <u>awaiting</u> an answer. If the loan is granted, the money is often presented at an official meeting known as a loan closing. The borrower signs the loan documents. A person's <u>signature</u> is a symbol that reflects the signer's legal promise to repay the loan.

Credit cards are also a type of loan. Although they may require less paperwork, the <u>philosophy</u> behind this type of credit is the same. The cardholder is the borrower. The credit card company is the lender. The cardholder signs a contract that is a promise to repay the amounts charged. If they wish, cardholders can repay a minimum amount each month. The rest of the debt remains. Interest is added as a fee for using credit.

Loans are legal contracts, so borrowers and lenders must be careful not to break any laws. Borrowers must sign only their own names. They <u>commit</u> the crime of fraud if they sign someone else's name to a document. Lenders must follow laws about fairness in lending. They must provide honest information about interest rates.

1. Underline the words that explain what borrowers <u>guarantee</u>. Then, tell what *guarantee* means.

2. Circle the <u>motives</u> for borrowing money. Then, describe two other *motives* for borrowing money.

3. Circle the word that is a synonym for <u>sufficiently</u>. Then describe what *sufficiently* means.

4. Circle the task that some might find <u>disagreeable</u>. Write a sentence about a *disagreeable* chore.

5. Circle the words that tell what borrowers will spend time <u>awaiting</u>. Then, tell about something you are *awaiting* now.

6. Underline the words that describe what a <u>signature</u> means on a loan. Then, describe one place where you have placed your *signature*.

7. Underline the sentences that explain the <u>philosophy</u> of credit cards. Describe the *philosophy* behind a custom, such as shaking hands or clapping after a performance.

8. Circle the words that describe what borrowers <u>commit</u> if they sign another person's name. Then, tell what *commit* means.

"A Problem" by Anton Chekhov
Reading Warm-up B

Read the following passage. Pay special attention to the underlined words. Then, read it again, and complete the activities. Use a separate sheet of paper for your written answers.

Corinna Matthews sat patiently outside the coach's office. As more and more time passed, Corinna's unchanging and <u>indifferent</u> expression suggested that she didn't care how long she was kept waiting.

Corinna's swim coach, Dr. Adams, was having a conference with her parents. Corinna could not hear what was being said, although the coach's voice was so forceful that she could hear echoes of his <u>emphatic</u> words.

"Corinna has repeatedly missed swim practice this semester," Dr. Adams explained to Mr. and Mrs. Matthews. "She missed three practices this week alone, and as a <u>consequence</u>, she will not be allowed to participate in this weekend's competition."

Mrs. Matthews nodded her agreement. "We noticed that Corinna lost her drive for swimming after Yelena joined the team. We are afraid that Yelena is a bad influence and is leading our daughter <u>astray</u>."

The coach said, "I have also noticed that Corinna has seemed less motivated since Yelena was <u>initiated</u> into the swim team. In fact, they both miss practices."

"We know that you are one of the most <u>distinguished</u> teachers in this school and respect your opinion," said Mr. Matthews. "Perhaps if we all talk with Corinna together, we can help her take a hard look at her priorities."

"Excellent," said Dr. Adams. "Let's call her in."

When Corinna walked into the office and sat down, she stared <u>blandly</u> forward, trying to show no expression at all.

Dr. Adams told Corinna that she would not be allowed to participate in the swim meet this weekend and then explained why.

"You're right," <u>asserted</u> Corinna. "I do need to change my priorities. Swimming is no longer as important to me as it was."

She looked defiantly at her parents and the coach. They stared back as their hope for a simple solution quickly disappeared.

1. Underline the words that tell what Corinna's <u>indifferent</u> expression showed. Then tell something to which you are *indifferent*.

2. Circle the synonym for <u>emphatic</u>. Then, tell what *emphatic* means.

3. Underline the <u>consequence</u> Corinna will face. Then, describe a possible *consequence* of not studying for a test.

4. Explain how you can tell if someone is trying to lead you *astray*.

5. Circle the words that tell what Yelena was <u>initiated</u> into. Then, describe a group into which you might be *initiated*.

6. Describe a *distinguished* person in your community.

7. Underline the words that explain how Corinna did something <u>blandly</u>. Then, tell what *blandly* means.

8. Underline the words that Corinna <u>asserted</u>. Then, tell something that you have *asserted* to a friend or family member.

"A Problem" by Anton Chekhov
Literary Analysis: Characterization

Characters are the people, animals, or objects who perform the actions and experience the events of a story. An author reveals the personalities of characters in a story by using **direct** or **indirect characterization.** With direct characterization, an author makes direct statements about a character. With indirect characterization, the author reveals a character's traits through his or her **dialogue,** actions, thoughts, and appearance, as well as what other people in the story think of the character.

To better understand characters, think about the information you learn about characters and how you learn it. Think also about **character development**—changes the character undergoes through the course of the story or new information that the author reveals about the character.

A. DIRECTIONS: *Complete the following chart with examples from the story of direct and indirect characterization of each character listed. If there is no example of either direct or indirect characterization, explain why you think the author chose not to use that form of characterization.*

Character	Examples of Direct Characterization	Examples of Indirect Characterization
Example: The Treasury official	The author describes him as taciturn, dull-witted, and rheumatic.	He sits mostly silent and fails to support his opinion; he mutters his replies to the Colonel.
1. Sasha		
2. The Colonel		
3. Ivan Markovitch		

B. DIRECTIONS: *In a brief essay, indicate whether direct or indirect characterization makes you feel you know a character better. Explain your answer.*

_____

_____

_____

_____

_____

_____

Name _____ Date _____

Reading: Relate Characters and Events to Your Own Experiences to Make Inferences

An **inference** is something you figure out about information that is not directly stated in a story. One way to make inferences is to **relate characters and events to your own experiences.** For example, at the beginning of the story the author states that the family was careful to keep something secret from the servants. Though you may not have servants, you might be able to relate to the desire to keep your family's personal business within the family. By thinking about a similar situation in your own life, it can help you to infer that the Uskov family is dealing with something they feel might be embarrassing if it is made public. Personal observations and experiences such as these can help you to better understand characters in literature.

DIRECTIONS: *Complete the following chart with personal experiences you can relate to each passage and an inference you are able to make based on your experiences. If you do not have a personal experience you can directly relate to the passage, make an educated guess based on observations of people you know.*

Passage From Story	Personal Experience Related to Passage	Inference
1. "Shall we be false to civic duty," Ivan Markovitch exclaimed passionately, "if instead of punishing an erring boy we hold out to him a helping hand?"		
2. Every minute he [Sasha] was on the point of jumping up, bursting into the study and shouting in answer to the detestable metallic voice of the Colonel: "You are lying!"		
3. But then he [Sasha] remembered he had not a farthing, that the companions he was going to would despise him at once for his empty pockets. He must get hold of some money, come what may!		
4. But debt is not a crime, and it is unusual for a man not to be in debt.		

"A Problem" by Anton Chekhov
Vocabulary Builder

Word List

candid	taciturn	subdued

A. DIRECTIONS: *Match each word in the left column with its definition in the right column. Write the letter of the definition on the line next to the word it defines.*

___ 1. candid   A. quiet; lacking energy

___ 2. taciturn   B. silent; not liking to talk

___ 3. subdued   C. honest; direct

B. DIRECTIONS: *Create two different sentences for each of the Word List words. You may use different forms of the vocabulary word for your second sentence. Write sentences that reveal the meaning of the words through context clues.*

Examples for the word *ventured*: A. Though the shadows in the dark yard scared me, I <u>ventured</u> out to try to find my dog.

B. I couldn't believe that my timid little puppy would <u>venture</u> out of the house so late.

1. A. _____

  B. _____

2. A. _____

  B. _____

3. A. _____

  B. _____

C. DIRECTIONS: *In the blank, write the letter of the word that best completes the meaning of the sentence.*

____ 1. I could not believe that I was hearing my normally _____ sister give a long speech encouraging a large audience to donate to her favorite charity.

    A. taciturn   B. candid   C. contrary   D. generous

____ 2. After the team lost the big game, the mood of the fans was _____ as they left the stadium.

    A. taciturn   B. bland   C. jubilant   D. subdued

Name _____ Date _____

Support for Writing a Retelling

For your retelling, use the following story map to list the main events of "A Problem."

The Main Conflict or Problem:

Event 1:

Event 2:

Event 3:

Event 4:

Event 5:

Event 6:

The Resolution or Solution to the Problem:

The Ending:

Now, use this story map to help you retell the story from the moneylender's point of view and then from the perspective of Sasha as an old man.

"A Problem" by Anton Chekhov
Support for Extend Your Learning

Listening and Speaking

Use the following chart to help you and your partner organize your overview of "A Problem." List the major characters in the first column. Write examples of each character's speech in the second column. In the third column, identify social and regional factors that affect each character's speech.

Character	Example of Speech	Social and Regional Factors

Research and Technology

On the following lines, list and evaluate the sources you find for your research on social status in Russia during the nineteenth century. Use your notes to write your report on the accuracy and reliability of the sources. Attach a separate sheet of paper if you need more space.

Source 1: _____

_____

Source 2: _____

_____

Source 3: _____

_____

Source 4: _____

_____

"A Problem" by Anton Chekhov

Enrichment: Connecting to the Humanities by Examining Personal Honor

The dual theme of honor and dishonor runs through "A Problem." As you read the story, you will most likely ask yourself, "What does it mean to be an honorable person?"

In Chekhov's story, the main character, Sasha Uskov, causes "a problem" for his family that threatens to tarnish his family's honor. However, the action needed to protect the family's reputation is not necessarily an honorable one.

DIRECTIONS: *As you read "A Problem," complete the following chart. Define "honor" as it is demonstrated by the characters and events. Then, identify five examples of honor or dishonor illustrated in the story. Explain why you think each example is a good illustration of honor or dishonor. You may explain from a character's point of view or from your own point of view.*

Definition of honor as it is demonstrated by the characters and events: _____

_____

_____

Example of Honor or Dishonor	Explanation
1.	
2.	
3.	
4.	
5.	

"A Visit to Grandmother" by William Melvin Kelley
"A Problem" by Anton Chekhov
Build Language Skills: Vocabulary

Word Roots

The word *formulate* can be traced back to the Latin root word *forma*, meaning "shape" or "form." The word *formulate* means "to express in a fixed or definite way"—that is, to give shape or form to a way of expressing things. The meanings of other words containing this root word also involve the idea of shape or form. Examples of other words that come from *forma* include *formal*, *information*, *formative*, and *formula*.

A. DIRECTIONS: *Fill in the following word map for the word* formulate.

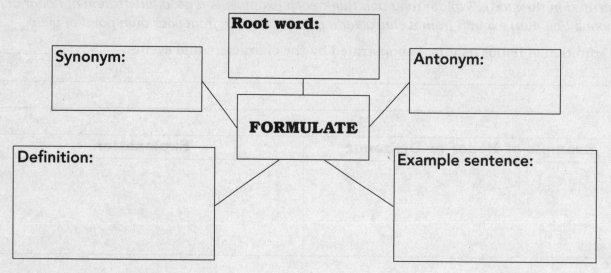

Academic Vocabulary Practice

B. DIRECTIONS: *Create two different sentences for each of the following words. You may use different forms of the vocabulary word for your second sentence.*

Example: *formulate*

We will meet next week to <u>formulate</u> a plan for our group's history fair project.

I <u>formulated</u> my ideas by diagramming them on a computer before I began constructing my model.

1. perspective _____

_____

2. anticipate _____

_____

3. indicate _____

_____

4. discern _____

_____

Name _____ Date _____

Build Language Skills: Grammar

Regular Verbs

A verb has four principal parts: the present, the present participle, the past, and the past participle. The present and past forms function as verbs. The present participle and the past participle can also act as adjectives. Most of the verbs in the English language are regular; the past and past participle of a regular verb are formed by adding *-ed* or *-d* to the present form. The past and past participle of regular verbs have the same form. The following chart lists the principal parts of two verbs—*visit* and *discuss*.

Principal Parts of Regular Verbs

Present	Present Participle	Past	Past Participle
visit	(is, are, was, were) visiting	visited	(has, have, had) visited
discuss	(is, are, was, were) discussing	discussed	(has, have, had) discussed

A. PRACTICE: *Identify the principal part used to form each of the underlined verbs.*

Example:

__past__ Chig <u>noticed</u> an ugly look on his father's face.

_____ 1. Ronald is <u>cooking</u> dinner while the children talk.

_____ 2. Charley had <u>wanted</u> to go to college.

_____ 3. Lucille <u>asked</u> her mother to ride in the car with her.

_____ 4. "I <u>believe</u> their behavior will improve," Jennifer said.

B. Writing Application: *Write sentences by following the following instructions.*

Example: Write a sentence using the past participle form of the verb *prepare*.
Sasha <u>had prepared</u> himself for the possibility that he might have to go to court.

1. Write a sentence using the past participle of the verb *talk*.

_____

2. Write a sentence using the present form of the verb *agree*.

_____

3. Write a sentence using the present participle of the verb *decide*.

_____

4. Write a sentence using the past of *laugh*.

_____

"A Problem" by Anton Chekhov
Selection Test A

Critical Reading *Identify the letter of the choice that best answers the question.*

___ 1. At the beginning of "A Problem," the Uskovs send half their servants out to the theater or the circus, while the rest stay in the kitchen. Why do they do this?
   A. To reward the servants for doing their jobs well.
   B. To keep the servants from finding out what Sasha did.
   C. To show Ivan Markovitch how wealthy and powerful the Uskovs are.
   D. To give the Colonel's wife, her sister, and the governess some privacy.

___ 2. Why did Sasha write a note he could not pay?
   A. He wanted to keep up with his wealthy friends who looked down on him for not having money.
   B. He hated his uncle, the Colonel, and hoped to get him in trouble with the bank.
   C. He had always dreamed of visiting Siberia, and cashing the note was the only way to get sent there.
   D. He wanted to give the money to the poor, who were starving and cold.

___ 3. How does Sasha feel about having been caught doing wrong in "A Problem"?
   A. ashamed
   B. indifferent
   C. terrified
   D. depressed

___ 4. What is the Colonel's reason for arguing against helping Sasha?
   A. He believes they can successfully keep the story out of the papers.
   B. He believes Sasha will do the same thing again if they help him this time.
   C. He dislikes Ivan Markovitch and automatically disagrees with everything Ivan says.
   D. He knows that Sasha really wants to go to Siberia and does not want to stand in his way.

___ 5. Sasha becomes angry when he hears the Colonel call him a criminal. Which of the following would best help you to understand why Sasha reacts this way?
   A. thinking about how Sasha lost both his parents when he was very young
   B. thinking about a time when you had a fun day with your friends
   C. thinking about the Colonel's background as an army officer
   D. thinking about how you would feel if someone called you a criminal

____ 6. Which of the following is NOT one of the reasons Ivan Markovitch gives for help-
ing Sasha?
   A. because Sasha grew up without parents to guide him
   B. because Sasha's dead mother would want them to help him
   C. because Sasha's friend Handrikov said he would pay the debt
   D. because Sasha was already being punished by his guilty conscience

____ 7. Why does the Colonel change his mind in "A Problem"?
   A. Ivan makes him feel sorry for Sasha's dead mother by saying that he thinks
      she is present in the room, weeping for her boy.
   B. Sasha falls on his knees and begs the Colonel for help, which impresses the
      Colonel enough to change his mind.
   C. The Treasury official finally convinces the Colonel that it would be terrible if
      the story got into the newspapers.
   D. The Colonel's wife convinces him that Sasha is really a good boy who never
      meant to hurt anyone.

____ 8. Which of the following is an example of direct characterization in "A Problem"?
   A. when Sasha thinks to himself that he is not a criminal
   B. when Ivan Markovitch speaks for Sasha to the other uncles
   C. when the author states that Sasha was sick of life and found it very hard
   D. when the Colonel leaves by another door so that he won't have to see Sasha

____ 9. Which of the following is an example of indirect characterization in "A Problem"?
   A. when the Treasury official is described as taciturn and dull-witted
   B. when the reader discovers that Sasha is twenty-five years old
   C. when the author states that Ivan Markovitch is kind-hearted
   D. when Sasha thinks to himself that he is not a criminal

____ 10. In "A Problem," Sasha's character is revealed mostly through
   A. description of his appearance.
   B. description of his personality.
   C. his thoughts and actions.
   D. what other characters think about him.

____ 11. How does Ivan Markovitch feel when Sasha asks for another loan?
   A. useful
   B. horrified
   C. happy to oblige
   D. concerned

Vocabulary and Grammar

___ 12. In "A Problem," the author describes the quiet Treasury official as taciturn. Which of the following is an activity that a taciturn person would be most likely to enjoy?
A. playing a board game with friends
B. reading a book alone
C. going to a family reunion
D. working as a retail store clerk

___ 13. After losing the big game, the team members spoke in _____ voices as they entered the locker room.
A. taciturn
B. subdued
C. candid
D. indifferent

___ 14. Which of the following is an example of someone who is being candid?
A. a person on trial choosing not to testify
B. a news reporter making up facts to support his story
C. an athlete taking all the credit for his team's victory
D. a girl giving an honest opinion about her friend's new outfit

___ 15. Sasha was happy when he found out that his uncles _____ to pay his debt for him.
A. choose
B. chose
C. chosen
D. will have chosen

Essay

16. In an essay, state what you would have done if you were one of Sasha's uncles. Would you have helped him repay his debt? Explain your reasons and give examples from "A Problem" to support your position.

17. Think about the end of "A Problem." In an essay, explain what you think is likely to happen next and why. Consider how Sasha is characterized through his behavior toward Ivan Markovitch at the end of the story. Remember also that Sasha accepts the idea that he is a criminal after all.

"A Problem" by Anton Chekhov
Selection Test B

Critical Reading *Identify the letter of the choice that best completes the statement or answers the question.*

____ 1. At the beginning of "A Problem," the Uskov family is very careful to keep the servants from finding out the family secret. Which of the following would best help you to understand why this is important to the Uskovs?
A. thinking about a time when you had a particularly fun day with your friends
B. thinking about how things have changed between the time the story was written and now
C. thinking about how the servants must feel about being sent away
D. thinking about a situation that your family prefers to keep to itself and not share with others

____ 2. Which of the following is NOT a reason that Sasha cashed a false promissory note in "A Problem"?
A. His friends were getting tired of him sponging off them.
B. He wanted money to spend while partying with his friends.
C. He wanted to pay his friends back for their generosity and kindness.
D. His friends cashed false notes regularly, so he believed it was normal and acceptable.

____ 3. What does Sasha's uncle mean when he says that it would be "civic cowardice" to help Sasha?
A. that Sasha is a coward
B. that the family should not hide behind Sasha's problems
C. that civic duty is more important than family honor
D. that by protecting Sasha from punishment they would be breaking the law

____ 4. What does the Colonel argue the uncles should do about Sasha in "A Problem"?
A. pay the debt to save the family's honor and keep the story out of the papers
B. not pay the debt because he believes Sasha will do the same thing again
C. make him work off the debt by becoming a servant in the family's household
D. send him to military school to learn some discipline

____ 5. While listening to his uncles' discussion, Sasha feels indifferent about his fate. How does the author reveal this aspect of Sasha's character?
A. through his actions
B. through his dialogue
C. through his appearance
D. through his thoughts

____ 6. While he is sitting by the door listening to his uncles argue, Sasha experiences several negative emotions. Which of the following would most help you to understand his reactions?
A. thinking about how many people are in debt in the United States today
B. thinking about a time you overheard strangers arguing in a public place
C. thinking about how the uncles must feel as they discuss their nephew's fate
D. thinking about a time you got in trouble and had to wait for your punishment

_____ 7. In "A Problem," how does Sasha convince himself at first that he is not a criminal?
    A. He thinks that, since he did not intend to hurt anyone, what he did was not a criminal act.
    B. He knows that the courts always let debtors go and never punish them.
    C. He listens to Ivan telling his other uncles that he has done nothing wrong.
    D. He thinks that, since Handrikov had agreed to pay the debt for him, he is not responsible.

_____ 8. In "A Problem," how does Sasha Uskov feel when leaving the Colonel's home with his uncle after the council meeting?
    A. He feels grateful to his uncle for standing up for him.
    B. He feels humbled by his uncles' kindness and is determined to change.
    C. He feels free and wants to party with his friends.
    D. He regrets the trouble that he has caused his family.

_____ 9. How does Ivan Markovitch feel at the end of "A Problem" and why?
    A. ecstatic because he has convinced the uncles to pay Sasha's debt
    B. sad because his dear sister is no longer alive to guide his nephew Sasha
    C. pleased because Sasha has invited him to go celebrate with him and his friends
    D. horrified because Sasha demands more money and clearly has not learned his lesson

_____ 10. Sasha initially rejects the idea that he is a criminal. At the end, however, he decides that he is a criminal after all. Why?
    A. His uncles have decided to let him go to court and take his punishment.
    B. He realizes that his friends are all criminals, so he thinks he must be one too.
    C. He realizes that he has just essentially robbed his kind-hearted uncle so that he can go to a party.
    D. He feels hopeless about ever getting out of debt and wants to do something wicked to help him forget his troubles.

_____ 11. Which line from "A Problem" best illustrates Sasha's character?
    A. "In short, the family was dear to him for many reasons."
    B. "It made no difference to him where he was: here in the hall, in prison, or in Siberia."
    C. "And it's not in my character to bring myself to commit a crime."
    D. "When I have the money I help the poor."

_____ 12. Which of the following sentences from "A Problem" is an example of direct characterization?
    A. "Ivan Markovitch talked further of family honor."
    B. "He was sick of life and found it insufferably hard."
    C. "'What have I done wrong besides?' Sasha wondered."
    D. "He went out of the study and sat down again on the chair near the door."

_____ 13. Which of the following is an example of indirect characterization in "A Problem"?
    A. when the Treasury official is described as taciturn and dull-witted
    B. when the reader discovers that Sasha is twenty-five years old
    C. when the author states that Ivan Markovitch is kind-hearted
    D. when Sasha thinks to himself that he is not a criminal

_____ 14. Based on the events in "A Problem," which of the following is most likely to happen next?

A. Ivan will begin joining Sasha at the parties with his friends.

B. Sasha will realize his mistakes and change his behavior for the better.

C. Sasha will cash another false note, but this time his uncles will not help him.

D. The uncles will pay off Sasha's debt and give him a great deal of money.

Vocabulary and Grammar

_____ 15. Sasha's other paternal uncle, a _____ man, sits silently throughout Ivan Markovitch's defense of Sasha.

A. prodigious

B. sublime

C. guileless

D. taciturn

_____ 16. What is the best way to rewrite the following sentence so that the italicized vocabulary word makes sense?

The fans screamed wildly in *subdued* voices when the team scored another touchdown.

A. The fans became subdued when the team won another game.

B. The subdued fans yelled wildly when the team scored another touchdown.

C. The fans were subdued as they left the stadium after the team lost another game.

D. The fans, subdued, yelled angrily when the referee made a call in favor of the other team.

_____ 17. Which of the following is an example of someone who is being candid?

A. a girl giving an honest opinion about her friend's new outfit

B. a child happily eating all his vegetables and drinking his milk

C. a basketball player winning the Most Valuable Player award

D. a shoplifter sneaking something out of a store without paying

_____ 18. In which of the following sentences is the past participle of an irregular verb used correctly?

A. Sasha's friends have spent a great deal of money on parties.

B. Sasha have spend all of his money and is now in debt.

C. Sasha's uncles did not want to spent their money for Sasha's mistake.

D. Sasha will have spent even more money in the future.

_____ 19. Sasha _____ money from the bank when he cashed a note he could not pay.

A. steal

B. stole

C. stealed

D. will have stolen

Essay

20. In Chekhov's story "A Problem," Sasha Uskov's behavior causes "a problem" for his family. In an essay, describe the serious problem that Sasha causes, how he reacts to the problem, how his family reacts to the problem, and how his family goes about trying to resolve the problem.

21. Think about the end of "A Problem." In an essay, explain what you think is likely to happen next. Support your answer with logic and evidence from the story.

Vocabulary Warm-up Word Lists

Study these words from "The Streets of the Cañón." Then, apply your knowledge to the activities that follow.

Word List A

apprehension [a pri HEN shuhn] *n.* fear or worry
  Todd felt <u>apprehension</u> as the date of semester midterms approached.

assurance [uh SHOOR uhns] *n.* statement of commitment that inspires confidence
  The doctor gave me her <u>assurance</u> that the fracture would heal quickly.

decisively [dee SY siv lee] *adv.* quickly and with determination
  Elaine moved <u>decisively</u> to block her opponent's shot.

historian [his TAWR ee uhn] *n.* a person who studies past events
  The local <u>historian</u> also knew the stories behind historical events.

humanity [hyoo MAN uh tee] *n.* human beings; the state of being humane
  <u>Humanity</u> has a hard time recovering from the devastating effects of war.

interruption [in tuh RUHP shuhn] *n.* a stop or pause in what is happening
  A power outage caused an <u>interruption</u> in our viewing of the movie.

mottled [MOT uhld] *v.* marked with spots of different shades
  The peeling sunburn <u>mottled</u> her skin with pink and white blotches.

prominent [PROM uh nuhnt] *adj.* conspicuous; easily seen
  The largest gift was a <u>prominent</u> package, visible to all in the room.

Word List B

chaperone [SHA puh rohn] *n.* one who stays with a young person at social events
  My mother acted as a <u>chaperone</u> on our school trip.

doubtless [DOWT lis] *adj.* certain
  We were <u>doubtless</u> that the undefeated champion would win the crown.

humbly [HUM blee] *adv.* modestly; without pride
  She accepted praise <u>humbly</u>, giving everyone else credit for her work.

intricate [IN truh kit] *adj.* complicated, detailed
  This pattern is far too <u>intricate</u> for someone just learning to crochet.

merged [MURJD] *v.* joined together
  When the businesses <u>merged</u>, they tried to retain all the employees.

pungent [PUHN juhnt] *adj.* having a sharp or bitter smell or taste
  I love the <u>pungent</u> taste of highly spiced foods.

virtuous [VER choo uhs] *adj.* having good character
  The <u>virtuous</u> youngster had learned to always tell the truth.

whitewashed [WYT wahsht] *adj.* painted white by a special mixture
  The <u>whitewashed</u> walls reflected the heat of the sun.

"The Streets of the Cañón" by Josephina Niggli
Vocabulary Warm-up Exercises

Exercise A *Fill in each blank in the paragraph below with an appropriate word from Word List A. Use each word only once.*

The moonlight [1] _____ the faces of those gathered outside in the park, making patterns on their foreheads. A [2] _____ was giving a talk about periods of greatness in [3] _____ when suddenly the listeners heard thunder. The speaker did not allow the noise to serve as an [4] _____. She just talked right over it. Still, others felt [5] _____ as they noticed the wind pick up. One [6] _____ flash of lightning right over the speaker's head was hard even for her to ignore. While she offered her audience [7] _____ that there was no cause for alarm, people moved [8] _____ toward the edge of the park to find their cars.

Exercise B *Answer the question with complete explanations.*

Example: If the girl accepted her award <u>humbly</u>, would everyone be angry at her arrogance? Why or why not?

> *They wouldn't be angry because <u>humbly</u> means "with modesty," not "with arrogance."*

1. If Jim was <u>doubtless</u> that he could find his way, should Sally be worried?

   _____

2. If Naomi is <u>virtuous</u>, should you trust her with your best belongings?

   _____

3. If a wall is <u>whitewashed</u>, will the result be dreary and dark?

   _____

4. If two roads <u>merged</u> after a light, how many roads would you see after the light?

   _____

5. If a maze is <u>intricate</u>, will it be easy to get through?

   _____

6. If Aunt Kim was a <u>chaperone</u> at the party, were the guests over 25 years old?

   _____

7. If the greens had a <u>pungent</u> taste, would you describe them as sweet?

   _____

"The Streets of the Cañón" by Josephina Niggli

Reading Warm-up A

Read the following passage. Pay special attention to the underlined words. Then, read it again, and complete the activities. Use a separate sheet of paper for your written answers.

One of the greatest feuds in Mexican history was between the Mayan Indians and the descendants of Spanish settlers in the Yucatan Peninsula. The descendants of the original Spanish settlers maintained political power and treated the Indians poorly for a long time. Then, during the late eighteenth century, they began to take over land for plantations. They made the Indians work for them and pay heavy taxes. When Mexico gained independence from Spain in the early nineteenth century, the European descendants still seemed to deny the basic <u>humanity</u> of the Indians, treating them as if they weren't people like themselves.

In 1848, the Mayas moved <u>decisively</u> and without hesitation to fight the oppression they suffered. They fought with fury. The goal of the Mayas was to drive all non-Indians out of the peninsula. Once the non-Indians realized the Mayas were ready to fight, they felt great <u>apprehension</u> and fear. They were nearly ready to leave the peninsula when an <u>interruption</u> occurred in the fighting. Mayas recognized a clear, <u>prominent</u> signal from nature. Winged ants <u>mottled</u> the sunlight as they filled the sky in irregular patterns. The Mayas knew that this was an indication that they should begin planting. They left the battle. This gave the non-Indians time to strengthen their position.

After that, no one could realistically give <u>assurance</u> to the Mayas that they could win. In fact, there were many times during the decades of struggle that the Mexican government declared that the battles were over. Still, for a long time, any people of European descent arriving in this region had reason to fear the Maya.

A <u>historian</u> who studied Mexico's past and this struggle referred to this conflict as the "Caste Wars." This term has become the common name for what occurred. Eventually, tensions lessened, and the Mayas' condition improved somewhat.

1. Underline the phrase that describes how the Europeans denied the <u>humanity</u> of the Mayas. Then tell what *humanity* means.

2. Circle the words that explain what <u>decisively</u> means. Use *decisively* in a sentence.

3. Circle the words that tell who felt <u>apprehension</u>. Tell what *apprehension* is.

4. Circle the words that tell what the Mayas had to do that caused an <u>interruption</u> in the fighting. What might cause an *interruption* in your daily routine?

5. Underline the phrase that tells what <u>prominent</u> sign the Mayas saw. Then explain what *prominent* means.

6. Circle the word that tells what was <u>mottled</u> by winged ants. Describe what this might look like.

7. Underline the phrase that tells what <u>assurance</u> the Mayas were *not* able to get. Explain what *assurance* means.

8. Circle the words that tell what this <u>historian</u> studied. Name something else that a *historian* might study in relation to this article.

"The Streets of the Cañón" by Josephina Niggli
Reading Warm-up B

Read the following passage. Pay special attention to the underlined words. Then, read it again, and complete the activities. Use a separate sheet of paper for your written answers.

When Jeremy began to court Lupe, he had no idea how intricate and complex his strategies would become to win her, or just how important she would be in his life. Doubtless he was struck by her intelligence and beauty, as nearly anyone would have been. However, coming from a big city in Texas, he had no experience in dealing with parents who expected to have a chaperone accompany the couple on all of their dates.

In Jeremy's case, Lupe's parents were particularly cautious with their sweet, virtuous daughter because his background was so different from their own. He didn't even speak their tongue! Jeremy felt bewitched. Soon his attraction to Lupe merged with the challenge of their cultural differences, and their courtship became his focus. While he had sophistication and worldliness from his urban lifestyle, she had humor, kindness, and an unspoiled manner that she had learned in her more rural surroundings. He had never known anyone like her. He longed to make her a part of his big-city life. Whether she could bear to leave her family, friends, and home was the issue that stood before them. In the meantime, Jeremy tried to gain the trust of Lupe's parents by treating them with respect and treating their daughter gallantly.

When Jeremy visited, María Guadalupe (as Lupe was formally called) sat humbly with her aunt in the sitting room of her small, whitewashed home. He would present both women with simple and elegant gifts. A sharp, pungent cooking odor invariably wafted through the room at that hour. He longed to have just a few moments alone with Lupe before he joined her family for a meal.

Eventually, they were able to slip away from Tía Marisol's sharp eye for a bit. Fifty years later, as they both looked back fondly on those days, they agreed that their life together was well worth the wait.

1. Circle the word that means nearly the same thing as intricate. Use the word *intricate* in a sentence.

2. Underline the phrase that tells what Jeremy was doubtless struck by. Explain what *doubtless* means.

3. Write what you think a chaperone is expected to do.

4. Name three people whom you could describe as virtuous. Why would you describe them this way?

5. Underline the phrase that tells what merged with Jeremy's attraction to Lupe. Then tell what *merged* means.

6. In your own words, describe what it means for Lupe to sit humbly.

7. Circle the word that tells what was whitewashed. Explain what *whitewashed* means.

8. Name three foods that have a pungent flavor.

"The Street of the Cañon" by Josephina Niggli
Literary Analysis: Setting

All stories have a **setting**—the time and the place of the story's events. To establish a setting, writers use **descriptions,** or word-pictures, to appeal to the senses. Settings shape stories by helping to determine plot as well as characters' concerns and values.

A story may have an overall setting as well as specific settings. There may be more than one setting as the action moves from place to place, and from one time to another. In Shakespeare's *Romeo and Juliet,* for example, the overall setting is Verona, Italy, in the sixteenth century, but the specific time and place changes from scene to scene.

A. DIRECTIONS: *In the "Setting" column, fill in the overall time, overall place, specific time, and specific place in "The Street of the Cañon." In the "Evidence" column, fill in the detail from the story that gives you the information for the setting. In the "Impact" column, write how overall and specific times and places matter to the story. What effect, if any, does each have?*

"The Street of the Cañon"			
	Setting	**Evidence**	**Impact**
Overall Time:			
Overall Place:			
Specific Time:			
Specific Place:			

B. DIRECTIONS: *Write a brief summary of a version of "The Street of the Cañon" set today in your region of the United States. To adapt the story to its new setting, think about situations that can cause rivalries or competition between communities.*

_____

_____

_____

_____

_____

_____

_____

Name _____ Date _____

"The Street of the Cañon" by Josephina Niggli
Reading: Make Inferences and Read on to Find Additional Support

An **inference** is an insight, based on stated details, about information that is not stated. As you read, check your inferences against new information and revise them if needed.

DIRECTIONS: *For each passage from the story, write an inference you can draw from it. Then, write a detail from later in the story that either proves or disproves your inference.*

Example: A tall slender man, a package clutched tightly against his side, slipped from shadow to shadow. Once a dog barked, and the man's black suit merged into the blackness of a wall. But no voice called out, and after a moment he slid into the narrow dirt-packed street again. . . .

Inference: The man is frightened of someone and is trying to escape.

Detail that proves or disproves the inference: The man enters a party, so he does not seem to be trying to escape after all. He was being sneaky, but he was not frightened.

1. The fan in her small hand snapped shut. She tapped its parchment tip against her mouth and slipped away to join the dancing couples in the front room. The gestures of a fan translate into a coded language on the frontier. The stranger raised one eyebrow as he interpreted the signal.

   Inference: _____

   Detail that proves or disproves your inference: _____

   _____

2. This request [to dance] startled her [Sarita's chaperone's] eyes into popping open beneath the heavy brows. "So, my young rooster, would you flirt with me, and I old enough to be your grandmother?"

   Inference: _____

   Detail that proves or disproves your inference: _____

   _____

3. His eyes on the patio, he asked blandly, "You say the leader was one Pepe Gonzalez? The name seems to have a familiar sound."

   Inference: _____

   Detail that proves or disproves your inference: _____

   _____

4. "This is no cheese from Linares. . . . Years ago, when the great Don Rómolo Balderas was still alive, we had such cheese as this—ay, in those days we had it."

   Inference: _____

   Detail that proves or disproves your inference: _____

   _____

Name _____ Date _____

"The Street of the Cañon" by Josephina Niggli
Vocabulary Builder

Word List

nonchalantly	imperiously	plausibility

A. DIRECTIONS: *Match each word in the left column with its definition in the right column. Write the letter of the definition on the line next to the word it defines.*

___ 1. nonchalantly   A. casually; indifferently

___ 2. imperiously   B. believability; seeming truth

___ 3. plausibility   C. arrogantly

B. DIRECTIONS: *Revise or rewrite each sentence so that the underlined vocabulary word is used logically. Be sure to keep the vocabulary word in your revision.*

    Example: The stranger from Hidalgo walked <u>cautiously</u> down the streets of the village, not concerned at all about anyone seeing him.

           The stranger from Hidalgo walked <u>cautiously</u> down the streets of the village, hoping no one would see him.

1. The polite party guests thanked their host <u>imperiously</u> for his hospitality.

    _____

    _____

2. Due to the <u>plausibility</u> of his story, not a single person there believed him.

    _____

    _____

3. Accustomed to getting good grades, she glanced <u>nonchalantly</u> at the D- she received on her research paper.

    _____

    _____

C. DIRECTIONS: *Circle the letter of the word that is most nearly opposite in meaning to the word in capital letters. Because some of the choices are close in meaning, carefully consider all the choices before deciding which is best.*

___ 1. NONCHALANTLY
    A. casually   B. anxiously   C. arrogantly   D. carefully

___ 2. IMPERIOUSLY
    A. softly   B. humbly   C. rudely   D. openly

___ 3. PLAUSIBILITY
    A. belief   B. possibility   C. workability   D. impossibility

"The Street of the Cañon" by Josephina Niggli

Support for Writing a Letter to a Friend and a Book Review

Fill in the following story map to help you summarize "The Street of the Cañon."

The Main Conflict or Problem:

Event 1:	Event 2:	Event 3:

Event 4:	Event 5:	Event 6:

The Resolution or Solution to the Problem:

The Ending:

Now, use your completed story map to help you write your personal letter and book review. Remember to use language appropriate for each audience and provide information that each audience would expect.

"The Street of the Cañon" by Josephina Niggli
Support for Extend Your Learning

Listening and Speaking

To help you prepare for your class discussion on the similarities and differences between "The Highwayman" and "The Street of the Cañon," fill in the following graphic organizer. Write things that are unique to "The Highwayman" in the left-hand oval, things that are unique to "The Street of the Cañon" in the right-hand oval, and things that are similar in both the poem and the story in the center section where the ovals overlap.

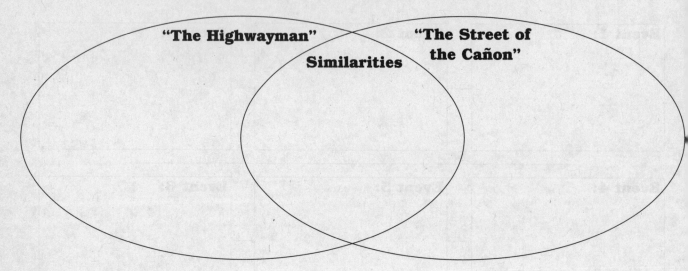

Research and Technology

Fill in the following boxes with some notes about the story's setting and mood. Use your notes to help you select and evaluate artwork for your visual art presentation.

Setting	Mood

Name _____ Date _____

"The Street of the Cañon" by Josephina Niggli
Enrichment: Connecting to Cultures

On the night Pepe Gonzalez pays an unusual visit to San Juan Iglesias, he walks cautiously down dark, unwelcoming streets and then enters a home filled with music and "whirling dancers." Pepe is from Hidalgo, an enemy village, and before this night his only meetings with people from San Juan Iglesias were hostile ones. Tonight, however, people are distracted by the music and festive atmosphere, and nobody recognizes him as an enemy. He finds a dance partner and together they join a circle of dancers, talking and enjoying each other's company.

Dancing, one of the oldest art forms, has always been popular as a way for people to relax, entertain, celebrate, and socialize. While theater dance is usually performed by professionals to entertain an audience, social dancing is an activity meant to be enjoyed by all people at parties, ceremonies, weddings, and other gatherings. Social dance finds its roots in primitive cultures and in early folk dances; it began as a way for people to connect themselves with a group and to celebrate religion or important events. Some of the earliest forms of social dances include the square dance, waltz, polka, and minuet. Latin American dances include the tango and the rhumba. New forms of recreational and social dancing continue to appear as music and social customs evolve and change.

DIRECTIONS: *Review "The Street of the Cañon," and then respond to the following topics.*

1. Explain the importance of dance to the story. Describe how Josephina Niggli incorporates descriptions of dance into the conversation between Sarita and Pepe. How do the dance movements contrast with the relationship the two are supposed to have, given they are from feuding villages?

   _____

   _____

   _____

2. Knowing that social dance has always been a way in many cultures for people to socialize and connect themselves with a group, explain why Pepe might have chosen to make his daring appearance in San Juan Iglesias at a party featuring dance. What is he trying to do?

   _____

   _____

   _____

3. Why do you think social dance has always been such a popular activity in many cultures? How does the dancing in "The Street of the Cañon" compare with dances you have seen or enjoyed?

   _____

   _____

   _____

Name _____ Date _____

Critical Reading *Identify the letter of the choice that best answers the question.*

_____ 1. Where is "The Street of the Cañon" set?
A. the village of Hidalgo
B. the village of San Juan Iglesias
C. the village of the Three Marys
D. the village of Sabinas Valley

_____ 2. What can you infer about the stranger after reading the first few paragraphs of "The Street of the Cañon"?
A. He is carrying cheese to a party.
B. He is on a casual walk through a neighboring town.
C. He does not want anyone to see from which direction he came.
D. He plans to dance at the party with a young lady he has met before.

_____ 3. At the beginning of "The Street of the Cañon," why is the stranger careful to keep people from noticing the package he is carrying?
A. He does not want to share it with anyone.
B. He feels guilty about giving Sarita cheese for her birthday.
C. He knows it will make them angry when they find out what it is.
D. He thinks they will steal it from him.

_____ 4. In "The Street of the Cañon," why does the stranger go to the party?
A. to steal the bones of a famous man born in Hidalgo
B. to wish Sarita a happy birthday and ask her to marry him
C. to show that his father makes the best cheese in the valley
D. to play a prank on the people of San Juan Iglesias

_____ 5. The stranger asks the orchestra to play the *Virgencita*, the favorite song of Hidalgo. What does Sarita think of his request?
A. that he is making a bad joke
B. that he is a man from the village of Hidalgo
C. that he does not know the song would make people in her village angry
D. that it is a strange request since the song does not have a good rhythm

_____ 6. What is the stranger, Pepe Gonzalez, hiding from the young woman as they dance?
A. that he is from Hidalgo
B. that he does not know how to dance
C. that he is secretly in love with her chaperone
D. that he plans to steal something from her home

_____ 7. In "The Street of the Cañon," why do the people of Hidalgo and San Juan Iglesias dislike each other?

    A. Both villages want to be leaders in cheese production.

    B. Both villages want to have the bones of a famous historian.

    C. Both villages want to control the Valley of the Three Marys.

    D. Both villages claim ownership of a chest full of gold that was found.

_____ 8. When talking about Pepe Gonzalez, Sarita says, "He has a talent . . . for doing the impossible. When all the world says a thing cannot be done, he does it to prove the world wrong." Based on this statement, what can you infer about how Sarita feels about Pepe?

    A. She does not care about him one way or the other.

    B. She hates him intensely simply because he is from Hidalgo.

    C. She admires him, even though she is angry about what he did.

    D. She fears him and worries about what he might do to her village.

_____ 9. Why does the stranger leave the party in "The Street of the Cañon"?

    A. He has another party to attend.

    B. He needs to get home because it is late.

    C. He worries that Sarita will think he likes her if he stays.

    D. He knows the crowd will soon figure out that he is from Hidalgo.

_____ 10. Which of the following details helps the reader identify the time period of "The Street of the Cañon"?

    A. There is dancing at the party.

    B. The stranger brings cheese to the party.

    C. The candymaker's arm was broken.

    D. The men from Hidalgo rode horses.

_____ 11. Sarita's party takes place at night and all the villagers are gathered there. How do these details help make the party a good setting for the stranger to accomplish his goal?

    A. He can arrive and escape without people seeing him.

    B. It will take longer for the party guests to find the cheese.

    C. It will be less obvious that he is not a very good dancer.

    D. He will not have to go home until the next morning.

Vocabulary and Grammar

___ 12. Jarred's parents expect him to earn high grades. If Jarred hands his report card to his parents nonchalantly, what kind of reaction do you think he expects them to have?
   A. extreme excitement
   B. intense anger
   C. pleased acceptance
   D. deep sadness

___ 13. An imperious person is someone who is being arrogant. In which of the following situations is a person behaving imperiously?
   A. a young child begging for an after-school snack
   B. an older woman feeding squirrels in a neighborhood park
   C. a wealthy man demanding to be seated in an exclusive restaurant
   D. a baseball fan shouting excitedly as his favorite player hits a home run

___ 14. Pepe Gonzalez _____ a special cheese to the party.
   A. brung
   B. bringed
   C. brought
   D. bringing

Essay

15. In an essay, explain what makes Sarita suspect that the stranger is Pepe Gonzalez in "The Street of the Cañon." Think about the things the stranger says to Sarita while they are dancing, how he reacts to what she says, and how the cheese helps her put all the clues together.

16. Think about the dangers the man from Hidalgo faces by going to the party in San Juan Iglesias. In an essay, explain why these particular dangers might not apply in a story set in a different town or a different time than "The Street of the Cañon."

"The Street of the Cañon" by Josephina Niggli
Selection Test B

Critical Reading *Identify the letter of the choice that best completes the statement or answers the question.*

____ 1. What is the setting of "The Street of the Cañon"?
   A. a small village in Spain about 50 years ago
   B. the Mexican village of Hidalgo during the 1800s
   C. a small town in the United States about 50 years ago
   D. the Mexican village of San Juan Iglesias during the 1800s

____ 2. What might readers logically infer about the stranger after reading the details presented in the opening lines of "The Street of the Cañon"?
   A. He is carrying cheese to a party.
   B. He is on a casual walk through a neighboring town.
   C. He plans to dance at the party with a certain person.
   D. He is deliberately going where he will be unwelcome.

____ 3. In "The Street of the Cañon," why is the stranger drawn to the young girl with "laughing black eyes"?
   A. She is an old friend.
   B. She seems frightened and unsure of herself.
   C. He recognizes her and plans to dance with her.
   D. She is the only person at the party who seems friendly.

____ 4. When the stranger asks the orchestra to play the *Virgencita,* the favorite song of Hidalgo, Sarita thinks the stranger is
   A. making a foolish and tasteless joke.
   B. unaware of the significance of the song.
   C. a man from the village of Hidalgo.
   D. trying to embarrass and upset her.

____ 5. What is the stranger hiding from the young woman in "The Street of the Cañon"?
   A. that he is from Hidalgo
   B. that he is not enjoying the party
   C. that he is enjoying her company
   D. that he has never been to San Juan Iglesias before

____ 6. What is the most recent cause of tension between Hidalgo and San Juan Iglesias in "The Street of the Cañon"?
   A. Both want to be leaders in cheese production.
   B. Both want to control the Valley of the Three Marys.
   C. Both claim ownership of the bones of a famous historian.
   D. Both claim ownership of a chest full of gold that was found.

_____ 7. Based on what Sarita says as she dances with the stranger, what can a reader infer about what her reaction will be when she learns she has danced with a person from Hidalgo?
A. She will want to meet other Hidalgo people.
B. She will be pleasantly surprised.
C. She will be shocked and confused.
D. She will leave the party.

_____ 8. Why does the author include the following passage, written from the stranger's point of view?

> The Hidalgo man twisted his mouth remembering how Rubén the candymaker had ridden across the whitewashed line high on the cañon trail that marked the division between the Three Marys' and the Sabinas' sides of the mountains, and then had fallen in a faint from his saddle because his left arm was broken. There was no candy in Hidalgo for six weeks. . .

A. to discount Sarita's perspective on the situation
B. to introduce Rubén as a character
C. to show the brutality of the fight between the two villages
D. to present the stranger's perspective on the events described by Sarita

_____ 9. In "The Street of the Cañon," what do the stranger's actions reveal about his personality?
A. He is gentle and kind.
B. He is bold and manipulative.
C. He is a coward.
D. He is interested only in parties.

_____ 10. What is Sarita's attitude as she describes Pepe's reputation for "doing the impossible"?
A. contempt for his escapades
B. fear of his wildness
C. amusement at the rumors
D. admiration for his courage

_____ 11. What can you infer about why the stranger leaves the party in "The Street of the Cañon"?
A. He needs to get home because it is late.
B. He feels Sarita will think he likes her if he stays.
C. He feels guilty for being at a party at San Juan Iglesias.
D. He knows the crowd will soon figure out that he is from Hidalgo.

_____ 12. At the end of "The Street of the Cañon," what causes an uproar among the guests?
A. They realize someone from Hidalgo is at the party.
B. The stranger makes his identity known to Don Romeo.
C. The goat cheese brought by the stranger is spoiled.
D. Sarita realizes she has been dancing with Pepe Gonzalez.

_____ 13. What can you infer about how Sarita feels when she realizes with whom she has been dancing?
A. She is surprised and intrigued with the idea that she was dancing with Pepe Gonzalez.
B. She is filled with rage that Pepe Gonzalez would have the nerve to come to her party.
C. She is frightened that Pepe Gonzalez will come back and harm her.
D. She hopes her friends will be jealous when they find out she danced with Pepe.

____ 14. Which of the following lines from the story best explains Pepe's motivation for crashing the party in "The Street of the Cañon"?
A. "Don Rómolo Balderas was the greatest historian in the entire Republic."
B. "When all the world says a thing cannot be done, he does it to prove the world wrong."
C. "But most of all there were cheeses, for the Three Marys was a cheese-eating valley."
D. "Such fine manners were not common to the town of San Juan Iglesias."

____ 15. Which of the following details from "The Street of the Cañon" does NOT help the reader to know the historical period in which the story is set?
A. Tío Daniel refers to the northern frontier.
B. Sarita has a chaperone at the party.
C. The stranger brings cheese to the party.
D. The men from Hidalgo rode horses.

Vocabulary and Grammar

____ 16. Which of the following is the best synonym for the word *nonchalantly*?
A. timidly
B. arrogantly
C. slowly
D. casually

____ 17. In which of the following situations is a person behaving <u>imperiously</u>?
A. a young child begging for an after-school snack
B. a rebellious teenager staying out past her curfew
C. a wealthy man demanding to be seated in an exclusive restaurant
D. a baseball fan shouting excitedly as his favorite player hits a home run

____ 18. The chaperone allowed it, so Sarita and Pepe _____ to dance.
A. begun
B. began
C. beginned
D. will have begun

____ 19. In which of the following sentences is the past participle of an irregular verb used correctly?
A. Pepe brung cheese from Hidalgo to the party.
B. Pepe bringed cheese from Hidalgo to the party.
C. Pepe has brought cheese from Hidalgo to the party.
D. Pepe will be bringing cheese from Hidalgo to the party.

Essay

20. In an essay, explain why the party is a good setting for Pepe to play his prank. Think about what he needs in order for his prank to be successful. Use details from "The Street of the Cañon" to support your essay.

21. Think about the ending of "The Street of the Cañon." In an essay, explain what you think would happen if the story went on to describe the next week or so in the characters' lives. Use details from the story to support your prediction.

Vocabulary Warm-up Word Lists

Study these words from "There Will Come Soft Rains." Then, apply your knowledge to the activities that follow.

Word List A

hysterically [hi STER uh klee] *adv.* laughing or crying in an out-of-control manner
The child cried <u>hysterically</u> when he lost his teddy bear.

linoleum [li NOH lee uhm] *n.* a washable floor covering with a strong, shiny surface
<u>Linoleum</u> floors are back in fashion for retro and vintage kitchen designs.

preference [PREF uhr ens] *n.* liking one thing better than another
You show a <u>preference</u> for one candidate over the others when you vote.

quenching [KWENCH ing] *v.* satisfying a thirst
The tea wasn't <u>quenching</u> my thirst the way water does.

radioactive [ray dee oh AK tiv] *adj.* emitting energy as unstable atoms break down
Contact with <u>radioactive</u> substances like uranium can be dangerous.

reveal [ri VEEL] *v.* show or make known
The actor wouldn't <u>reveal</u> his age to anyone.

tragic [TRAJ ik] *adj.* very unfortunate or sad
Romeo and Juliet tells the <u>tragic</u> story of star-crossed lovers.

wavered [WAY verd] *v.* felt uncertain or unsteady
I <u>wavered</u> between feeling happy and sad about graduating.

Word List B

charred [CHARD] *v.* blackened by fire or burning
The chef <u>charred</u> the catfish just the way Marie liked it.

circuits [SUR kits] *n.* routes for electricity
The <u>circuits</u> overloaded when Ted plugged in both the computer and TV.

cluttered [KLUHT erd] *adj.* overcrowded with objects
Though the room was clean, it was <u>cluttered</u> with too many knickknacks.

ejected [ee JEKT id] *adj.* came out of with force
The cork was <u>ejected</u> when the bottle of carbonated liquid was shaken.

frenzy [FREN zee] *n.* chaotic activity
The audience was in a <u>frenzy</u> as they danced to the band's greatest hit.

froth [FRAWTH] *n.* small bubbles formed on the top of a liquid
The <u>froth</u> from the smoothie made a mustache over Jimmy's upper lip.

preoccupation [pree ahk yoo PAY shuhn] *n.* something that takes all your attention
His <u>preoccupation</u> with UFOs distracted him from his astronomy studies.

reinforcements [ree in FAWRS muhnts] *n.* items used to strengthen things
I used glue and tape as <u>reinforcements</u> when I framed and hung the photo.

Name _____ Date _____

"There Will Come Soft Rains" by Ray Bradbury
Vocabulary Warm-up Exercises

Exercise A *Fill in each blank in the paragraph below with an appropriate word from Word List A. Use each word only once.*

The neon sign at the old diner had a [1] _____ glow. The cook behind the counter usually spent her nights grumbling under her breath while her customers [2] _____ between a choice of chicken and biscuits or the fried chicken platter. Sometimes it seemed that nobody these days could express a clear [3] _____ about what food to eat. Customers knew what they wanted to drink, though, [4] _____ their thirst with the free water as soon as they sat down. Over the years, the cook had seen people [5] _____ plenty about themselves as their tears spilled on the [6] _____ floor. There was nothing, though, that was so [7] _____ that she couldn't get them laughing [8] _____ at one of her well-timed jokes.

Exercise B *For each item, use a word from Word List B to replace the underlined word or group of words without changing its meaning. Write your answers as complete sentences.*

Example: The fish was <u>blackened</u> from the grill.
  The fish was <u>charred</u> from the grill.

1. The <u>paths of electricity</u> could be switched off at the breaker.
   _____

2. The nails served as <u>strengtheners</u> to the glue that held the boards together.
   _____

3. The chef's current <u>obsession</u> is Jamaican food.
   _____

4. The birds moved in a <u>flurry</u> to get the seeds that Kim had scattered.
   _____

5. The <u>bubbles</u> on my hot chocolate tasted warm and sweet.
   _____

6. The <u>messy</u> shelves were full of jumbled toys.
   _____

7. The toddler <u>pushed out</u> the video when she pressed the button.
   _____

"There Will Come Soft Rains" by Ray Bradbury
Reading Warm-up A

Read the following passage. Pay special attention to the underlined words. Then, read it again, and complete the activities. Use a separate sheet of paper for your written answers.

Seventeen-year-old Jenna didn't want to <u>reveal</u> her invention to anyone. She felt anxious as she dragged her computer files into innocent-looking folders, trying desperately to make sure that her notes were secure. Next week, she could relax. Next week, Jenna would make her work public.

Jenna was part of an elite group of high-school students gathered from across the country to take part in a special science program. Her friends in the Young Inventors' Workshop had worked on what might be called "everyday" innovations. For example, Maggie had worked on improving the look and durability of old-fashioned <u>linoleum</u> floors. Derek had worked on easy-to-wear water packs for <u>quenching</u> athletes' thirst. Eileen and Ben had <u>wavered</u> between projects. They had not been able to decide whether to build on someone else's innovation or to hold out for a truly unique idea.

Jenna had gotten to work immediately. She had a <u>preference</u> for inventions that could truly help the world. To that end, she was trying to figure out a better way to store <u>radioactive</u> waste. She knew it could be dangerous to keep the high-level waste stored in the containers that were currently available. In fact, some believed the use of the current containers could lead to <u>tragic</u> results.

Jenna was almost ready to present her solution, but she feared that someone would get into her files and take credit for her ideas. Maggie and Derek thought she was being silly, but they didn't know just how important her project was. Jenna stayed awake long nights working on the details of her invention and fretting over what might happen with it. It was no wonder, then, that she reacted almost <u>hysterically</u> when she saw one of the workshop advisors browsing through her computer.

"Relax, Jenna," he said. "I'm just doing a virus scan. You know, if humanity is worth saving, then at least some of us must be worth trusting."

1. Circle the words that tell what Jenna didn't want to <u>reveal</u>. Then tell what *reveal* means.

2. Underline the phrase that tells what Maggie wanted to improve in <u>linoleum</u> floors. Explain what *linoleum* is.

3. Circle the word that tells what Derek worked on <u>quenching</u>. Tell what *quenching* means.

4. Underline the sentence that explains why Eileen and Ben <u>wavered</u> between projects. Explain what *wavered* means.

5. Underline the phrase that tells what Jenna had a <u>preference</u> for. Explain what *preferences* are.

6. Underline the words that tell why Jenna wanted to figure out a better way to store <u>radioactive</u> waste.

7. Rewrite the sentence with the word <u>tragic</u>, using a synonym for the word.

8. Underline the words that tell why Jenna reacted almost <u>hysterically</u>. Describe how someone who reacts almost *hysterically* might look, sound, and act.

"There Will Come Soft Rains" by Ray Bradbury
Reading Warm-up B

Read the following passage. Pay special attention to the underlined words. Then, read it again, and complete the activities. Use a separate sheet of paper for your written answers.

Will your next home be "smart"? When developers talk about "smart homes," they mean a couple of things. First of all, they are talking about how different electronic devices "talk" to each other. In smart homes, the electric <u>circuits</u> of the different parts of the home are networked so that they can communicate with one another.

Imagine hearing your alarm bell ring. You wake up knowing that a <u>frenzy</u> of activity is taking place. Your cappuccino is beginning to brew, and the milk is steamed into a <u>froth</u>, while toast is crisping in the toaster oven. At the same time, the water for your shower is turned on.

In this "smart" world, the home's appliances along with the heating and cooling systems should work in a way that helps save energy. For example, during the winter, the heat would automatically readjust to a cooler temperature when people leave the house. The closing door would cue the system to reset itself. If the flow of electricity were to be interrupted, battery-operated systems would serve as back-up <u>reinforcements</u> to keep everything running smoothly.

The kitchen has become a special <u>preoccupation</u> for innovators. With a sleek, open style in fashion, the simplest appliance is being designed to perform multiple functions. The <u>cluttered</u> countertops of today's kitchens may be a thing of the past if people start buying refrigerators with television screens built onto the front. Cookbooks can be put into storage if these same refrigerators suggest recipes based on the food they have inside. These refrigerators might even help cooks decide what should be <u>ejected</u> from the shelves as they analyze what's too old to use.

One simple item that could change how we cook is the smart oven mitt. This device would help us avoid overcooked dinners. We used to check the food in the oven to tell us whether it was done and whether the flame had <u>charred</u> the meat in the broiler. Will tomorrow's consumers decide that they need their refrigerators, ovens, and even oven mitts to give them suggestions and advice?

1. Underline the phrase that tells how the <u>circuits</u> of the home will be able to communicate. Then tell what *circuits* are.

2. Describe a <u>frenzy</u> of activity you have been a part of.

3. Circle the words that tell what is steamed into a <u>froth</u>. Explain what *froth* is.

4. When would the battery-operated systems provide <u>reinforcements</u> to the electronic systems?

5. Circle the word that tells what innovators' <u>preoccupation</u> has become. Tell what *preoccupation* means.

6. Write a sentence about what might be on top of <u>cluttered</u> counters.

7. Describe what items being <u>ejected</u> from a refrigerator might look like.

8. Circle the word that is a synonym for <u>charred</u>. Explain what *charred* means.

Name _____ Date _____

"There Will Come Soft Rains" by Ray Bradbury
Literary Analysis: Setting

All stories have a **setting**—the time and the place of the story's events. To establish a setting, writers use **descriptions,** or word-pictures, to appeal to the senses. Settings shape stories by helping to determine plot as well as characters' concerns and values.

A story may have an overall setting as well as specific settings. There may be more than one setting as the action moves from place to place, and from one time to another. In Shakespeare's *Romeo and Juliet,* for example, the overall setting is Verona, Italy, in the sixteenth century, but the specific time and place changes from scene to scene.

You should pay attention to details about the setting, just as you pay attention to other information in the story. What details give you information about the time and place of a story, and what is the effect of those details? Use the following charts to organize what you learn about the settings of the story.

A. DIRECTIONS: *In the "Setting" column, fill in the overall time, overall place, specific time, and specific place in "There Will Come Soft Rains." In the "Evidence" column, fill in the detail from the story that gives you the information for the setting. In the "Impact" column, write how overall and specific times and places matter to the story. What effect, if any, does each have on the story?*

"There Will Come Soft Rains"			
	Setting	**Evidence**	**Impact**
Overall Time:			
Overall Place:			
Specific Time:			
Specific Place:			

B. DIRECTIONS: *How might "There Will Come Soft Rains" have been different if set in a different time and place? How might it have been the same? Write a brief summary of the story as it would be if its setting were today in your region of the United States.*

_____

_____

_____

_____

"There Will Come Soft Rains" by Ray Bradbury
Reading: Make Inferences and Read on to Find Additional Support

An **inference** is an insight, based on stated details, about information that is not stated. Making inferences helps you make connections between facts or events. After making an inference, **read on** to find additional support. If other details disprove your inference, change it.

DIRECTIONS: *On the lines following each passage from the story, write an inference you can draw from it. Then, write a detail from later in the story that either proves or disproves your inference.*

Example: In the living room the voice-clock sang, *"Tick-tock, seven o'clock, time to get up, time to get up, seven o'clock!"* as if it were afraid that nobody would. The morning house lay empty.

Inference: The family that lives in the house has gone away on vacation.

Detail that proves or disproves the inference: A few paragraphs later, it is revealed that the family's car is still in the garage. It is unlikely that they left without it, so something is probably wrong.

1. In the kitchen the breakfast stove gave a hissing sigh and ejected from its warm interior eight pieces of perfectly browned toast, eight eggs sunnyside up, sixteen slices of bacon, two coffees, and two cool glasses of milk.

   Inference: _____

   Detail that proves or disproves your inference: _____

   _____

2. The entire west face of the house was black, save for five places. Here the silhouette in paint of a man mowing a lawn. Here, as in a photograph, a woman bent to pick flowers. Still farther over, their images burned on wood in one titanic instant, a small boy, hands flung into the air; higher up, the image of a thrown ball, and opposite him a girl, hands raised to catch a ball which never came down.

   Inference: _____

   Detail that proves or disproves your inference: _____

   _____

3. The dog, once huge and fleshy, but now gone to bone and covered with sores, moved in and through the house, tracking mud.

   Inference: _____

   Detail that proves or disproves your inference: _____

   _____

"There Will Come Soft Rains" by Ray Bradbury
Vocabulary Builder

Word List

titanic	fluttered	tremulous

A. DIRECTIONS: *Match each word in the left column with its definition in the right column. Write the letter of the definition on the line next to the word it defines.*

___ 1. titanic   **A.** flapped or vibrated rapidly

___ 2. fluttered   **B.** trembling; quivering; timid; fearful

___ 3. tremulous   **C.** powerful or of great size

B. DIRECTIONS: *Revise or rewrite each sentence so that the underlined vocabulary word is used logically. Be sure to keep the vocabulary word in your revision.*

> **Example:** The house <u>shuddered</u> as it went peacefully through its morning routine.
> The house <u>shuddered</u> as the fire ate away at its walls.

1. The large rock in the front yard <u>fluttered</u> in the afternoon sunshine.

   _____

   _____

2. Her voice was loud and <u>tremulous</u> as she confidently gave the best speech of her life.

   _____

   _____

3. The pebble made a <u>titanic</u> splash as it hit the surface of the pond.

   _____

   _____

C. DIRECTIONS: *Circle the letter of the word that is nearest in meaning to the capitalized word.*

1. TREMULOUS
   A. trembling
   B. vast
   C. prestigious
   D. frozen

2. TITANIC
   A. metallic
   B. immense
   C. nautical
   D. ferocious

3. FLUTTERED
   A. waved
   B. trembled
   C. flapped
   D. flipped

"There Will Come Soft Rains" by Ray Bradbury

Support for Writing a Letter to a Friend and a Book Review

Fill in the following story map to help you summarize "There Will Come Soft Rains."

The Main Conflict or Problem:

Event 1:

Event 2:

Event 3:

Event 4:

Event 5:

Event 6:

The Resolution or Solution to the Problem:

The Ending:

Now, use your completed story map to help you write your personal letter and book review. Remember to use language appropriate for each audience and provide information that each audience would expect and find interesting.

"There Will Come Soft Rains" by Ray Bradbury
Support for Extend Your Learning

Listening and Speaking

To help you prepare for your class discussion on the similarities and differences between Teasdale's poem and Bradbury's story, fill in the following graphic organizer. Write things that are unique to the poem in the left-hand oval, things that are unique to the story in the right-hand oval, and things that are similar in both the poem and the story in the center section where the ovals overlap.

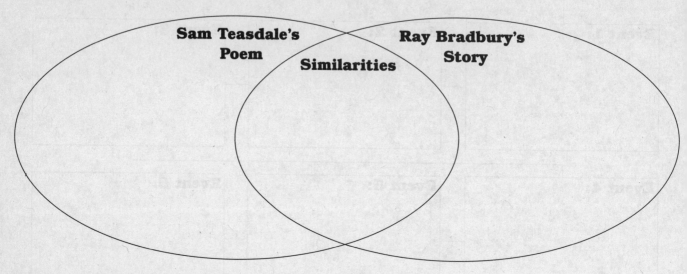

Sam Teasdale's
Poem

Similarities

Ray Bradbury's
Story

Research and Technology

Fill in the following boxes with some notes about the story's setting and mood. Use your notes to help you select and evaluate artwork for your visual art presentation.

Setting	Mood

"There Will Come Soft Rains" by Ray Bradbury
Enrichment: Connecting to Technology

In Ray Bradbury's "There Will Come Soft Rains," a fantastic house lives on after its inhabitants have perished. The story graphically dramatizes ways in which technology can seem miraculous in some situations, but incredibly dangerous in others.

Although we do not have all the labor-saving devices in the story, we are getting closer all the time. Automatic thermostats heat and cool our homes according to schedules and temperatures of our choosing. We can shop at home via computer or telephone. Our ovens can clean themselves. We can see news from anywhere at any time.

But these advances are not without cost. Economists, anthropologists, and ecologists call these costs "tradeoffs." You don't have to grow your own food, but you are also entirely dependent on someone else. You have saved labor, but lost self-sufficiency. Some of these tradeoffs are cultural. We can cook an entire dinner in five minutes in a microwave, but most of us do not take the time to teach someone else what we know about cooking.

What are some of the tradeoffs of modern devices? Use the following chart to consider the way the world is changing. Which ones do you consider worth the price?

DIRECTIONS: For each device or technology in the left column, list some benefits in the center column. In the right column, list some potential tradeoffs.

Device or Technology	Benefits	Tradeoffs
Automatic sprinkler systems:		
Digital recording devices:		
Cellular telephones:		
Online shopping:		
Central air conditioning:		
Online banking:		
Electronic surveillance:		
Cable television:		

"The Street of the Cañon" by Josephina Niggli
"There Will Come Soft Rains" by Ray Bradbury
Build Language Skills: Vocabulary

Word Roots

The word *perspective* combines the Latin root *-spec-* with the prefix *-per-*. *-Spec-* can be traced back to the Latin verb *specere*, meaning "to look." Other words containing the root *-spec-* also have to do with ways of literally or figuratively looking or seeing, such as *inspect, retrospect, suspect,* and *speculate.*

A. DIRECTIONS: *Using a dictionary, briefly explain what the root contributes to the meaning of each of the following words as shown in this example:*

spectacle: The root *-spec-* has to do with looking or seeing, and a spectacle is something that is amazing to see.

1. perspective: _____

2. inspect: _____

3. retrospect: _____

4. suspect: _____

Academic Vocabulary Practice

B. DIRECTIONS: *Decide whether each of the following statements is true or false based on the meaning of the italicized word. Explain your answers.*

Example: A person who *inspects* luggage at an airport opens people's suitcases.
True—an inspector has to look closely and thoroughly at items being inspected.

1. A school's prom committee meets to *formulate* plans for the dance.

   _____

   _____

2. If a story is told from one person's *perspective*, the reader understands what all the characters are thinking.

   _____

   _____

3. One can *anticipate* something that happened last week.

   _____

   _____

4. A listener can *indicate* that he or she understands by nodding his or her head.

   _____

   _____

5. If there is very little evidence at a crime scene, it is difficult for a detective to *discern* clues.

   _____

   _____

"The Street of the Cañon" by Josephina Niggli
"There Will Come Soft Rains" by Ray Bradbury

Build Language Skills: Grammar

Irregular Verbs

A verb has four principal parts: the present, the present participle, the past, and the past participle. Many very common verbs are irregular. This means that the past and past participle are not formed by adding -ed or -d to the present form. The past and the past participle of irregular verbs are formed in various ways. Two irregular verbs, *spend* and *bring*, are shown in the following chart.

Principal Parts of Irregular Verbs

Present	Present Participle	Past	Past Participle
spend	(is, are, was, were) spending	spent	(has, have, had) spent
bring	(is, are, was, were) bringing	brought	(has, have, had) brought

A. PRACTICE: *Identify the principal part used to form each underlined verb.*

Example:

___past___ Pepe <u>kept</u> the package under his arm until he reached the table.

____ 1. Pepe <u>laid</u> the cheese on the table where he knew people would find it.

____ 2. When Pepe left the party, he <u>had taught</u> the people of San Juan Iglesias that he did not look or act like the devil they thought he was.

____ 3. San Juan Iglesias <u>is keeping</u> the bones of the famous historian.

____ 4. An atomic bomb <u>struck</u> the city.

____ 5. The house <u>had kept</u> its peace for many days.

____ 6. The sun <u>will rise</u> again over the ruined city.

B. Writing Application: *Write sentences following the instructions. Check a dictionary if you are unsure of the correct irregular forms.*

    Example: Write a sentence using the past participle form of the verb *write*.

        Ray Bradbury <u>has written</u> many stories about the consequences of future technological growth.

1. Write a sentence using the past participle form of the verb *shrink*.

_____

2. Write a sentence using the present form of the verb *freeze*.

_____

3. Write a sentence using the present participle form of the verb *burst*.

_____

"There Will Come Soft Rains" by Ray Bradbury
Selection Test A

Critical Reading *Identify the letter of the choice that best answers the question.*

_____ 1. What is the setting of "There Will Come Soft Rains"?
   A. on a Pacific island in 2026
   B. in a small town in California in 1950
   C. in a city in California in the near future
   D. on a Pacific island a few years after World War II

_____ 2. How is the setting of "There Will Come Soft Rains" revealed to the reader?
   A. The date and location are burned into the side of the house.
   B. The house states the time, date, and location at the beginning of the story.
   C. The reader must figure it out based on a variety of clues throughout the story.
   D. There is a newspaper on the kitchen table that shows the date and location of the story.

_____ 3. Where are the human beings in "There Will Come Soft Rains"?
   A. They are all at work or at school.
   B. They have all moved to a different city.
   C. They have all been destroyed by a nuclear war.
   D. They are all being held prisoner in the basement of the automated house.

_____ 4. Which of the following details helps you figure out what has happened to the owners of the house in "There Will Come Soft Rains"?
   A. Mrs. McClellan likes to listen to poetry in the evenings.
   B. The stove prepares a breakfast that goes uneaten.
   C. There are silhouettes of four people burned into the side of the house.
   D. The house carefully keeps itself clean and protects itself from harm.

_____ 5. At the beginning of the story, the stove prepares eight pieces of toast, eight eggs, sixteen slices of bacon, two coffees, and two glasses of milk. What can you figure out about the McClellan family based on this information?
   A. The family is having guests over for breakfast.
   B. Two of the family members are allergic to milk.
   C. The stove usually burns the toast and undercooks the eggs.
   D. There are four family members, and two of them are children.

_____ 6. What is the purpose of the robot mice in "There Will Come Soft Rains"?
  A. to entertain the family's cat
  B. to clean the floors of the house
  C. to feed and groom the family's dog
  D. to serve the food prepared by the stove

_____ 7. What happens to the family's dog in "There Will Come Soft Rains"?
  A. It dies of radiation sickness and starvation.
  B. It wandered away before the beginning of the story.
  C. The house takes care of it, but it becomes ill from loneliness and bad food.
  D. It is taken in by another family because the McClellans can no longer take care of it.

_____ 8. What was the last thing the McClellan children did before the story begins?
  A. They played a game of catch.
  B. They listened to poetry before bedtime.
  C. They watched the animal scenes in the nursery.
  D. They ate eggs, toast, and bacon prepared by the stove.

_____ 9. What is the poem by Sara Teasdale about?
  A. the beauty of a soft rain shower in the springtime
  B. how she wishes she owned a high-tech automated house
  C. that nature would not care if humans disappeared entirely
  D. that spring always comes to an end when the heat of summer arrives

_____ 10. How does the automated house "die" in "There Will Come Soft Rains"?
  A. It is blown up in a nuclear blast.
  B. The electronic mice tear it down.
  C. It catches on fire and is unable to put the fire out.
  D. Its owners leave it and it eventually stops functioning.

_____ 11. In "There Will Come Soft Rains," machines, not humans, perform all house chores. Which of the following adjectives best describes the feeling that is created by this setting?
  A. cheerful
  B. frightening
  C. reassuring
  D. impersonal

Vocabulary and Grammar

___ 12. Read the following sentence and then choose the best synonym for the word *titanic.*

> With a titanic effort, the world champion bodybuilder heaved the massive weights up over his head.

A. timid

B. powerful

C. unsinkable

D. moderate

___ 13. Which of the following situations is most likely to make a person feel tremulous?

A. being threatened by a violent person

B. hearing one's favorite song on the radio

C. getting a good grade on a research paper

D. finding out that an exam has been moved to a later date.

___ 14. Choose the correct form of the irregular verb *sleep* to complete the following sentence.

> The McClellan children _____ in a nursery that had glowing animals on the walls.

A. sleeped

B. slept

C. sleeping

D. had sleep

Essay

15. Ray Bradbury published "There Will Come Soft Rains" in 1950. How well do you think he predicted the way houses would look and function in the twenty-first century? In an essay, evaluate Bradbury's predictions by comparing them to the way things are today. You may also make an educated guess about how things will continue to change in the next 20 years.

16. In "There Will Come Soft Rains," Bradbury personifies the house and its machines. In other words, he writes as if the house and its machines have thoughts and emotions like people. For example, he writes that the house makes its wake-up call as if afraid that nobody would wake up. What are some more examples of emotions Bradbury gives to the house and its machines? Do they really have emotions? Why do you think Bradbury uses personification in this story? Write your response in an essay.

"There Will Come Soft Rains" by Ray Bradbury
Selection Test B

Critical Reading *Identify the letter of the choice that best completes the statement or answers the question.*

____ 1. In "There Will Come Soft Rains," human beings
   A. have all been destroyed by the automated house.
   B. have all been destroyed in a nuclear war.
   C. have left the planet for a safer destination.
   D. are prisoners of the technology they have invented.

____ 2. Which of the following details helps you infer what is going on at the beginning of "There Will Come Soft Rains"?
   A. "This was the one house left standing."
   B. "Until this day, how well the house had kept its peace."
   C. "The rooms were acrawl with the small cleaning animals, all rubber and metal."
   D. "Somewhere in the walls, relays clicked, memory tapes glided under electric eyes."

____ 3. What can you infer from the following passage from "There Will Come Soft Rains"?

   In the kitchen the breakfast stove gave a hissing sigh and ejected from its warm interior eight pieces of perfectly browned toast, eight eggs sunnyside up, sixteen slices of bacon, two coffees, and two cool glasses of milk.

   A. The family is having guests over for breakfast.
   B. Two of the family members are allergic to milk.
   C. The stove usually burns the toast and undercooks the eggs.
   D. There are four family members, and two of them are children.

____ 4. In "There Will Come Soft Rains," why does the house continue its activity even when it no longer makes sense to do so?
   A. It is sad and misses the family.
   B. It is damaged and malfunctioning.
   C. It is simply following its programming.
   D. It hopes another family will be moving in soon.

____ 5. Which of the following sentences from "There Will Come Soft Rains" contributes directly to the setting?
   A. "Today is Mr. Featherstone's birthday."
   B. "Bridge tables sprouted from patio walls."
   C. "A dog whined, shivering on the front porch."
   D. "It repeated the date three times for memory's sake."

____ 6. Why did Bradbury choose a fully automated house instead of a factory or a school as the setting for "There Will Come Soft Rains"?
   A. A house is small enough to describe in a short story.
   B. It is unlikely that a larger building would survive the blast.
   C. The homey details emphasize the horror of nuclear destruction.
   D. A factory or school would require less automation than the house.

____ 7. In "There Will Come Soft Rains," what mood is created by a setting in which all domestic functions are performed by machines and none by human beings?
A. cheerful and exhilarating
B. repulsive and horrifying
C. homey and reassuring
D. impersonal and chilling

____ 8. What can the reader infer about the McClellan family based on the way their house is programmed in "There Will Come Soft Rains"?
A. They live a quiet, orderly life.
B. They are active in politics.
C. Both parents have full-time jobs.
D. Mrs. McClellan is blind.

____ 9. What was the last thing the family did before "There Will Come Soft Rains" begins?
A. listen to poetry before bedtime
B. mow the lawn, pick flowers, and play ball
C. reprogram the house to function without them
D. wash the car, feed the dog, and buy groceries

____ 10. By portraying the house as "alive" and the family as painted silhouettes, Bradbury
A. stresses the importance of strong family values.
B. expresses the idea that human life is insignificant.
C. reverses expectations of human and nonhuman roles.
D. shows how technology can enhance human lives.

____ 11. What happens to the family's dog in "There Will Come Soft Rains"?
A. It dies of radiation sickness and starvation.
B. It dies in the fire that burns down the house.
C. The house takes care of it, but it is lonely without the family.
D. It wanders away in search of food because the house does not feed it.

____ 12. The setting of "There Will Come Soft Rains" suggests that human beings
A. are dependent on machines.
B. have evolved into androids.
C. view nature as distasteful.
D. have no free choice.

____ 13. Given the events that took place shortly before "There Will Come Soft Rains" begins, the automated house may represent the
A. last hope for humane family values.
B. answer to the problem of global war.
C. dangers of technology.
D. inherent evil of totalitarian systems.

____ 14. In "There Will Come Soft Rains," what starts the fire in the house?
   A. One of the cleaning mice shorts out inside the wall.
   B. The house accidentally starts a grease fire while cooking some bacon.
   C. The family dog knocks over a candle while trying to get into the kitchen.
   D. A falling tree limb knocks a bottle of flammable cleaning solution onto the stove.

____ 15. Why is the house unable to put out the fire in "There Will Come Soft Rains"?
   A. The windows are broken and the water has run out.
   B. The family forgot to program the house to put out fires.
   C. No one comes when the house calls for emergency assistance.
   D. The house malfunctions and does not even try to extinguish the fire.

Vocabulary and Grammar

____ 16. Which of the following is an antonym of *titanic*?
   A. timid
   B. powerful
   C. unsinkable
   D. inconsequential

____ 17. Which of the following people is most likely to feel *tremulous*?
   A. a child who has just learned to write his name
   B. a young man who has just been in a car accident
   C. a teen who has just finished a difficult research project
   D. an older woman who has just purchased a new winter coat

____ 18. The house was the only building that still _____ in a city of rubble and ashes.
   A. stands
   B. standing
   C. stood
   D. standed

____ 19. In which of the following sentences is the irregular verb *rise* used correctly?
   A. The next morning, the sun rose over a ruined city.
   B. The next morning, the sun risen over a ruined city.
   C. The next morning, the sun rising over a ruined city.
   D. The next morning, the sun rised over a ruined city.

Essay

20. In "There Will Come Soft Rains," Bradbury explores the idea that technology can be both helpful and dangerous to human beings. In an essay, explain ways in which the story shows these two sides of technology.

21. Ray Bradbury published "There Will Come Soft Rains" in 1950. In an essay, discuss whether or not you think Bradbury's vision of the future in "There Will Come Soft Rains" is believable and realistic in reference to the modern world. Use examples from the story and from real life to support your opinion.

22. Near the end of Bradbury's "There Will Come Soft Rains," he pays tribute to poet Sara Teasdale by including a poem she wrote. What effect does this poem have on the story? Write an essay that discusses the meaning of the poem and its effects on the story.

Vocabulary Warm-up Word Lists

Study these words from the selections. Then, complete the activities that follow.

Word List A

eternal [ee TER nuhl] *adj.* continuing forever
   The newlyweds hoped for eternal happiness.

heirs [AIRZ] *n.* people who legally receive money or property of a person who has died
   The heirs to the fortune gave the money they inherited to charity.

moreover [mawr OH ver] *adv.* in addition
   The clown was very professional; moreover, he was hilarious.

offensive [uh FEN siv] *adj.* insulting and likely to upset people
   Though Ted didn't mean to be rude, people found his jokes offensive.

qualifications [kwahl ih fih KAY shuhnz] *n.* qualities that make someone a good choice
   Thanks to her computer training, she met all the qualifications for the job.

render [REN der] *v.* give; yield; pay; do a service
   My parents expect me to render a complete account of my evening out.

restless [REST lis] *adj.* unable to be still, especially due to nervousness or boredom
   Todd felt so restless during the dull movie that he went to the lobby for snacks twice.

sequestered [si KWES terd] *v.* set apart; separated
   The child with the flu was sequestered in her room for a week.

Word List B

chariots [CHAR ee uhts] *n.* ancient two-wheeled horse-drawn vehicles
   Roman chariots have been unearthed at the site of ancient battles.

leisurely [LEE zhur lee] *adj.* unhurried
   We toured the museum at a leisurely pace.

nevertheless [nev er thuh LES] *adv.* in spite of that
   I know you are probably right, but nevertheless, I'll do things my way.

professionally [pruh FESH uhn uhl lee] *adv.* in a way guided by rules, not feelings
   The police officer acted professionally even when the driver began to yell.

trifling [TRY fling] *adj.* having little value or importance
   Jane made some trifling contributions to the group discussion.

trophy [TROH fee] *n.* a prize, often a cup or plaque, awarded or received for victory
   Each baseball player got a trophy when the team won the championship.

underfoot [uhn der FOOT] *adv.* on the ground, beneath your feet
   The gravel on the country road crunched underfoot.

writings [RY tingz] *n.* books, stories, poems, letters, and the like, in general
   The English teacher had her students read all her favorite writings.

86

Name _____ Date _____

"One Thousand Dollars" by O. Henry
"By the Waters of Babylon" by Stephen Vincent Benét
Vocabulary Warm-up Exercises

Exercise A *Fill in each blank in the paragraph below with an appropriate word from Word List A. Use each word only once.*

Mr. Doane's loved ones gathered at the hospital. The wait that had seemed

[1] _____ was now over. After being [2] _____ for days in

the quarantine area, Mr. Doane had died. [3] _____, there had already

been a first reading of the will. The [4] _____ group now gathered at the

hospital had been summoned according to its contents. Mr. Doane's loved ones were

now his [5] _____. There were questions that each was eager to ask, yet

nobody wanted to appear rude or [6] _____ by bringing up the will just

yet. Still, they wondered which of them had the [7] _____ to handle the

estate. Who could [8] _____ the legal advice to guide them?

Exercise B *Revise each sentence so that the underlined vocabulary word is used in a logical way. Be sure to keep the vocabulary word in your revision.*

Example: The mechanic did the job <u>professionally</u>, so we yelled at him.
The mechanic did the job <u>professionally</u>, so we thanked him.

1. I know you are happy; <u>nevertheless</u>, I am happy.
   _____

2. She gave me a <u>trifling</u> amount of money, so I was rich.
   _____

3. The losing team got a <u>trophy</u>, and the winning team got nothing.
   _____

4. Drivers drove <u>chariots</u> pulled by teams of dogs.
   _____

5. I was out of breath after my <u>leisurely</u> walk.
   _____

6. There were lots of clouds <u>underfoot</u>.
   _____

7. The information was in the <u>writings</u>, so no one could find it again.
   _____

Name _____   Date _____

"One Thousand Dollars" by O. Henry
"By the Waters of Babylon" by Stephen Vincent Benét
Reading Warm-up A

Read the following passage. Pay special attention to the underlined words. Then, read it again, and complete the activities. Use a separate sheet of paper for your written answers.

When Howard Hughes died in 1976, nearly four hundred people claimed to be <u>heirs</u> to his estate. The famous movie producer, aviator, and businessman left roughly 2 billion dollars. During his last years, Hughes lived <u>sequestered</u> in the Desert Inn in Las Vegas, away from any sort of public life. After a while, the owners asked him to leave the premises. Hughes, once so <u>restless</u> that he flew all over the world, ended up buying the hotel from the owners so he could stay put.

It is not clear whether Hughes was still able to <u>render</u> clear instructions about his will toward the end of his life. He had been married and divorced twice and had no children from those marriages. He had no single obvious heir. <u>Moreover</u>, instead of close friends, he had a staff of people who gave him food and medication.

Eventually, several wills turned up. One named Melvin Dummar, a man who worked in a mine in Nevada, as one of Hughes's heirs. Why would the billionaire recluse leave part of his fortune to Dummar, who was not even a relative? What <u>qualifications</u> did Dummar have to deserve Hughes's <u>eternal</u>, everlasting gratitude? Dummar said it was because he once gave Hughes a ride in his car.

According to Dummar, one night in 1967, he saw a man lying in the dirt in the desert. Dummar offered to help him. The man asked him for a lift to Las Vegas, about 150 miles away. Dummar agreed, and it was only at the end of the trip that Hughes revealed who he was. As Dummar tells it, the two men never met again. And yet, eleven years later, when Hughes died, he supposedly left one-sixteenth of his fortune (roughly 156 million dollars) to Melvin Dummar. The will that named Dummar as one of Hughes's heirs was declared a forgery by a Nevada court. In fact, all of the wills were declared fakes. The fortune was split among Hughes's many cousins. Dummar found talk of forgery <u>offensive</u> and distasteful. He still maintains that he gave Howard Hughes that ride.

1. Circle the number of people who claimed to be <u>heirs</u> to the Hughes estate. Tell what *heirs* are.

2. Underline the phrase that tells where Hughes lived <u>sequestered</u>. Explain what *sequestered* means.

3. Circle the words that show that Hughes had become the opposite of <u>restless</u>. Then tell what it feels like to be *restless*.

4. Circle the word that tells what Hughes may or may not have been able to <u>render</u>. Tell what *render* means.

5. Rewrite the sentence that uses the word <u>moreover</u>. Find a word or phrase that means the same thing as *moreover*.

6. Underline the sentence that describes Dummar's <u>qualifications</u>. Write some *qualifications* that you have for the workplace.

7. Circle the word that means the same as <u>eternal</u>. Use the word *eternal* in a sentence.

8. Circle the word that is a synonym for <u>offensive</u>. Explain why Dummar found talk of forgery *offensive*.

"One Thousand Dollars" by O. Henry
"By the Waters of Babylon" by Stephen Vincent Benét
Reading Warm-up B

Read the following passage. Pay special attention to the underlined words. Then, read it again, and complete the activities. Use a separate sheet of paper for your written answers.

You've surely heard the expression "When in Rome, do as the Romans do." However, you may not have realized that there's no need to travel all the way to Italy to emulate first-century Romans. If you read any of the countless descriptive <u>writings</u> about the Colosseum, you will soon realize that in our own modern society, we often "do" just as the Romans did.

The Colosseum is an elliptical four-story structure, <u>professionally</u> designed by the architects of the day. There were 80 entrances, of which 76 were numbered. These numbers corresponded to the numbers on spectators' tickets. This allowed for the orderly entrance of up to 50,000 eager spectators. It is this very system that is still used today at stadiums around the globe. Of course, these same doors permitted spectators to exit without the sort of mad rush that leaves people trampled <u>underfoot</u>.

Roman nobles often arrived at the Colosseum in <u>leisurely</u> style, carried on litters by their slaves or servants. When the emperor and his entourage arrived, they had no need to push through the crowds. There were two entrances reserved just for their use. The remaining two entrances were used by the gladiators, who entered in dramatic processions at the beginning of the day's event. The most prominent gladiators rode around the arena in <u>chariots</u>.

The combat that followed was no <u>trifling</u> matter. Gladiators fought until one of the two combatants was poised to kill the other. Then the crowd would signal a thumbs-up, meaning "free him," or a thumbs-down, meaning "kill him." <u>Nevertheless</u>, it was the emperor who had the final word. The winning gladiator did not receive any sort of <u>trophy</u>, but he was occasionally granted his freedom.

Though traffic flow in modern colosseums is still based on the Roman model, competitors are surely grateful that fans no longer have the same influence on the outcome.

1. Underline the phrase that indicates that there are many <u>writings</u> about the Colosseum. Name the subject of some *writings* you have read.

2. Circle the words that tell what was <u>professionally</u> designed. Write about something else that is usually *professionally* designed by an architect.

3. Explain how people in the Colosseum might be trampled <u>underfoot</u>.

4. Underline the phrase that describes how the nobles arrived in <u>leisurely</u> style. Then explain what *leisurely* means.

5. Circle the words that shows who rode in the <u>chariots</u>. Write about another context where *chariots* might be used.

6. Explain why the combat was no <u>trifling</u> matter.

7. Rewrite this sentence, using a synonym for <u>nevertheless</u>.

8. Underline that phrase that tells what drivers might get instead of a <u>trophy</u>. Tell what a *trophy* is.

Name _____ Date _____

"One Thousand Dollars" by O. Henry
"By the Waters of Babylon" by Stephen Vincent Benét
Literary Analysis: Point of View

Point of view is the perspective from which a story is told. Most stories are told from either first-person point of view or third-person point of view.

In **first-person point of view,** the narrator is one of the characters and refers to himself or herself with the pronouns *I* or *me.* In "By the Waters of Babylon," for example, the story's narrator is also its main character, John.

In **third-person point of view,** the narrator does not participate in the action. Instead, the narrator refers to characters by the third-person pronouns *he, she, him, her, they,* and *them.* "One Thousand Dollars" is told in third-person point of view. A narrator outside the story tells about the actions and experiences of the main character, Bob Gillian.

Sometimes, a writer gives the reader more information than the narrator or a character has. By doing so, the writer creates **dramatic irony,** a forceful contrast between what the reader knows to be true and what the narrator or character believes.

DIRECTIONS: *Write your answers to the following questions.*

1. How can you tell that "One Thousand Dollars" is told in third-person point of view? _____
_____

2. At the end of "One Thousand Dollars," what do Gillian and the reader know that the law-yers do *not* know? _____
_____

3. Reread the last sentence of "One Thousand Dollars." How does this sentence create dra-matic irony? _____
_____

4. Does this dramatic irony make you see other people in a new light? Why or why not?
_____

5. **A.** Give one quote from "By the Waters of Babylon" that helps you identify John as the story's first-person narrator. _____
_____

   B. Now, circle the word or words in the quote that reveal the point of view.

6. What does John know that the reader does *not* know? _____
_____

7. Give one detail from "By the Waters of Babylon" about which the reader has more knowl-edge than John does. _____
_____

8. What mood is created by the story's dramatic irony? _____

"One Thousand Dollars" by O. Henry
"By the Waters of Babylon" by Stephen Vincent Benét
Vocabulary Builder

Word List

stipulates	prudent	purified	nevertheless

A. DIRECTIONS: *Each sentence below features a word from the Word List. Explain whether each sentence makes sense, given the meaning of the underlined word. If it does not make sense, write a new sentence using the word correctly.*

1. Lake water should be <u>purified</u> before it is consumed.

   _____

   _____

2. It was <u>prudent</u> of James to rollerblade without a helmet.

   _____

   _____

3. Greta is sleepy; *nevertheless*, she wants to go to bed.

   _____

   _____

4. The entry form <u>stipulates</u> that all contestants must be under 18 years of age.

   _____

   _____

B. DIRECTIONS: *Write each word from the Word List next to its correct definition.*

____ 1. exercising sound judgment; cautious

____ 2. in spite of that; however

____ 3. cleansed; made pure

____ 4. includes specifically as part of an agreement

Name _____ Date _____

"One Thousand Dollars" by O. Henry
"By the Waters of Babylon" by Stephen Vincent Benét
Support for Writing to Compare Literary Works

Before you draft your essay comparing how each author uses point of view to create irony, complete the graphic organizers below.

One Thousand Dollars
What truth is revealed at the end of the story?
Who sees the truth? (Consider the narrator, the story's characters and the reader.)   Who does not?
What is ironic about the story's ending? (Do the reader, the characters, or the narrator continue to hold any wrong assumptions?)   How does the ironic ending affect the way you see yourself, the world, or others?

By the Waters of Babylon
What truth is revealed at the end of the story?
Who sees the truth? (Consider the narrator, the story's characters and the reader.)   Who does not?
What is ironic about the story's ending? (Do the reader, the characters, or the narrator continue to hold any wrong assumptions?)   How does the ironic ending affect the way you see yourself, the world, or others?

Now, use your notes to write an essay comparing how point of view creates irony in each story. In your essay, explain which use of irony you found more effective, and why.

"One Thousand Dollars" by O. Henry
"By the Waters of Babylon" by Stephen Vincent Benét
Selection Test A

Critical Reading *Identify the letter of the choice that best answers the question.*

____ 1. In "One Thousand Dollars," what problem does Gillian face?
  A. He cannot find the person to whom his uncle has left $1,000.
  B. He does not know how to spend the $1,000 he has inherited.
  C. He cannot convince the lawyers that the $1,000 is his.
  D. He does not want to spend $1,000 on Lotta Lauriere, but feels he must.

____ 2. In "One Thousand Dollars," what is Old Bryson's attitude toward Gillian?
  A. He finds Gillian annoying and immature.
  B. He respects Gillian.
  C. He envies Gillian's money and therefore tolerates him.
  D. He feels sorry for Gillian and therefore tries to help him.

____ 3. In "One Thousand Dollars," how are Gillian's true feelings for Miss Hayden revealed?
  A. through his actions only
  B. through his words only
  C. through his words and his actions
  D. through the first-person narrator

____ 4. At the end of "One Thousand Dollars," why does Gillian rip up the note he has written?
  A. because he does not know how to spend the $50,000
  B. because he does not want the lawyers to think poorly of him
  C. because he decides that he wants the $50,000 after all
  D. because he wants Miss Hayden to receive the $50,000

____ 5. What creates irony at the end of "One Thousand Dollars"?
  A. The lawyers know something that Gillian does not.
  B. Gillian does a good deed.
  C. The reader knows something that the lawyers do not.
  D. Gillian acts selfishly.

_____ **6.** In "By the Waters of Babylon," how is John's society different from the one that came before it?
  A. Priests govern the society.
  B. Technology is more advanced.
  C. People eat only plants.
  D. There is no warfare.

_____ **7.** In "By the Waters of Babylon," why does John go to the Place of the Gods?
  A. to become more powerful
  B. to seek knowledge
  C. to find metal
  D. to anger his father

_____ **8.** In "By the Waters of Babylon," John sees the city "as it had been when the gods were alive." What is he seeing?
  A. a view of another planet
  B. New York City as it had been
  C. the future
  D. a myth

_____ **9.** In "By the Waters of Babylon," what does John finally realize about the gods?
  A. that they did not know how to read
  B. that they used magic to cook and wash
  C. that they still lived in the city
  D. that they were people

_____ **10.** What creates irony in "By the Waters of Babylon"?
  A. John finally understands the truth about the gods.
  B. John goes to the Place of the Gods even though it is forbidden.
  C. The narrator knows more about the "Place of the Gods" than the reader does.
  D. The reader knows more about the "Place of the Gods" than John does.

_____ **11.** Which sentence from "One Thousand Dollars" or "By the Waters of Babylon" reflects first-person point of view?
  A. After a time, I myself was allowed to go into the dead houses and search for metal.
  B. "I thank you very much, sir," said Gillian, and out he went to his cab.
  C. The towers are not all broken—here and there one still stands.
  D. Without touching the envelope, Mr. Tolman went to a door and called his partner, Sharp.

___ 12. Which is true of both "One Thousand Dollars" and "By the Waters of Babylon"?

A. They are set in the past.

B. They are set in the future.

C. They are set in a different time period from our own.

D. They are set in our own time period.

___ 13. Which is a theme of both "One Thousand Dollars" and "By the Waters of Babylon"?

A. Things are not always what they seem to be.

B. If you do what is forbidden, you will pay the price.

C. Love can change the world.

D. Life is not always fair.

Vocabulary

___ 14. How might the priests in "By the Waters of Babylon" have *purified* the metal?

A. by bending and twisting it

B. by placing it in fire

C. by covering it with dirt

D. by throwing it away

___ 15. On a cold day, which of these actions would be *prudent*?

A. going barefoot

B. going for a jog

C. wearing a coat

D. wearing shorts

Essay

16. "One Thousand Dollars" and "By the Waters of Babylon" are told from different points of view, or perspectives. In an essay, identify the point of view from which each story is told. Next, describe the narrator of each story. Finally, explain whether the narrator knows more or less about the story's characters and events than the reader does. Provide examples from the stories to support your ideas.

17. Both "One Thousand Dollars" and "By the Waters of Babylon" invite their readers to see something in a new way. In a brief essay, explain how each story does this. Pay particular attention to the end of each story. Provide examples from the stories to support your points.

"One Thousand Dollars" by O. Henry
"By the Waters of Babylon" by Stephen Vincent Benét
Selection Test B

Critical Reading *Identify the letter of the choice that best completes the statement or answers the question.*

____ 1. In "One Thousand Dollars," how does Gillian respond to his $1,000 inheritance?
   A. He is angry that his uncle did not leave him more money.
   B. He finds it an awkward amount of money to have to spend.
   C. He is overjoyed that his uncle left him such a large sum of money.
   D. He knows that if he spends it wisely, he will receive much more money.

____ 2. In "One Thousand Dollars," Old Bryson's reaction to Gillian suggests that
   A. some of Gillian's acquaintances like him only because he is wealthy.
   B. many of Gillian's acquaintances will be jealous of his inheritance.
   C. most of Gillian's acquaintances want what is best for him.
   D. some of Gillian's acquaintances find him immature and unlikable.

____ 3. In "One Thousand Dollars," which word best describes Lotta Lauriere's response to Gillian?
   A. dismissive
   B. affectionate
   C. hostile
   D. puzzled

____ 4. In "One Thousand Dollars," why does Gillian give the money to Miriam Hayden?
   A. because he loves her
   B. because he wants to impress her
   C. because she asks him for it
   D. because he can't think of anything else to do with it

____ 5. What creates irony at the end of "One Thousand Dollars"?
   A. The lawyers know something about Gillian that the reader does not.
   B. The narrator knows something about Gillian that the lawyers do not.
   C. The reader knows something about Gillian that the lawyers do not.
   D. The lawyers, the reader, and the narrator all discover the truth about Gillian.

____ 6. Which best describes the narrator in "One Thousand Dollars"?
   A. first-person
   B. omniscient third-person
   C. limited third-person
   D. naive first-person

____ 7. In "By the Waters of Babylon," which period represents "the beginning of time" for John's society?
   A. before the evolution of the human species
   B. before the onset of the Industrial Revolution
   C. after human beings learned to use fire
   D. after the destruction of modern civilization

____ 8. John's references to gods and magic in "By the Waters of Babylon" suggest that
    A. John is young.
    B. his people lack knowledge of technology.
    C. the People of the Hills are social outcasts.
    D. the Great Burning was a recent event.

____ 9. What conclusion can be drawn from this passage from "By the Waters of Babylon"?
    There was also the shattered image of a man or a god. It had been made of white stone and he wore his hair tied back like a woman's. His name was ASHING. . . .
    A. The image is a statue of Washington.
    B. The gods had a leader named ASHING.
    C. Some people considered Washington a god.
    D. The gods had greater respect for men than for women.

____ 10. John's discovery that the "gods" were men makes him realize that
    A. he can no longer be considered a priest.
    B. his people are capable of similar feats.
    C. New York City was once a sacred place.
    D. the Hill People are completely insignificant.

____ 11. Which sentence best reflects the point of view in "By the Waters of Babylon"?
    A. The north and the west and the south are good hunting ground. . . .
    B. It is eight suns' journey to the east and a man passes by many Dead Places.
    C. After a time, I myself was allowed to go into the dead houses and search for metal.
    D. There was a washing-place but no water—perhaps the gods washed in air.

____ 12. The point of view used in "By the Waters of Babylon" causes the reader to
    A. strongly identify with John.
    B. judge the narrator to be ignorant.
    C. believe in magic.
    D. see the world in a new way.

____ 13. Which of the following is true of the narrators in both stories?
    A. They are both omniscient.
    B. They both know more than the reader knows.
    C. They are both first-person narrators.
    D. They both have limited knowledge.

____ 14. How are Gillian in "One Thousand Dollars" and John in "By the Waters of Babylon" alike?
    A. Both take actions that others may perceive to be foolish.
    B. Neither is treated fairly by his elders.
    C. Both allow fear and uncertainty to determine their actions.
    D. Neither comes to understand an important truth.

____ 15. In both stories, dramatic irony is used to create
    A. a humorous tone.
    B. suspense.
    C. third-person point of view.
    D. a dreamy mood.

___ 16. Both "One Thousand Dollars" and "By the Waters of Babylon" are set
A. in New York City, and in the past.
B. in Europe, and in the future.
C. in New York City, and in a different time period from our own.
D. in Europe, and in our own time period.

___ 17. Which is a theme of both "One Thousand Dollars" and "By the Waters of Babylon"?
A. Things are not always what they seem to be.
B. It is best to seek advice before making an important decision.
C. Small acts of love can change the world.
D. Waste not, want not.

___ 18. At the end of both "One Thousand Dollars" and "By the Waters of Babylon," the reader is left with a feeling of
A. doom.
B. amusement.
C. hope.
D. regret.

Vocabulary

___ 19. What does *nevertheless* mean in this sentence from "By the Waters of Babylon"?

The god who lived there must have been a wise god and full of knowledge. I felt I had a right there, as I sought knowledge also. Nevertheless, it was strange.

A. because of this
B. in addition
C. amazingly
D. in spite of this

___ 20. Which of these actions is *prudent*?
A. sleeping until noon
B. packing carefully for a camping trip
C. strongly disagreeing with another person
D. riding a bike without a helmet

Essay

21. In an essay, choose an alternate point of view for either "One Thousand Dollars" or "By the Waters of Babylon." Explain how the story would have been different if this alternate point of view had been used. In your opinion, would this point of view have made the story better, or did the author choose the most effective point of view to begin with?

22. Dramatic irony can create a variety of feelings in the reader, from intense pity to discomfort. In an essay, explain the feelings generated by the irony in both "One Thousand Dollars" and "By the Waters of Babylon." Define, as precisely as you can, the source of your reaction to the ending of each story. Then, explain whether the feeling prompted you to see yourself, someone else, or the world around in you in a new light.

23. The authors of both "One Thousand Dollars" and "By the Waters of Babylon" create dramatic irony by using a certain point of view. In an essay, identify the point of view used in each story. Then, explain how point of view is responsible for the irony in each work.

Name _____   Date _____

Writing Workshop—Unit 2, Part 1
Narration: Short Story

Prewriting: Gathering Details

Complete the following character chart to make the characters of your story more interesting and specific.

	Appearance	Dreams	Fears	Habits	Quirks
Character 1					
Character 2					
Character 3					
Character 4					

Drafting: Making a Plot Diagram

Complete the following plot diagram by jotting down the major events of your story to keep your writing on track.

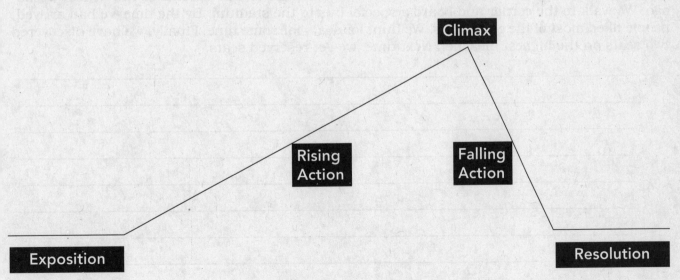

Writing Workshop—Unit 2, Part 1
Short Story: Integrating Grammar Skills

Applying Consistent Verb Tenses

The different forms that verbs take to show time are called **tenses.** Study these examples of the six verb tenses in English.

Present Tense:	We often *dine* at Joe's.
Past Tense:	Yesterday we *dined* at Joe's.
Future Tense:	Tomorrow we *will dine* at Joe's.
Present Perfect Tense:	We *have dined* at Joe's many times.
Past Perfect Tense:	We *had dined* at Joe's before going to the movies.
Future Perfect Tense:	By tomorrow, we *will have dined* at Joe's three times this month.

Use the perfect tenses to clarify a sequence of actions within the past, present, or future.

Unclear:	By the time we *finished* our meal, the rain *started.*
Clear:	By the time we *finished* our meal, the rain *had started.*

Identifying Correct Tenses

A. DIRECTIONS: *Circle the verb in parentheses that best completes each sentence.*

1. Because the bus is already late, I probably (arrive, will arrive) late to school.
2. Yesterday, the bus (comes, came) late because we received a heavy dusting of snow.
3. The bus (reached, had reached) Oak Street before the snow started.
4. Today, no snow (has fallen, had fallen) yet, but it is still very cold.

Fixing Mixed Verb Tenses

B. DIRECTIONS: *On the following lines, rewrite the paragraph to correct errors in verb tense.*

Last week, my sister Pat and I attended a football game. Pat purchased the tickets weeks ago. We walk to the corner and board a special bus to the stadium. By the time we had arrived, people filled most of the good seats. We hunt for seats for some time. Finally, we have discovered two seats on the highest bleacher. Next time, we get reserved seats.

_____

_____

_____

_____

_____

_____

_____

Unit 2: Short Stories
Part 1 Benchmark Test 3

MULTIPLE CHOICE

Literary Analysis *Read the selection. Then, answer the questions that follow.*

It is not often that you meet someone who is truly different. Emma is different. She is completely unconcerned with the rest of the world, often barely acknowledging its existence. And when you live in Manhattan, it isn't easy to ignore the rest of the world. Chaotic throngs of people rush through each crosswalk. Traffic, noise, and filth are omnipresent. Manhattan is not like the Blue Ridge Mountains. But Emma doesn't seem to notice.

1. The selection includes an example of which of the following kinds of characterization?
   A. indirect
   B. abstract
   C. direct
   D. omniscient

2. Which method of character development does this selection employ?
   A. dialogue
   B. description
   C. character interaction
   D. conflict

3. What inference can you make about Emma from the details in the selection?
   A. Emma is from the Blue Ridge Mountains.
   B. Emma does not like the noise of the city.
   C. Emma is very uncomfortable in the city.
   D. Emma currently lives outside of New York.

4. Which of the following techniques might be used to develop character indirectly?
   A. figurative language
   B. first-person point of view
   C. omniscient narrator
   D. dialogue

Read the selection. Then, answer the questions that follow.

Asleep, Corky completely forgot where he was. But the minute his eyes fluttered open, he remembered every hideous detail. The bars on the tiny, unreachable window; the thin, lumpy mattress; the cracked sink and lidless toilet; the cold floor; the marks scratched into the unpainted damp walls: these sights slammed him back into his new reality.

5. What is the most reasonable inference to make about the setting of this selection?
   A. The setting is present-day America.
   B. The setting is a prison.
   C. The setting is long ago.
   D. The setting is a boarding school.

6. How important is the setting likely to be to the plot of this selection?
   A. not important
   B. slightly important
   C. quite important
   D. extremely important

7. Setting includes which of the following?
   A. time and place
   B. time and character
   C. place and plot
   D. place and theme

8. What is the point of view of the narrator in this sentence?

   Ruth picked up a hairbrush, looked at it quizzically, and threw it at the mirror.

   A. first person
   B. naive first person
   C. third person omniscient
   D. third person limited

9. What is the point of view of the narrator in this sentence?

   I looked at the paper and was stunned to realize that I had finally passed a chemistry exam.

   A. first person
   B. third person limited
   C. third person omniscient
   D. naive first person

10. What is the point of view of the narrator in this sentence?

    As Sam brought his fist down, he yelled and pictured the board cracking in two.

    A. first person
    B. naive first person
    C. third person omniscient
    D. third person limited

11. Compared to the reader, how much does a naive first-person narrator know about events?
    A. the same
    B. less
    C. more
    D. much more

12. On how many characters does a limited third-person narrator focus?
    A. one
    B. a couple
    C. several
    D. all of them

Reading Skills *Read the selection. Then, answer the questions that follow.*

There was a feller here once by the name of Jim Smily, in the winter of '49—or maybe it was the spring of '50—I don't recollect exactly, somehow, though what makes me think it was one or the other is because I remember the big flume wasn't finished when he first come to the camp; but anyway, he was the curiosest man about always betting on anything that turned up you ever see, if he could get anybody to bet on the other side, and if he couldn't he'd change sides—any way that suited the other man would suit him—any way just so's he got a bet, he was satisfied. But still, he was lucky—uncommon lucky; he most always come out winner.

—Mark Twain (from "Jim Smily and His Jumping Frog")

13. What inference can you make about Simon Wheeler, the character who is telling the story?
    A. He has had little formal education.
    B. He is a skilled storyteller.
    C. He lives out west.
    D. He is a friend of Jim Smily.

14. What can you infer about Wheeler's storytelling style?
    A. It is concise.
    B. It is grandiose.
    C. It is meandering.
    D. It is formal.

15. Which of the following will best help a reader make an inference about a character?
    A. predicting what the character would do next
    B. forming a mental image of the character
    C. comparing the character to an actual person
    D. imagining how the character will influence the plot

16. Which would be the best reason for a reader to change an inference about a character?
    A. when someone else who has read the selection contradicts the reader's inference
    B. when the selection presents new information about the character
    C. when the theme of the selection is revealed
    D. when new characters who are integral to the plot are introduced

17. What is most important for you to consider when making an inference about a character?
   A. the author's opinion of and information about the character
   B. details in the selection
   C. the reader's experience and details in the selection
   D. the reader's experience

18. A Web site identified by which of the following URLs would likely have the most reliable information?
   A. .edu
   B. .org
   C. .com
   D. .net

19. What would best help users evaluate the credibility of a Web site?
   A. how many hits the site has gotten to date
   B. the ease of using the site
   C. the professional appearance of the graphics
   D. when the site was last updated

20. What is the best way to check information from a Web site?
   A. decide whether it seems to make sense
   B. compare it to information from another site
   C. compare it to a reliable print source
   D. ask a classmate to evaluate the information

Vocabulary

21. Given the meaning of the word root -spec-, what is the meaning of *spectator*?
   A. particle of dust
   B. audience member
   C. hopeful person
   D. participant

22. Knowing the word *inspect* helps you see that -spec- has which of these meanings?
   A. see
   B. judge
   C. buy
   D. donate

23. Given the meaning of the word root -form-, what is the meaning of *transform*?
   A. change view
   B. change understanding
   C. change place
   D. change shape

24. Knowing the word *reform* helps you see that *-form-* has which of the following meanings?
   A. alter
   B. change
   C. shape
   D. prison

Grammar

25. How are past and past participle verb parts formed?
   A. by adding *-ing*
   B. by adding *-es*
   C. by adding *-ed*
   D. by adding *-ment*

26. What is the verb part in this sentence?

   Micah is running in the marathon this weekend.

   A. present
   B. present participle
   C. past
   D. past participle

27. What is the verb part in this sentence?

   Candace made brownies for after the game.

   A. present
   B. present participle
   C. past
   D. past participle

28. Which of the following verbs is irregular?
   A. want
   B. show
   C. jump
   D. say

29. Which of the following verbs is irregular?
   A. forbid
   B. sequester
   C. harangue
   D. triumph

30. Which of the following verbs is the most irregular?
   A. build
   B. show
   C. shine
   D. be

31. How many basic tenses does English have?
    A. 3
    B. 4
    C. 5
    D. 6

32. When is mixing tenses necessary?
    A. whenever the author decides to mix them
    B. when the passage refers to different times
    C. when the passage describes an event that happened far in the past
    D. when the author is using perfect tenses

33. How many tenses are mixed in the following example?

    Whenever the dog wanted to go out, he stands at the door panting. He waited at the door for hours until I had gotten home.

    A. 2
    B. 3
    C. 4
    D. 5

ESSAY

34. Demonstrate the importance of point of view by retelling a short story from a point of view different from the original. For example, if the story you choose is told in third person omniscient, change it to first person or third person limited.

35. What have you read lately that you simply adored—or absolutely detested? Choose a book to which you reacted strongly, and review it for your classmates. Include a very brief summary, but avoid upsetting readers by giving away the ending. Support your opinions of the book with details and quotations from the text.

36. Challenge yourself to write a believable but very short story with characters nothing like you and your friends and a setting far from home and way in the past or far into the future. Choose details of character and setting as well as point of view carefully so that you can make the most impact with the fewest words.

Name _____

Unit 2: Short Stories
Part 2 Concept Map

Literary Analysis: Short Story

A Short Story — has — a theme — and sometimes — uses symbolism

(demonstrated in this selection)
Selection name: _____

(demonstrated in this selection)
Selection name: _____

Basic Elements of Short Stories

- Plot
- Conflict
- Character
- Characterization
- Setting
- Theme

Reading Skills and Strategies: Draw Conclusions

You can draw a conslusion — by — recognizing key details — and by — identifying patterns in the symbols being used

Academic Vocabulary words you you can use to discuss drawing conclusions

_____
_____
_____
_____
_____

(demonstrated in this selection)
Selection name: _____

Reading Informational Materials: Literary Reviews

Drawing conclusions can help you — to — evaluate a critic's's judgments

Comparing Literary Works: Irony and Paradox

are created when the writer —

makes a forceful contrast between words or expectations and reality (*irony*)

expresses two contradicting ideas that can be described in a statement (*paradox*)

(demonstrated in these selections)
Selection names:
1.
2.

Part 2 Student Log

Complete this chart to track your assignments.

Writing	Extend Your Learning	Writing Workshop	Other Assignments

Unit 2: Short Stories
Part 2 Diagnostic Test 4

MULTIPLE CHOICE

Read the selections. Then answer the questions that follow.

Besides being a founding father, Benjamin Franklin was an inventor, a scientist, a writer, and a diplomat. A practical man, Franklin devoted himself to improving everyday life. His boundless imagination led to inventions still in use today, such as bifocal glasses, the odometer, the lightning rod, and the Franklin stove.

While he was postmaster, Franklin wanted to determine the length of certain delivery routes, so he created an odometer, a device to measure and record distance by counting the rotations of a wheel's axle.

In the 1700s, when Franklin lived, most American houses were made of wood and heated by fireplaces. Because the chimney loses so much heat, Franklin devised an iron stove with a flue to keep more warmth inside the home. Keeping the fire contained in an iron box burned fuel more efficiently and was safer.

Franklin also found a way to protect buildings from fires started by lightning. He mounted an iron rod on the roof of the building, and then he attached a metal cable to the rod, stretching it to the ground and burying it. The rod attracted and channeled the lightning, rendering it harmless.

Perhaps Franklin's greatest invention, however, was himself. He demonstrated that a poor American could educate himself and become a famous citizen of the world.

1. Which of the following descriptions best applies to Benjamin Franklin?
   A. scientist, inventor, one of the early presidents of the United States
   B. founding father, postmaster, writer of Declaration of Independence
   C. inventor, writer, founding father, president, writer of the Constitution
   D. founding father, scientist, inventor, writer, diplomat

2. What was Benjamin Franklin's main focus for his inventions?
   A. boundless imagination
   B. practical matters
   C. government
   D. everyday life

3. Which of the following is one of Franklin's inventions?
   A. a wheel axle
   B. the telescope
   C. speedometers
   D. an iron stove

4. How did Franklin's invention measure the length of mail delivery routes?
   A. by counting the rotations of a wheel's axle
   B. by using a speedometer to calculate the time to travel the route
   C. by using an odometer attached to a stretched metal cable
   D. by taking measurements of the distance based on the stars

5. How was Franklin's stove an improvement on the fireplace?
   A. It took up less space in a room than the standard fireplace.
   B. It kept the heat from being lost through a chimney.
   C. It was much more attractive than a stone fireplace.
   D. It was able to burn more wood than the ordinary fireplace.

6. Which of the following best explains how a lightning rod works?
   - A. An iron rod is attached to the roof of a house, dispersing the lightning's energy.
   - B. Lightning flows up a metal cable and out through a metal rod on the roof.
   - C. An iron rod attached to the roof attracts lightning and channels it to the ground through a cable.
   - D. An iron rod attracts and channels lightning to an electric generator.

7. Why was lightning a danger to people in colonial times?
   - A. Because there were fewer houses, they were more likely to be struck by lightning.
   - B. The climate of the times was much stormier and produced more lightning.
   - C. People of colonial times were more susceptible to being struck by lightning.
   - D. Most houses were wood, and when lightning struck it started fires.

8. Which of the following is considered by some to be Franklin's greatest invention?
   - A. himself
   - B. the Franklin stove
   - C. bifocal glasses
   - D. the lightning rod

Read the selection. Then, answer the questions that follow.

Unlike most of ancient Greece where the arts were taught and valued, in the city-state of Sparta, warfare dominated every aspect of life. Spartan boys went to school to become strong and skilled soldiers. Typical juvenile games were forbidden, since all Spartans, even the children, were expected to practice self-discipline and self-denial. To serve Sparta properly, children had to be trained from an early age.

At age six, Spartan boys and girls were taken from their homes and sent to military academies. They were taught reading and writing, however most instruction was in survival skills. The girls needed to become strong mothers and loyal wives, while the boys had to prepare for military duty. The boys were deliberately underfed, treated harshly, exposed to the elements, and made to march long distances without shoes. If they stole food, there was no penalty unless they were caught in the act. Then they would get a severe beating and be expected to show no emotion. Holding back feelings was considered a sign of strength.

When they were twenty, the young men were tested on their leadership, fitness, and military skills. If they passed, they became soldiers and legal citizens of Sparta. If not, they were deprived of political rights, cast out of the army, and refused citizenship.

9. How was the city-state of Sparta unlike most of ancient Greece?
   - A. Most ancient Greek states were interested only in warfare.
   - B. Most of Greece valued the arts and taught the arts to the children.
   - C. Sparta was located in an area outside of what was ancient Greece.
   - D. Most ancient Greek states except for Sparta strictly disciplined their children.

10. What dominated life in ancient Sparta?
   - A. training of children
   - B. juvenile games
   - C. the arts
   - D. warfare

11. What was expected of children in Sparta?
    A. to become skilled at juvenile games
    B. to become self-disciplined
    C. to excel in the study of the arts
    D. to be loyal to their families

12. What happened to Spartan children at the age of six?
    A. They began a course of home tutoring.
    B. They were forced to live alone.
    C. They were sent to military academies.
    D. They began to attend school.

13. How was training similar for boys and girls?
    A. Both were instructed in basic weapons skills.
    B. Both were taught reading, writing, and survival skills.
    C. Both learned about Spartan military history.
    D. Both were prepared to become strong and loving parents.

14. Which of the following best describes the training that Spartan boys underwent?
    A. They underwent intense training in the arts, as well as in military skills.
    B. They were forced to endure hunger, cold, and harsh punishment.
    C. They were taught to hold back their feelings.
    D. They were taught military skills.

15. What happened to young men who did not pass the test of leadership, fitness, and military skills?
    A. They were refused the right to become an officer in the military.
    B. They were forced to endure another five years of training.
    C. They not allowed to become citizens, have political rights, or join the army.
    D. They were required to serve as soldiers for two years before testing again.

Vocabulary Warm-up Word Lists

Study these words from "How Much Land Does a Man Need?" Then apply your knowledge to the activities that follow.

Word List A

bargaining [BAR guhn ing] *v.* working toward reaching an agreement
  The buyer and seller were still <u>bargaining</u> over the price.

blundered [BLUHN derd] *v.* made a foolish mistake
  My sister <u>blundered</u> when she thought she could learn her lines in two days.

civilly [SIV uh lee] *adv.* politely
  Treat people <u>civilly</u> and they will respect you.

hazy [HAY zee] *adj.* cloudy; smoky; dust-filled air
  The wind-blown dust made the air <u>hazy</u>.

interpreter [in TER prit er] *n.* translator of spoken language
  The talk was in Spanish, but we listened in English through an <u>interpreter</u>.

quarreled [KWAHR uhld] *v.* argued bitterly; disputed
  The umpire and the runner <u>quarreled</u> over the tag at home plate.

remainder [ri MAYN duhr] *n.* the amount left over
  Please do the <u>remainder</u> of the assignment tonight for homework.

wooded [WOOD id] *adj.* covered with trees
  Most of the trees on the <u>wooded</u> land are pines.

Word List B

afresh [uh FRESH] *adv.* begin again
  Moving to another school let her start <u>afresh</u> with a new group of friends.

burdening [BER duhn ing] *v.* putting a heavy load on; loading
  Are you <u>burdening</u> the horse with too much weight?

communal [kuh MYOO nuhl] *adj.* owned or shared by a group or the public
  Everyone in our neighborhood works in the <u>communal</u> garden.

envious [EN vee us] *adj.* wanting what someone has; jealous
  She was so <u>envious</u> of my necklace that she bought one of her own.

formerly [FAWR mer lee] *adv.* in the past
  Our principal was <u>formerly</u> a math teacher.

proverb [PRAH verb] *n.* short, popular saying
  The <u>proverb</u> on the pillow reads "Home, Sweet Home."

recurred [ri KERD] *v.* happened again
  The problem <u>recurred</u> until we finally discovered how to fix it.

sowed [SOHD] *v.* scattered seeds over soil; planted
  The farmer <u>sowed</u> corn in the newly plowed field.

Name _____ Date _____

"How Much Land Does a Man Need?" by Leo Tolstoy
Vocabulary Warm-up Exercises

Exercise A *Fill in each blank in the paragraph below with an appropriate word from Word List A. Use each word only once.*

The two men met on the [1] _____ lot in order to decide its future.
Each man brought his own [2] _____ to translate the other man's
statements. The discussion began [3] _____, with polite suggestions
and comments. First one man offered to buy the other's land. Straight away,
they began [4] _____ to settle on a fair price. But then the buyer
[5] _____ badly when he mentioned that he planned to cut down all the
trees and build a parking lot. The [6] _____ of the discussion was far
from polite. The men and their translators [7] _____ loudly for an hour
and then gave up. They walked away in opposite directions. Both the men and the hope
for a deal faded quickly into the [8] _____ afternoon.

Exercise B *Write a complete sentence to answer each question. For each item, use a word
from Word List B to replace each underlined word without changing its meaning.*

Example: What is a project you could start <u>again</u>?
I could start <u>afresh</u> with the doghouse I was building last year.

1. Do you think a <u>group-owned</u> garden would be a success in your area?

   _____

2. Why might watching television make you <u>jealous</u> of other people?

   _____

3. What is something that has <u>repeatedly happened</u> this year?

   _____

4. What is a favorite <u>saying</u> that everyone in your family knows?

   _____

5. Why might it be a mistake to be <u>loading</u> a bicycle with extra weight?

   _____

6. What do you think was <u>once</u> on the land around your school?

   _____

7. Why are crops <u>planted</u> at different times?

   _____

Name _____   Date _____

"How Much Land Does a Man Need?" by Leo Tolstoy
Reading Warm-up A

Read the following passage. Pay special attention to the underlined words. Then, read it again, and complete the activities. Use a separate sheet of paper for your written answers.

A farmer and his daughter lived a quiet life until a foreigner bought the land beside their farm and installed a fence between the properties, making the farmer furious.

"How can he be so rude?" he asked his daughter. "Well, he has <u>blundered</u> terribly if he thinks I will tolerate this kind of disrespect."

Fortunately for the farmer, his daughter knew how to speak the neighbor's language, so she could act as <u>interpreter</u> for the two men. The next day, father and daughter visited the foreigner next door. With the daughter translating, the farmer insisted that the neighbor remove the fence, but the neighbor refused. The farmer and the neighbor <u>quarreled</u> about the fence every day for a month.

"I am not <u>bargaining</u> with him anymore," the farmer shouted one night at home. "I am making a demand."

The next day, the farmer and his daughter marched next door. It was so <u>hazy</u> that the farmer did not see the neighbor until he bumped into the man. Within moments, the two men were shouting. The daughter tried to keep up, translating for both men, but the argument only grew louder.

"Wait," the daughter suddenly called to her father, "he says he is sorry. He knows he was wrong and has an idea." She explained that the neighbor offered to plant trees instead of building a fence. This would create a <u>wooded</u> patch that would be a beautiful, natural border. The farmer loved the idea, and soon the neighbors were shaking hands and even hugged before parting.

Walking home, the farmer said smugly to his daughter, "You wanted to give in, but I taught him a lesson. From now on he is going to be very different. Instead of treating us rudely, he will always treat us <u>civilly</u>. His magnificent idea of a woods is proof of his respect for us."

The daughter smiled for the <u>remainder</u> of the walk home, knowing that the idea for the woods was not the neighbor's, but her own. Tired of the endless fighting, she simply told both men that the other was sorry.

1. Underline the words that describe how the neighbor <u>blundered</u>. Then, tell what *blundered* means.

2. Underline the words that tell why the daughter could be an <u>interpreter</u>. Then, tell why people might need an *interpreter*.

3. Circle the words that tell what the neighbors <u>quarreled</u> about. Then, tell what *quarreled* means.

4. Underline the words that mean the opposite of <u>bargaining</u>. Then, tell one possible result of *bargaining*.

5. Underline the words that tell what happened because the day was <u>hazy</u>. Then, tell what *hazy* means.

6. Describe what a *wooded* patch might look like.

7. Circle the antonym for <u>civilly</u>. Then, tell what *civilly* means.

8. Describe what you might do with the <u>remainder</u> of today. Tell what *remainder* means.

Name _____ Date _____

"How Much Land Does a Man Need?" by Leo Tolstoy
Reading Warm-up B

Read the following passage. Pay special attention to the underlined words. Then, read it again, and complete the activities. Use a separate sheet of paper for your written answers.

You might have heard the proverb "Variety is the spice of life." This familiar saying suggests that making changes can make your life more interesting. Long ago, many farming communities made an important discovery. They learned that variety can be more than interesting—it can be necessary. Crop rotation is a way to use variety to make sure that land remains productive.

Early farmers probably noticed that growing the same crop year after year was burdening the soil. The nutrients in the soil were exhausted, and the land soon became infertile. After several years, crops that once grew well would begin to grow poorly in the same field.

At some point, planters discovered that changing the crops grown on the same land could help restore lost nutrients. They discovered the effectiveness of crop rotation. During the Middle Ages, farmers developed a three-year crop rotation cycle. They sowed rye or winter wheat during the first year, followed by oats or barley in the second year. During the third year, the land was left fallow, or unplanted. After one year of rest, the land was planted afresh with rye or winter wheat.

Farmers discovered that by rotating crops in this way, land that had formerly been infertile was now productive. These methods came to benefit all types of farms, from individual farms with only one owner to communal farms in which ownership is shared by a group of people.

Crop rotation not only helps renew soil nutrients but also serves as an effective tool in pest control. When problems with pests have recurred, researchers have tried to find ways to limit the damage done by harmful insects and bacteria. Changing crops can help break pests' life cycles by taking away their food source.

Modern farming technology has changed a great deal since the Middle Ages, but crop rotation remains one of the most effective ways to keep soil fertile. Still, farmers of the Middle Ages would probably be envious if they saw the plentiful results of modern research.

1. Underline the proverb. Then, tell what a *proverb* is.

2. Underline the words that tell the results of burdening the soil. Then, tell what *burdening* means.

3. Circle the words that tell what farmers sowed in the first year of crop rotation. Then, name three other crops that might be *sowed*.

4. Describe something that you could do *afresh*.

5. Circle the word that describes what the land was formerly like. Then, tell what *formerly* means.

6. Underline the words that define communal farms. Then, describe another *communal* property.

7. Circle the words that tell what recurred. Then, write about something that has *recurred* in your school.

8. Underline the words that tell what might make farmers of the Middle Ages envious. Then, tell something that might make a modern farmer *envious*.

Name _____ Date _____

"How Much Land Does a Man Need?" by Leo Tolstoy
Literary Analysis: Theme

The **theme** of a literary work is the central message it communicates. To express a theme, a writer may take one of these approaches: (1) directly state the theme of the work, or have a character directly state it; or (2) create patterns of story elements to suggest a larger meaning. Themes that appeal to all times and cultures are universal themes.

In many cases, a theme reflects a **philosophical assumption**—the writer's basic beliefs about life. The writer's literary work may reflect this belief.

A. DIRECTIONS: *Write Tolstoy's philosophical assumption in "How Much Land Does a Man Need?" Then explain how three major events in the story reflect this philosophical assumption. Finally, write the central theme in your own words.*

Philosophical assumption: _____

_____

First major event and how it reflects Tolstoy's assumption: _____

_____

_____

Second major event and how it reflects Tolstoy's assumption: _____

_____

_____

_____

Third major event and how it reflects Tolstoy's assumption: _____

_____

_____

_____

Theme: _____

_____

B. DIRECTIONS: *Tolstoy's theme in "How Much Land Does a Man Need?" is a universal theme. In other words, it has meaning in all times and for all cultures. Explain how this theme applies to modern life in the United States.*

_____

_____

_____

_____

Name _____ Date _____

"How Much Land Does a Man Need?" by Leo Tolstoy
Reading: Recognize Key Details to Draw Conclusions About Theme

To identify the **theme** of a story, pay attention to **key details.** Combine later details with earlier ones to **draw a conclusion** about the author's message. There might be more than one theme in a story, but there is usually one central theme that is the guiding message the author intends to communicate. If the theme is not directly stated by the author or a character in the story, look for clues to help determine the theme. Clues can be found in details such as dialogue, setting, symbolism, conflict, plot action, and more.

DIRECTIONS: *Write the theme of "How Much Land Does a Man Need?" on the lines below. Then complete the chart by explaining how each detail helps a reader draw a conclusion about the theme of the story.*

Theme: _____

_____

Detail	Conclusion
Example: At the beginning of the story, the Devil hears Pahom thinking that, if he had enough land, he would fear nothing, not even the Devil.	By having the Devil listen in on Pahom's thoughts, Tolstoy shows that he thinks greed for property is a path to evil.
1. Pahom begins to argue with his neighbors and the judges because people are trespassing on his land. His place in the community gets worse, even though he is a landowner now.	
2. Pahom almost makes a deal for more land in his second home, when a passing dealer tells him about the land of the Bashkirs. He cancels his deal and goes to see the Bashkirs' land for himself.	
3. The night before he marks his land claim, Pahom does not sleep well. He dreams that every person who has tempted him with the promise of more land was the Devil in disguise.	
4. While Pahom is marking off the land he wants to claim, he cannot resist including a damp hollow where he believes flax would grow well.	
5. Pahom's servant buries him. All the land that Pahom needs in the end is a grave long enough for him to lie in—six feet.	

Name _____ Date _____

"How Much Land Does a Man Need?" by Leo Tolstoy
Vocabulary Builder

Word List

| piqued | disparaged | forbore | aggrieved |

A. DIRECTIONS: *Fill in the following chart with at least one synonym, at least one antonym, and an example sentence for each word.*

Word	Synonym	Antonym	Example Sentence
1. piqued			
2. disparaged			
3. forbore			
4. aggrieved			

B. DIRECTIONS: *In the blank, write the letter of the word that best completes the meaning of the sentence.*

1. Pahom felt _____ when his neighbors trespassed on his land and were not punished by the court.
   A. piqued   B. disparaged   C. forbore   D. aggrieved

2. Pahom's wife probably _____ from protesting against having to move hundreds of miles away to find more land.
   A. piqued   B. disparaged   C. forbore   D. aggrieved

3. In his mind, Pahom _____ those who would pay too much for too little land.
   A. piqued   B. disparaged   C. forbore   D. aggrieved

4. Pahom was _____ that he was not given enough communal land in his second home.
   A. piqued   B. disparaged   C. forbore   D. aggrieved

"How Much Land Does a Man Need?" by Leo Tolstoy
Support for Writing a Character Analysis

For your character analysis, use the following graphic organizer to help you identify the main traits that define Pahom. Then fill in examples of incidents and descriptions in the story that show these traits.

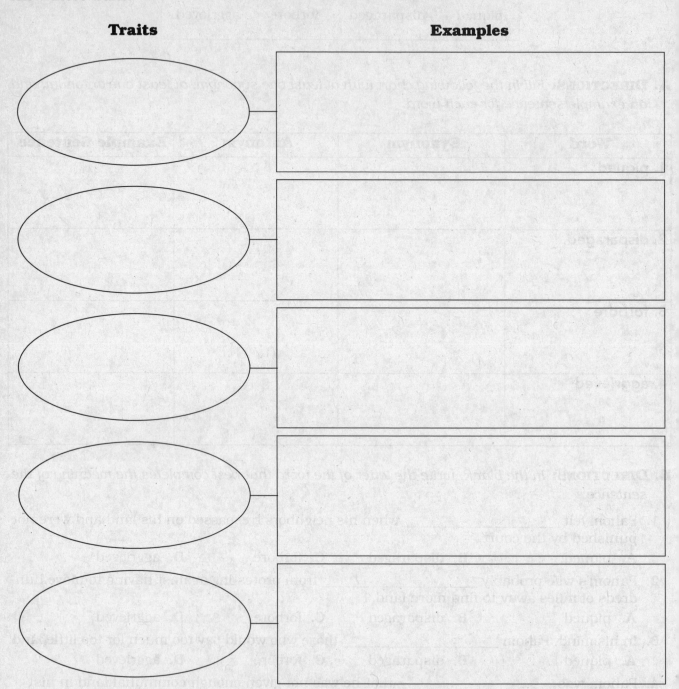

Now, use this graphic organizer to help you write a brief character analysis of Pahom.

"How Much Land Does a Man Need?" by Leo Tolstoy
Support for Extend Your Learning

Listening and Speaking

Use the following chart to help you and your group decide how Tolstoy's theme does or does not apply to modern life. Write several people's statements of the story's theme or message in the top box. Circle the one on which your group agrees. Then write reasons why this theme does or does not apply to modern life in the boxes below.

Statements of the story's message:

Reasons why the theme DOES apply to modern life:	Reasons why the theme DOES NOT apply to modern life:

Research and Technology

Use the chart below to help you brainstorm a list of visual aids that you and your group might create for your presentation. For each idea, identify one or more resources that are available to you that might help you create your visual aid.

Visual Aid	Resources
A map showing the proportion of urban and rural populations in Russia in 1875	
A flow chart showing ways in which property was acquired	

"How Much Land Does a Man Need?" by Leo Tolstoy
Enrichment: Social Studies

Prior to Alexander II's abolition of serfdom in Russia in 1861, the only distinguishing feature between a serf (peasant) and a slave was the plot of land to which he or she was tied. However, even with their new freedom under Alexander II's reforms, most serfs could not afford to buy their own land or farms. In fact, most serfs were outraged that they needed to pay for land that they considered, by rights, already theirs. The serfs' definition of their relationship to the nobility and to the land could be summed up in the phrase "We are yours, but the land is ours." The difference between the peasants' social conditions and those of the landowning nobility continued to widen. One reason for the increase in poverty was the Russian government's regard for agriculture as a source of revenue. Even though many peasants prospered after liberation, they were crushed with taxes on sugar, tobacco, matches, and oil.

Around the time Alexander II implemented his reforms, Karl Marx and Friedrich Engels published their *Communist Manifesto.* In the *Manifesto,* Marx and Engels argue that workers have been exploited by the ruling class throughout human history. The principles of Karl Marx, Friedrich Engels, and Vladimir Lenin inspired the movements that brought about communism, which is a political system based on common property or upon the equal distribution of wealth. Early university-educated communist activists saw the peasants as a great potential force for revolutionary action, and many elements fueled the Russian Revolution. As peasants competed with each other to lease estate land from landowners, rents were driven up. Peasants then demanded that the government redistribute even greater portions of estate land. The revolution movement gathered momentum with peasant uprisings, workers' demonstrations, and strikes, but it was not powerful enough to replace the autocratic government with a democratic republic.

DIRECTIONS: *Use the information above to answer each of the following questions.*

1. Do you think the idea of communism would have appealed to Pahom? Why or why not?

   _____

   _____

   _____

   _____

2. What prevented many peasants from prospering economically?

   _____

   _____

   _____

   _____

3. What details in "How Much Land Does a Man Need?" illustrate the social and economic conditions of the peasant class, particularly those that communism was intended to correct?

   _____

   _____

   _____

   _____

"How Much Land Does a Man Need?" by Leo Tolstoy
Selection Test A

Critical Reading *Identify the letter of the choice that best answers the question.*

_____ 1. What does the story "How Much Land Does a Man Need?" focus on?
   A. Pahom's desire for more land
   B. Pahom's thirst for knowledge
   C. Pahom's wife's jealousy of her sister
   D. A dispute between peasants and landowners

_____ 2. What does Pahom believe would solve all his troubles?
   A. having enough land
   B. having more money
   C. making a deal with the Devil
   D. moving to the steppe

_____ 3. At the beginning of the story, Pahom claims, "If I had plenty of land, I shouldn't fear the Devil himself!" What is the Devil's reaction to this boast?
   A. He becomes frightened that Pahom might destroy him.
   B. He becomes angry at Pahom because he does not fear the Devil.
   C. He is happy because it reveals how the Devil can gain power over Pahom.
   D. He begins thinking of how he can keep Pahom from getting plenty of land.

_____ 4. Based on what happens to Pahom when he becomes a landowner, what is Tolstoy's attitude toward land ownership?
   A. Land ownership is life's highest achievement.
   B. Land ownership causes people to lose their sanity.
   C. Land ownership leads to greed and selfishness.
   D. Land ownership makes people appreciate their neighbors.

_____ 5. How does Pahom most likely feel about the Bashkirs when he first meets them?
   A. He fears their fierce nature and believes that they are devils.
   B. He respects them for their intelligence and bargaining skills.
   C. He worries that they might be deceiving him about the land.
   D. He believes they are foolish to give up their land so cheaply.

_____ 6. On the night before Pahom is to mark off his land, he has a disturbing dream. In it, he sees all the people who have led him to buy more land become the Devil, and he sees himself as a dead man. How does this dream help the reader to understand the theme of the story?

    A. It shows how Pahom regrets leaving his wife behind when he went on his journey to find more land.

    B. It shows how Pahom has a very active imagination, which led him into trouble in his younger days.

    C. It shows how his buying more and more land was a path to evil that will lead Pahom to lose everything in the end.

    D. It shows how the people who told him where to find more land were evil and that Pahom will likely outlive them.

_____ 7. What is the outcome of "How Much Land Does a Man Need?"

    A. Pahom gives his land away to local peasants.

    B. Pahom loses his life for just a little more land.

    C. Pahom tricks the Bashkirs into giving him more land.

    D. Pahom and his wife live happily on a forty-acre farm.

_____ 8. Which of the following pairs of adjectives best describes Pahom's character?

    A. lazy and dull

    B. wise and complex

    C. sympathetic and caring

    D. boastful and greedy

_____ 9. Tolstoy makes the philosophical assumption that people should not waste their lives on unimportant things. Which of the following details from the story is the best evidence of Tolstoy's philosophical assumption?

    A. The Bashkirs offer Pahom land in return for his peasants.

    B. Pahom's peasant neighbors and their animals trespass on his new land.

    C. Pahom buys his first farm by selling a horse and some bees, having his son work, and borrowing the rest.

    D. Pahom dies trying to get more land, but all the land he needs in the end is six feet of soil in which to bury him.

_____ 10. What lesson does the story "How Much Land Does a Man Need?" teach?

    A. the difference between acres and miles

    B. the difference between need and greed

    C. the difference between wealth and poverty

    D. the difference between urban and rural living

_____ 11. Which is NOT one of the messages of "How Much Land Does a Man Need?"

A. Land ownership causes greed and selfishness.

B. Land and other property are useless after death.

C. Reaching for too much can lead to the loss of everything.

D. It is foolish to listen to the stories of passing grain dealers.

Vocabulary and Grammar

_____ 12. Pahom was _____, or irritated, when his neighbors trespassed on his land.

A. disparaged

B. exhilarated

C. piqued

D. disappointed

_____ 13. Which of the following would most likely make a person feel *aggrieved*?

A. A peasant gets the opportunity to buy some of his neighbor's farmland.

B. A man's neighbors cut down his trees and let their cattle roam his land.

C. A woman's husband goes on a journey to find more land for his family.

D. A group of people offer land in exchange for gifts brought by a stranger.

_____ 14. Which of the following sentences contains a linking verb?

A. Pahom buys a farm.

B. Pahom is unhappy.

C. Pahom moves again.

D. Pahom dies.

_____ 15. Which of the following sentences contains an action verb?

A. Pahom's wife was jealous.

B. The Devil is happy.

C. Pahom marks his land.

D. Pahom becomes greedy.

Essay

16. Do you think that Pahom deserves what he gets? In an essay, explain why you do or do not believe Pahom deserves his fate. Use details from the story and from real life to support your response.

17. In an essay, state the theme of "How Much Land Does a Man Need?" and explain how you identified this theme. List details from the story that helped you determine the message Tolstoy is trying to express.

"How Much Land Does a Man Need?" by Leo Tolstoy
Selection Test B

Critical Reading *Identify the letter of the choice that best completes the statement or answers the question.*

_____ 1. Pahom believes all his troubles would be solved if
   A. he had enough land.
   B. he had more money.
   C. he made a pact with the Devil.
   D. he and his wife moved to the steppe.

_____ 2. Which line from the story best predicts how land ownership will affect Pahom?
   A. The land is all being sold, and I'll get none of it.
   B. Our only trouble is that we haven't land enough.
   C. If you were honest folk yourselves you wouldn't let a thief go free.
   D. Why should I suffer in this narrow hold, if one can live so well elsewhere?

_____ 3. What gave Pahom the opportunity to own his first piece of land?
   A. Pahom's wife inherited the land from her father.
   B. A woman close to his village decided to sell her land.
   C. Pahom won some land in a bet against his fellow peasants.
   D. A passing grain dealer told him about the land of the Bashkirs.

_____ 4. How does Pahom find out about the Bashkirs' land?
   A. A passing grain dealer tells him about it.
   B. The Devil tells him about it in a dream.
   C. He runs into a group of Bashkirs while traveling.
   D. He hears a rumor about it from his wife's sister.

_____ 5. Why does Tolstoy use the Bashkirs in his story and describe them as he does?
   A. He presents them as model landowners because they have fertile soil and comfortable lives.
   B. He uses them as a bad example, because they do not farm the land and do not work in the summer.
   C. He holds them up as an ideal because they are carefree and do not worry about accumulating wealth.
   D. He presents them as a symbol of a people under the influence of the Devil, who is disguised as their chief.

_____ 6. What is the Bashkirs' attitude toward land ownership in "How Much Land Does a Man Need?"
   A. They work hard to maintain their land.
   B. They feel their land is infertile and worthless.
   C. They hope to sell their land for as much as possible.
   D. They do not worry about building wealth with land.

_____ 7. On the night before Pahom is to mark off his land, he has a disturbing dream. Which of the following details from Pahom's dream gives the best clue to the theme of the story?
   A. the laughing Bashkir chief
   B. the sight of himself as a dead man
   C. the appearance of the peasant from the Volga
   D. the appearance of the Devil with hoofs and horns

_____ 8. The story "How Much Land Does a Man Need?" teaches the difference between
   A. acres and miles.
   B. urban and rural living.
   C. need and greed.
   D. wealth and poverty.

_____ 9. Which of the following is the best statement of the theme of "How Much Land Does a Man Need?"
   A. One should forgive one's neighbors for trespassing.
   B. Reaching for too much can lead to the loss of everything.
   C. It is foolish to listen to the stories of passing grain dealers.
   D. One must be prepared to move far away to find more land.

_____ 10. Which of the following lines from "How Much Land Does a Man Need?" best clarifies its theme?
   A. We may live roughly, but at least we're free from worry.
   B. Why should I suffer in this narrow hole, if one can live so well elsewhere?
   C. . . . though you often earn more than you need, you're very likely to lose all you have.
   D. I can't go on overlooking it, or they'll destroy all I have. They must be taught a lesson.

_____ 11. By describing how owning land affects Pahom, Tolstoy hints at his own philosophical assumption. He objected to private property because it led some people to
   A. become greedy and treat others badly.
   B. borrow money and make children work.
   C. mistreat the land and leave it exhausted.
   D. labor too hard and damage their health.

_____ 12. What is Tolstoy's answer to the question in the title "How Much Land Does a Man Need?"
   A. 13,000 acres of virgin steppe land
   B. about 40 acres, or just enough for a farm
   C. about six feet, or just enough to bury a man
   D. none, because all land should be shared

Vocabulary and Grammar

_____ 13. Pahom's wife was _____, or irritated, by her sister's boastful comments about the advantages of urban living.
   A. disparaged
   B. aggrieved
   C. piqued
   D. disappointed

_____ 14. Read the example sentence below. Then choose the best definition for the italicized word.
At first, Pahom *forbore* to prosecute his neighbors for trespassing on his land.
- A. refrained from
- B. plotted
- C. wronged
- D. offended

_____ 15. Which of the following sentences contains a linking verb?
- A. Pahom buys a farm near his village.
- B. Pahom is unhappy with his neighbors.
- C. Pahom moves his family to a bigger farm.
- D. Pahom dies trying to get even more land.

_____ 16. Which of the following sentences contains an action verb?
- A. Pahom's wife seems jealous of her sister.
- B. The Devil is happy about Pahom's boast.
- C. The grain dealer mentions the Bashkirs.
- D. Pahom becomes greedy for more land.

Essay

17. What is Tolstoy's answer to the question posed by the title "How Much Land Does a Man Need?" Do you agree or disagree with Tolstoy's answer? Write an essay supporting or refuting Tolstoy's position. Use details from the story to support your response.

18. Do you sympathize with Pahom? In an essay, explain how you feel about the character of Pahom and why. Describe Pahom's characteristics and how they factor into the theme and outcome of the story.

Vocabulary Warm-up Word Lists

Study these words from "Civil Peace." Then apply your knowledge to the activities that follow.

Word List A

agony [AG uh nee] *n.* great pain or suffering
    His <u>agony</u> increased when the doctor set the broken bone.

assortment [uh SAWRT muhnt] *n.* varied group
    I brought an <u>assortment</u> of nuts and dried fruits.

collapse [kuh LAPS] *v.* fall down; break down
    The walls will <u>collapse</u> if the roof is too heavy.

commandeered [kah muhn DEERD] *v.* seized for government use
    A garage near town was <u>commandeered</u> for storing army vehicles.

continuously [kuhn TIN yoo uhs lee] *adv.* going on without a break
    We were thirsty after dancing <u>continuously</u> for two hours.

immediate [i MEE dee it] *adj.* without delay; right away
    You need <u>immediate</u> medical care if you black out unexpectedly.

paralyzed [PA ruh lyzd] *v.* made inactive; frozen
    He was so <u>paralyzed</u> with fear he could not move.

rickety [RIK uh tee] *adj.* likely to fall down
    The <u>rickety</u> old chair wobbled when I sat down.

Word List B

accumulated [uh KYOOM yuh lay tid] *v.* piled up; gathered up little by little
    More garbage <u>accumulated</u> at the dump as people threw out more junk.

corporation [kawr puh RAY shuhn] *n.* a business that is one legal unit; a company
    The <u>corporation</u> employs more than eighty workers.

extraordinarily [ek strawr duh NER uh lee] *adv.* remarkably
    It was <u>extraordinarily</u> moving to hear the survivors relate their story.

fortnight [FAWRT nyt] *n.* two weeks
    i'd better get busy flossing, as I have a visit to the dentist in a <u>fortnight</u>.

heroic [hi ROH ik] *adj.* noble and courageous; like a hero
    With <u>heroic</u> strength, she kept the car from crushing the baby.

imperious [im PIR ee uhs] *adj.* arrogant; haughty
    His <u>imperious</u> tone made people think he was rude.

parched [PARCHT] *adj.* dry and hot
    The <u>parched</u> runner gulped down some water after crossing the finish line.

windfall [WIND fawl] *n.* unexpected good fortune
    Winning the prize money was a real <u>windfall</u> for me.

"Civil Peace" by Chinua Achebe
Vocabulary Warm-up Exercises

Exercise A *Fill in each blank in the paragraph below with an appropriate word from Word List A. Use each word only once.*

My mother's rusty old bicycle is so [1] _____ that it is as likely to [2] _____ as it is to move forward. I guess that's the reason that my mom [3] _____ my bicycle yesterday when she needed to run an [4] _____ of errands. My [5] _____ response was disappointment because I wanted to ride over to my friend's house. But then I remembered that I am almost [6] _____ borrowing my mother's in-line skates, so it seemed fair to lend her my bike. I decided to try to ride hers instead, but the wheels were so stiff that her bike was as good as [7] _____. Just getting the pedals to spin around once was pure [8] _____. It's a good thing it was such a nice day for a walk!

Exercise B *Answer the questions with complete explanations.*

1. Are <u>heroic</u> actions always based on strength and power?

_____

2. What are two ways that people might react to receiving a <u>windfall</u>?

_____

3. What might you do if you have <u>accumulated</u> a lot of loose papers from school?

_____

4. Would you rather work for yourself or for a <u>corporation</u>? Why?

_____

5. If you order a book online, do you think it will arrive within a <u>fortnight</u>?

_____

6. How might you plan an <u>extraordinarily</u> unusual menu for a party?

_____

7. What can you do if your mouth feels <u>parched</u>?

_____

8. Are most successful counselors <u>imperious</u>?

_____

"Civil Peace" by Chinua Achebe
Reading Warm-up A

Read the following passage. Pay special attention to the underlined words. Then, read it again, and complete the activities. Use a separate sheet of paper for your written answers.

Nigeria won its independence from British rule in 1960. However, the new nation was built on a <u>rickety</u> foundation that was almost certain to fall apart. Independent Nigeria was divided into three separate regions. The dream of a peaceful and unified nation was soon to <u>collapse</u> due to ethnic conflicts among these regions.

By 1966, a military government won control of Nigeria, replacing the struggling democracy. Soon, military officials were <u>commandeering</u> money, supplies, and housing from citizens. During this growing conflict, thousands of Ibo living in northern Nigeria were killed. Many Ibo fled to their eastern homeland. On May 30, 1967, the Ibo people declared their independence from Nigeria. They renamed their region Biafra. The country was plunged into civil war.

Nigeria's most <u>immediate</u> action was an economic blockade. This blockade essentially <u>paralyzed</u> the flow of resources, including food, into or out of Biafra. On July 6, 1967, Nigeria sent troops to retake the lands of Biafra. Although the army made slow progress, the blockade caused conditions to worsen <u>continuously</u>. Thousands of people were starving to death.

World opinion began to support the troubled nation of Biafra. Photographs of the <u>agony</u> and suffering inside Biafra spread around the world. Many governments and groups offered aid in the form of basic food and supplies. Nonetheless, the Nigerian government continued its campaign to regain control. Slowly, the region controlled by the Biafran government decreased in size.

The civil war lasted for nearly three years, ending with the surrender of Biafra on January 15, 1970. Historians estimate that as many as 1 million people died as a result of hunger, disease, and fighting. An <u>assortment</u> of laws were passed in an attempt to ease the ethnic and religious tensions. For example, laws made it illegal for political parties to be based on ethnic or tribal heritage. However, these laws have been difficult to apply.

1. Underline the words that tell what would happen because the foundation was <u>rickety</u>. Then, tell what *rickety* means.

2. Underline what was likely to <u>collapse</u>. Then, tell something else that might *collapse*.

3. Circle three things officials were <u>commandeering</u>. Tell what *commandeering* means.

4. Circle the <u>immediate</u> action taken by Nigeria. Tell what an *immediate* action is.

5. Circle the words that tell what was <u>paralyzed</u>. Then, tell what *paralyzed* means.

6. Underline the word that tells what worsened <u>continuously</u>. Describe something that has improved *continuously* in recent years.

7. Circle the synonym for <u>agony</u>. Then, tell what *agony* means.

8. Tell why you think Nigeria passed an *assortment* of laws rather than only one law.

Name _____ Date _____

Read the following passage. Pay special attention to the underlined words. Then, read it again, and complete the activities. Use a separate sheet of paper for your written answers.

Once again, Ajike Ojukwu stepped through his doorway to greet the desert morning. Within minutes, the hot air sucked the night's moisture from the tall man's body, leaving his lips <u>parched</u> and his eyes dry. This feeling was nothing unusual for Ojukwu, who simply accepted it and continued on.

Every day for a <u>fortnight</u>, Ojukwu had walked the five-mile journey with a steady pace and a cheerful attitude. For fourteen days he had been visiting the offices of the Ubar <u>Corporation</u> hoping to find that they were hiring. Ojukwu had worked for more than fifteen years in this coal mine, but had lost his job almost two years ago during the civil war. So far, each of his early morning visits to the office at the front entrance had ended the same way. An arrogant guard explained in an <u>imperious</u> tone that the Ubar Corporation did not need any more workers, after which he slammed the door.

Nonetheless, Ojukwu walked toward the mining office with a light heart and a steady stride. He had <u>accumulated</u> rejection after rejection for two weeks, but his hope was still bright.

When he arrived at the office door, a crowd of about two dozen men was gathered there, shouting for attention. Suddenly the door opened and the guard appeared. The crowd fell so <u>extraordinarily</u> silent you could hear each man breathing. At last the guard spoke.

"Today the Ubar Corporation has a position available for one new worker," the guard said with his usual haughty tone. The crowd jumped to attention, shouting their names and qualifications, but the guard's eye scanned the group slowly and finally rested on Ojukwu, who stood calmly in the back. He nodded at Ojukwu, who accepted this lucky <u>windfall</u> with his usual graceful calm.

Many of the men were jealous as they watched Ojukwu enter the office. Still, some of the men who knew Ojukwu were pleased that his <u>heroic</u> patience and good nature had finally been rewarded.

1. Underline the words that explain why Ojukwu's lips were <u>parched</u>. Then, tell what *parched* means.

2. Circle the words in the paragraph that define a <u>fortnight</u>. Then, tell something you might do a *fortnight* from now.

3. Describe a *corporation* in your city, town, or state.

4. Circle a synonym for <u>imperious</u>. Then, tell what *imperious* means.

5. Circle what Ojukwu had <u>accumulated</u>. Then, describe something you have *accumulated* at home.

6. Underline what happened when the crowd fell <u>extraordinarily</u> silent. Then, describe something *extraordinarily* interesting.

7. Describe a *windfall* you would like to receive.

8. Circle the words that describe Ojukwu's <u>heroic</u> qualities. Then, tell what *heroic* means.

"**Civil Peace**" by Chinua Achebe
Literary Analysis: Theme

The **theme** of a literary work is the central message it communicates. To express a theme, a writer may take one of these approaches: (1) directly state the theme of the work, or have a character directly state it; or (2) create patterns of story elements to suggest a larger meaning. Themes that appeal to all times and cultures are universal themes.

In many cases, a theme reflects a **philosophical assumption**—the writer's basic beliefs about life. The writer's literary work may reflect this belief.

A. DIRECTIONS: *Write Achebe's philosophical assumption in "Civil Peace." Then explain how three major events in the story reflect this philosophical assumption. Finally, write the central theme in your own words.*

Philosophical assumption: _____

_____

First major event and how it reflects Achebe's assumption: _____

_____

_____

_____

Second major event and how it reflects Achebe's assumption: _____

_____

_____

_____

Third major event and how it reflects Achebe's assumption: _____

_____

_____

_____

Theme: _____

_____

B. DIRECTIONS: *Achebe's theme in "Civil Peace" is a universal theme. In other words, it has meaning in all times and for all cultures. Explain how this theme applies to modern life in the United States.*

_____

_____

_____

_____

Name _____ Date _____

"**Civil Peace**" by Chinua Achebe
Reading: Recognize Key Details to Draw Conclusions About Theme

To identify the **theme** of a story, pay attention to **key details.** Combine later details with earlier ones to **draw a conclusion** about the author's message. There might be more than one theme in a story, but there is usually one central theme that is the guiding message the author intends to communicate. If the theme is not directly stated by the author or a character in the story, look for clues to help determine the theme. Clues can be found in details such as dialogue, setting, symbolism, conflict, plot action, and more.

DIRECTIONS: *Write the theme of "Civil Peace" on the lines below. Then complete the chart by explaining how each detail helps a reader draw a conclusion about the theme of the story.*

Theme: _____

_____

_____

Detail	Conclusion
Example: At the beginning of the story, Jonathan Iwegbu is thankful for his five remaining family members.	The author puts Jonathan's life in perspective by showing readers the violence and brutality of the war that has recently ended. Jonathan regards it as a miracle and a blessing that five members of his family managed to stay alive.
1. Jonathan discovers that his house is still standing. He is overwhelmed with disbelief and joy.	
2. Jonathan sells palm-wine, and his wife sells breakfast akara balls.	
3. Jonathan receives twenty pounds as an *egg-rasher* payment. He thinks that it is like Christmas to receive this money.	
4. Thieves come to take Jonathan's money. He does not fight them and makes a deal with them to give him his egg-rasher if they will not hunt him and his family.	
5. Jonathan's neighbors feel sorry for him, but he says, "I count it as nothing." He points out that he survived without the money before he got in.	

"Civil Peace" by Chinua Achebe
Vocabulary Builder

Word List

| disreputable | amenable | destitute | commiserate |

A. DIRECTIONS: *Fill in the following chart with at least one synonym, at least one antonym, and an example sentence for each word.*

Word	Synonym	Antonym	Example Sentence
1. disreputable			
2. amenable			
3. destitute			
4. commiserate			

B. DIRECTIONS: *Circle the letter of the word that best completes the meaning of the sentence.*

1. Jonathan Iwegbu is _____ to the idea of moving back to Enugu after the war.
   A. disreputable   B. amenable   C. destitute   D. commiserate

2. Jonathan is worried about _____ people who might try to steal his *egg-rasher* money.
   A. disreputable   B. amenable   C. destitute   D. commiserate

3. Jonathan's neighbors came to _____ with him about the theft of his money.
   A. disreputable   B. amenable   C. destitute   D. commiserate

4. Though Jonathan and his family are _____, they are thankful for what they have.
   A. disreputable   B. amenable   C. destitute   D. commiserate

Name _____ Date _____

"Civil Peace" by Chinua Achebe
Support for Writing a Character Analysis

For your character analysis, use the following graphic organizer to help you identify the main traits that define Jonathan Iwegbu. Then fill in examples of incidents and descriptions in the story that show these traits.

Traits   **Examples**

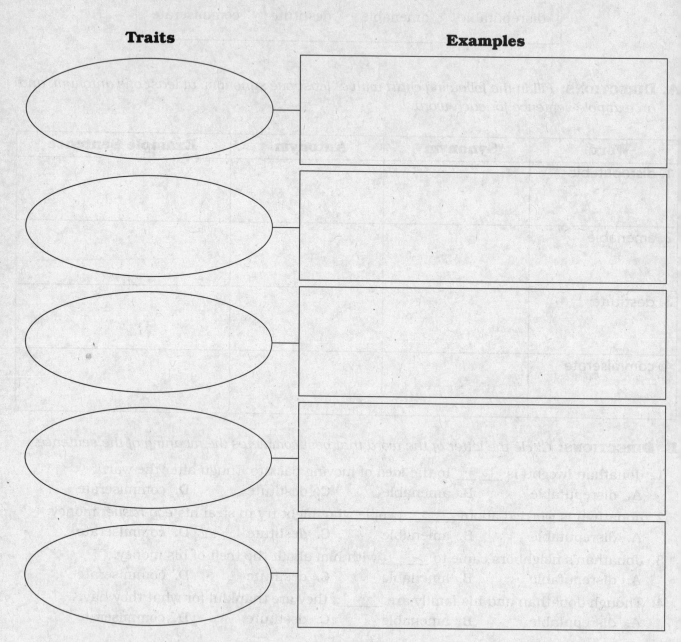

Now, use this graphic organizer to help you write a brief character analysis of Jonathan.

"Civil Peace" by Chinua Achebe
Support for Extend Your Learning

Listening and Speaking

Use the following chart to help you and your group decide how Achebe's theme does or does not apply to modern life. Write several students' statements of the story's theme or message in the top box. Circle the one on which your group agrees. Then write reasons why this theme does or does not apply to modern life in the boxes below.

Statements of the story's message:

Reasons why the theme DOES apply to modern life:	Reasons why the theme DOES NOT apply to modern life:

Research and Technology

Use the chart below to help you brainstorm a list of visual aids that you and your group might create for your presentation. For each idea, identify one or more resources that are available to you that might help you create your visual aid.

Visual Aid	Resources
A map showing the distribution of various tribes in Nigeria	
A timeline showing events from colonization through independence to the war	

Name _____ Date _____

Enrichment: Geography

"Civil Peace" is set in the African country of Nigeria. You can learn more about Nigeria by studying its geography. Work in a group of students to create a children's book about Nigeria. Each student should take one of the following topics related to the study of geography: landforms, bodies of water, climate, population, culture, government, economy, or history. Create one or two pages that briefly cover each topic and bind them together as a book to share with younger students. Illustrate difficult concepts whenever possible with maps, charts, graphs, timelines, and drawings.

DIRECTIONS: *Use the book map below to help you plan the pages of your group's book. Be sure to include a cover and a table of contents.*

p. 1	p. 2	p. 3	p. 4
p. 5	p. 6	p. 7	p. 8
p. 9	p. 10	p. 11	p. 12
p. 13	p. 14	p. 15	p. 16

"How Much Land Does a Man Need?" by Leo Tolstoy
"Civil Peace" by Chinua Achebe
Build Language Skills: Vocabulary

Etymology

The word *consequently* is the adverbial form of the word *consequence.* Its Latin root, *-sequi-,* means "follow." Therefore, *consequently* is used to link an effect to the action that was its cause. Other words containing the root *-sequi-* will also refer to the idea of following or coming as a result. Examples include the words *sequel, sequence,* and *non sequitur.*

A. DIRECTIONS: *Using a dictionary, briefly define each of the following words and then explain what the root contributes to the meaning.*

1. sequel: _____

   _____

2. sequence: _____

   _____

3. non sequitur: _____

   _____

Academic Vocabulary Practice

consequently	predominant	comprehend	coincide	infer

B. DIRECTIONS: *Use a thesaurus to find a synonym or a brief phrase that could replace each word in the academic vocabulary list. Then, write a sentence that makes the meaning clear.*

Example: *Vocabulary word: consequently   Synonym: therefore*

Sample sentence: The war had ended; <u>therefore</u>, people were finally able to return to their homes.

1. Vocabulary word: predominant   Synonym: _____

   Sample sentence: _____

2. Vocabulary word: comprehend   Synonym: _____

   Sample sentence: _____

3. Vocabulary word: coincide   Synonym: _____

   Sample sentence: _____

4. Vocabulary word: infer   Synonym: _____

   Sample sentence: _____

"How Much Land Does a Man Need?" by Leo Tolstoy

"Civil Peace" by Chinua Achebe

Build Language Skills: Grammar

Action and Linking Verbs

An **action verb** shows physical or mental action. A **linking verb** expresses a state of being or tells what the subject is by linking it to one or more words in the predicate. The most common linking verbs are forms of *be* (*is, are, was, were,* and so on). Other verbs are linking verbs if they can be replaced with a form of *be* and the sentence still makes sense.

Action verbs: Pahom *buys* some land from his neighbor. [shows physical action; cannot be replaced with a form of *be*]

Jonathan *values* his family's lives more than anything else. [shows mental action; cannot be replaced with a form of *be*]

Linking verbs: Pahom *is* content with his new farm for a while. [links *Pahom* to *content; is* is a form of *be*]

Jonathan *feels* grateful for his family's survival. [links *Jonathan* to *grateful;* can be replaced with *is*]

A. PRACTICE: *The following sentences are based on "How Much Land Does a Man Need?" or "Civil Peace." Identify each verb as either a linking verb or an action verb by writing LV or AV on the line before each sentence.*

Example:

_AV_ Pahom listened to his wife's discussion with her sister.

____ 1. The Devil was thrilled about Pahom's boast.

____ 2. The Devil gained power over Pahom through his greed for more land.

____ 3. Pahom remained unhappy, even with a larger farm.

____ 4. Jonathan seemed genuinely happy to find his home mostly intact.

____ 5. The Iwegbu family worked hard to get by after the war.

____ 6. The thieves took Jonathan's "egg-rasher" money.

B. Writing Application: *Write a paragraph based on either "How Much Land Does a Man Need?" or "Civil Peace." Use both action and linking verbs. Circle each verb and label it with LV or AV.*

_____

_____

_____

_____

_____

_____

_____

"Civil Peace" by Chinua Achebe
Selection Test A

Critical Reading *Identify the letter of the choice that best answers the question.*

____ 1. What does Jonathan Iwegbu value most in "Civil Peace"?
  A. his money
  B. his bicycle
  C. his home
  D. his family

____ 2. What does the phrase "happy survival" mean to Jonathan in "Civil Peace"?
  A. Put on a happy face.
  B. Beware of further violence.
  C. Congratulations on surviving the war.
  D. Survival does not ensure happiness.

____ 3. Why does Jonathan Iwegbu bury his bicycle?
  A. He no longer needs the bicycle to help him make a living.
  B. He wants to get rid of the bicycle because it is broken and rusted.
  C. He does not believe the officer who wanted it is really a soldier.
  D. He is worried that his child may injure himself while riding it.

____ 4. What does the phrase "Nothing puzzles God" mean in "Civil Peace"?
  A. That people should have faith in themselves.
  B. That people should have faith in God's plan.
  C. That God will punish those who fought in the war.
  D. That God does not like things that do not make sense.

____ 5. How does Jonathan Iwegbu feel when he finds his house intact?
  A. He is ashamed of his poor shelter.
  B. He wants to gloat to his neighbors.
  C. He feels like he has won a valuable prize.
  D. He feels like he has been punched in the stomach.

____ 6. Which of the following is NOT one of the ways Jonathan Iwegbu and his family earn money after the war?
  A. Jonathan opens a palm-wine bar.
  B. His son gets a job with the Treasury.
  C. His wife makes and sells breakfast akara balls.
  D. His children pick mangoes and sell them to soldiers' wives.

_____ 7. What do Jonathan's everyday actions in "Civil Peace" indicate about the country's economy after the war?

  A. Most people do not want to work.

  B. Many people are becoming very rich.

  C. The government provides jobs to everyone.

  D. People have to be resourceful to make money.

_____ 8. How does Jonathan Iwegbu deal with his losses?

  A. He turns to stealing from others to get by.

  B. He focuses on the good things that remain.

  C. He is angry at those who caused his losses.

  D. He spends his days feeling sorry for himself.

_____ 9. What is the outcome of Jonathan's confrontation with the thieves in "Civil Peace"?

  A. Jonathan gives them 100 pounds, but they demand even more.

  B. Jonathan's family shouts the alarm and the entire village comes running.

  C. Jonathan's son is killed by the thieves before Jonathan gives them his money.

  D. Jonathan gives them his "egg-rasher," and they leave him and his family alone.

_____ 10. How does the thieves' method of survival differ from Jonathan Iwegbu's?

  A. The thieves survive by stealing money while Jonathan survives by letting go of money.

  B. The thieves find many ways to get money while Jonathan only knows one way to get by.

  C. The thieves keep a good sense of humor while Jonathan mostly feels sorry for himself.

  D. They both steal to survive, but the thieves are willing to be violent while Jonathan is not.

_____ 11. At the end of "Civil Peace," Jonathan's neighbors feel sorry for him because he was robbed. He tells them,

> What is *egg-rasher*? Did I depend on it last week? Or is it greater than other things that went with the war? I say, let *egg-rasher* perish in the flames! Let it go where everything else has gone. Nothing puzzles God."

Based on these words along with Jonathan's words and actions throughout the story, what message does the author convey about survival?

  A. Survival without money and other possessions is meaningless.

  B. It is important to fight criminals, even at the cost of one's own life.

  C. In order to survive, one must be able to let go of what has been lost.

  D. One must find a way to hold onto money and possessions in order to survive.

___ 12. What is the theme of "Civil Peace"?

    A. One must fight crime at all costs.

    B. Poverty cannot be avoided after war.

    C. Where there is life there is hope.

    D. Money is necessary for survival.

Vocabulary and Grammar

___ 13. What is the best synonym for the word *amenable*?

    A. shameful

    B. disagreeable

    C. responsive

    D. powerful

___ 14. Which of the following people is most likely to be *destitute*?

    A. a homeless man

    B. a businesswoman

    C. an angry child

    D. a soldier at war

___ 15. Which of the following sentences contains a linking verb?

    A. Jonathan is grateful.

    B. Maria sells akara balls.

    C. The thieves demand money.

    D. Jonathan hides his *egg-rasher.*

Essay

16. In an essay, identify the theme of "Civil Peace." List details from the story that illustrate this theme. Consider how Achebe uses Jonathan's words and actions to help readers understand his message.

17. In an essay, describe the character of Jonathan Iwegbu. Give examples of his words and actions that show readers what kind of person he is. Then explain how you think most people in the United States today would react to circumstances like Jonathan's.

Name _____ Date _____

Critical Reading *Identify the letter of the choice that best completes the statement or answers the question.*

_____ 1. In "Civil Peace," what does Jonathan appear to value most?
A. the security of his savings
B. the condition of his bicycle
C. the preservation of his home
D. the safety of his family

_____ 2. How does Jonathan Iwegbu respond to the losses of war?
A. He turns to stealing from others to get by.
B. He spends his days feeling sorry for himself.
C. He is angry at those who caused his losses and vows revenge.
D. He decides to let go of what he has lost and focus on surviving.

_____ 3. Why does Jonathan Iwegbu bury his bicycle rather than give it to the officer who wanted it?
A. He does not believe the officer is really a soldier.
B. He needs the bicycle to help make a living during the war.
C. The bicycle is broken and Jonathan is worried for the officer's safety.
D. The officer is an enemy combatant and Jonathan does not want to help him.

_____ 4. Jonathan Iwegbu's reliance on the proverb "Nothing puzzles God" shows his
A. faith in the divine plan.
B. refusal to confront reality.
C. lack of faith in himself.
D. desire to acquire more education.

_____ 5. The main conflict in "Civil Peace" occurs when
A. Jonathan bribes the ragged soldier.
B. the thieves steal Jonathan's "egg-rasher."
C. Jonathan angrily rejects public sympathy.
D. the thieves argue among themselves.

_____ 6. In "Civil Peace," what does the leader of the thieves mean when he says "We no be bad tief"?
A. He is willing to make a deal with Jonathan.
B. He never fails to get money from his targets.
C. He is promising not to kill Jonathan and his family.
D. He and his gang have never been caught by police.

_____ 7. What deal does Jonathan work out with the thieves in "Civil Peace"?
A. He will give them 100 pounds the next morning if they will come back to get it.
B. He will give them his twenty-pound "egg-rasher" if they leave him and his family alone.
C. He will not raise the alarm to the police if they just walk away without hurting his family.
D. He will lead them to the houses of wealthier people if they agree not to take his money.

_____ 8. What is Jonathan's reaction to the theft of his twenty pounds in "Civil Peace"?
   A. despair
   B. bitterness
   C. outrage
   D. resignation

_____ 9. Why does Jonathan react as he does to the loss of his "egg-rasher" money?
   A. He believes that the thieves will use the money to help others in the community.
   B. It was not very much money, so he knows he can earn it again without effort.
   C. He knows that he survived without it before he got it, so he can survive without it now.
   D. He believes he is better off without the money because it would only have led him to evil.

_____ 10. How does the thieves' response to the losses of war differ from Jonathan Iwegbu's?
   A. Though they have both chosen to steal to get by, the thieves are willing to commit violence when they steal and Jonathan is not.
   B. The thieves have decided to survive by taking what they have lost from others, while Jonathan has chosen to work hard and forget about his losses.
   C. While Jonathan spends his days feeling sorry for himself, the thieves keep a very upbeat attitude as they go about improving their lives.
   D. The thieves forget about the war in order to focus on doing what they have to do to survive, but Jonathan dwells on thoughts of anger and revenge.

_____ 11. What is Achebe's philosophical assumption about survival?
   A. Survival without money and other possessions is meaningless.
   B. It is important to fight criminals, even at the cost of one's own life.
   C. In order to survive, one must be able to let go of what has been lost.
   D. One must find a way to hold onto money and possessions in order to survive.

_____ 12. What is the best statement of the theme of "Civil Peace"?
   A. Poverty breeds crime and despair.
   B. War ruins the lives of survivors.
   C. Where there is life there is hope.
   D. Honesty is the best policy.

_____ 13. What makes the theme of "Civil Peace" a universal theme?
   A. It has meaning for any time or culture.
   B. It can be interpreted on an astronomical level.
   C. There is just one possible interpretation of the story's theme.
   D. It only has meaning in the context of Nigeria after its civil war.

Vocabulary and Grammar

_____ 14. Which of the following is an example of someone being *amenable*?
   A. a neighbor sympathizing with Jonathan about the robbery
   B. Jonathan not caring very much about the loss of the "egg-rasher"
   C. Jonathan's wife praying that the thieves would not hurt her family
   D. the leader of the thieves being open to making a deal with Jonathan

_____ 15. Which of the following would someone who is *destitute* be most likely to do?
   A. buy jewelry for his wife
   B. work in exchange for a meal
   C. take a college class
   D. cry uncontrollably at weddings

_____ 16. Which of the following sentences contains a linking verb?
   A. Jonathan is surprised to find his house intact.
   B. Maria sells breakfast akara balls to earn money.
   C. Jonathan carefully keeps his money out of sight.
   D. The leader of the thieves demands 100 pounds.

_____ 17. Which of the following sentences contains an action verb?
   A. Jonathan feels blessed after the war.
   B. Maria seems content like her husband.
   C. Jonathan buries his bicycle.
   D. The family is terrified of the thieves.

Essay

18. In "Civil Peace," Jonathan Iwegbu relies on the proverb "Nothing puzzles God." What significance does the proverb hold for him? Does it provide an explanation for events, or is its meaning more complex? Write a brief essay in which you analyze the key statement's meaning.

19. Jonathan Iwegbu possesses a positive outlook on an arguably bleak life. In an essay, compare and contrast Jonathan's optimism with the reality of his life, naming at least three incidents from the story. Draw a conclusion about the reason for Jonathan's optimism. Does it arise because of the incidents, or for some reason unrelated to the incidents?

20. In "Civil Peace," Achebe makes a philosophical assumption about what is truly important in life. In an essay, explain Achebe's philosophical assumption and how this assumption influences the theme of the story. Note details from the story that help the reader to determine Achebe's philosophical assumption.

Vocabulary Warm-up Word Lists

Study these words from "The Masque of the Red Death." Then, complete the activities.

Word List A

acknowledged [ak NAHL ijd] *v.* accepted or admitted that something is true
I <u>acknowledged</u> that Mei was right after checking my answer on the key.

bizarre [bi ZAHR] *adj.* very unusual or strange
The combination of sushi and enchiladas struck me as rather <u>bizarre</u>.

expressive [ek SPRES iv] *adj.* showing one's thoughts or feelings
Her <u>expressive</u> face glowed with joy at the sight of her best friend.

revelers [REV uhl uhrz] *n.* people who are noisily enjoying festivities
The <u>revelers</u> at the New Year party began to sing Auld Lange Syne.

suite [SWEET] *n.* a set of rooms in a large building; a group of things forming a unit
The extended family booked a <u>suite</u> of rooms in the hotel for their reunion.

sustain [suh STAYN] *v.* to make something continue to exist over a period of time
They kept dance music playing all night long to <u>sustain</u> the party mood.

throng [THRAHNG] *n.* a crowd
A <u>throng</u> gathered to see the movie star.

unlimited [uhn LIM uh tid] *adj.* without any boundary
The <u>unlimited</u> expanse of the ocean stretched out in front of us.

Word List B

attained [uh TAYND] *v.* to have reached a place or a goal
The exhausted climbers finally <u>attained</u> the mountain's summit.

cowardice [KOW ur dis] *n.* a lack of bravery
He showed no <u>cowardice</u> as he rescued his brother from the burning room.

disregarded [dis ri GAHR did] *v.* having ignored something, especially something important or serious
His parents were upset when Josh <u>disregarded</u> the rule that required wearing a helmet.

embraced [em BRAYST] *v.* encompassed; taken in and included
The birds' migration period <u>embraced</u> all the weeks of autumn.

emphasis [EM fuh sis] *n.* special importance
The music school placed an <u>emphasis</u> on instrumental performance.

grotesque [groh TESK] *adj.* ugly or strange in a way that is unpleasant or frightening
The <u>grotesque</u> drawings of werewolves gave the child nightmares.

indulge [in DUHLJ] *v.* to let yourself do or have something that you enjoy
Jan will abandon her diet for now and <u>indulge</u> in the chocolate torte.

seclusion [si KLOO zhuhn] *n.* the state of being private and away from other people
Daniel lived in <u>seclusion</u> up in the mountains after tiring of city life.

"The Masque of the Red Death" by Edgar Allan Poe
Vocabulary Warm-up Exercises

Exercise A *Fill in each blank in the paragraph below with an appropriate word from Word List A. Use each word only once.*

The family rented a [1] _____ of rooms for their overnight stay in Chicago. They [2] _____ that it would be expensive, but they wanted to sleep in comfort since the rest of their trip would be so arduous. It was impossible to [3] _____ uninterrupted sleep throughout the night, though, when a group of [4] _____ next door refused to stop their party. There seemed to be a [5] _____ of people in the room with [6] _____ enthusiasm for making noise. First, the family was serenaded by an [7] _____ singer crooning along with a karaoke machine. Later, in a [8] _____ stunt, one of the partygoers climbed over onto their balcony. Finally, the family resorted to calling hotel security.

Exercise B *Answer the question with complete explanations.*

Example: If the students <u>disregarded</u> the rules, would the teacher be happy with them?
> *Their teacher wouldn't be happy because, if they <u>disregarded</u> the rules, they ignored them.*

1. If you <u>indulge</u> your appetite for a big meal, will you feel hungry?

_____

2. If Zach <u>attained</u> his dearest goal, would he be proud or disappointed?

_____

3. If Nan <u>embraced</u> the teacher's ideas, did she reject them?

_____

4. If Juan lives in <u>seclusion</u>, will he see a lot of people in his daily life?

_____

5. If a teen showed <u>cowardice</u> when encountering lizards, is it likely she would be chosen to lead a desert hike?

_____

6. If Rich's picture was <u>grotesque</u>, would it make people laugh or shudder?

_____

7. If the school places an <u>emphasis</u> on creativity, would you be surprised to learn that it offers music and art classes?

_____

"The Masque of the Red Death" by Edgar Allan Poe
Reading Warm-up A

Read the following passage. Pay special attention to the underlined words. Then, read it again, and complete the activities. Use a separate sheet of paper for your written answers.

After giving it lots of thought, Giulia decided to throw a costume party for her sixteenth birthday. She acknowledged that costumes weren't popular with everyone, but she wanted her party to seem larger than life.

"Giulia," said her best friend, Sandy, "the whole idea is just so strange and bizarre." It was impossible for Sandy to disguise the distaste in her expressive voice. "I have a party outfit that I'd love to wear, and I don't really want to have to come up with a costume!"

"I know, Sandy," said Giulia. "But there are so many parties where you can wear your party clothes. I want a party that revelers will never forget!"

Giulia decided that they should celebrate the years they'd been alive. On the invitations, she wrote, "Come as your favorite icon from the past 16 years!" She and Sandy brainstormed ideas for costumes. Giulia could be a president or perhaps a glamorous movie star. "Hmmm," Sandy thought, "maybe I'll be a TV character from the 1990s, or maybe I'll be a monster from a movie — but which one?" The possibilities seemed unlimited.

Sandy realized how much fun it could be to play a role and decided to help Giulia throw her party. They wanted everything to be perfect, including the setting. It wasn't as if they had a fancy suite, but they did have the entire backyard at Sandy's house. They decorated the yard with lanterns and glitter. Some friends who played in a band would play for the party. They wanted to sustain a mood of outlandish fun, which meant they didn't want to hear just any old pop songs. They asked the band to play the top songs from each of the past sixteen years.

On the night of the party, a throng of guests arrived right on time. Giulia laughed as she saw her friends dressed as characters from the 80s and 90s. She could sense their excitement, and she was ecstatic as the party began.

1. Underline the phrase that tells what Giulia acknowledged. Then explain what *acknowledged* means.

2. Circle the word that tells what Sandy's expressive voice revealed. Then tell what *expressive* means.

3. Circle the word that is a synonym for bizarre. Then use *bizarre* in a sentence.

4. Circle the word that tells where the revelers will be. Then explain what *revelers* are.

5. Rewrite the sentence that has the word unlimited, using your own words.

6. Circle the words that tell where the party would be held in place of a fancy suite. Explain why it would be nice to have a *suite* of rooms for a party.

7. Underline the phrase that tells the sort of mood Sandy and Giulia wanted to sustain. Then explain what *sustain* means.

8. Underline the words that describe the throng of guests. Write a sentence about a *throng* of people.

"The Masque of the Red Death" by Edgar Allan Poe
Reading Warm-up B

Read the following passage. Pay special attention to the underlined words. Then, read it again, and complete the activities. Use a separate sheet of paper for your written answers.

Are you looking for an entertaining read? If you don't let <u>cowardice</u> get the better of you, you might enjoy reading a ripping horror story. These stories are often full of <u>grotesque</u> characters who leave people shuddering at their sight. The setting is usually very important in a horror story, with darkness, gloom, and bad weather often establishing the tone. The plot in a horror story involves a good amount of suspense. The reader breathlessly turns the page, wanting to learn what will happen next and yet afraid to read that very thing.

Although sometimes critics have <u>disregarded</u> this genre as less than serious, many others have <u>embraced</u> it. The latter feel that authors like Mary Wollstonecraft Shelley, Bram Stoker, and Stephen King have <u>attained</u> their fame for good reason. Certainly, writers who have influenced the modern horror story include some of world literature's most distinguished authors. For example, Dante wrote about the tortures of hell in the *Inferno*; Goethe wrote about a man's pact with the devil in *Faust*; and Emily Brontë wrote about a man haunted by the ghost of his great love in *Wuthering Heights*.

Horror places an <u>emphasis</u> on what will scare the reader. Death, disease, or out-of-control technology are common elements of horror stories. Why would we want to feel horror—that strong combination of fear and disgust? Like children reading fairy tales, we can sometimes find comfort in dealing with the unknown in story form. Strangely, even things we know do not exist, like vampires and monsters, can seem real in a horror story. A skilled author can make our hair stand on end.

Notable horror story authors include Ambrose Bierce, Shirley Jackson, and, of course, Edgar Allan Poe. You may want to <u>indulge</u> your appetite for horror stories while you are in a safe place and among friends. Reading horror stories in <u>seclusion</u> might make for a scarier experience than you had bargained for.

1. Underline what you would be unable to do if <u>cowardice</u> got the better of you. Then, write a synonym for **cowardice**.

2. Underline the phrase that explains how <u>grotesque</u> characters affect others. Explain what **grotesque** means.

3. If critics have <u>disregarded</u> the horror genre, how have they treated it?

4. If people have <u>embraced</u> horror stories, how have they reacted to them? Write an antonym for **embraced**.

5. Circle the word that tells what Shelley, Stoker, and King have <u>attained</u>. Then tell what **attained** means.

6. Underline the words that tell what horror places an <u>emphasis</u> on. Then tell what writers of humor place an **emphasis** on.

7. What is a taste you have that you like to <u>indulge</u>? Write a sentence about it.

8. Explain why reading a horror story in <u>seclusion</u> might be very scary.

"**The Masque of the Red Death**" by Edgar Allan Poe
Literary Analysis: Symbolism

Symbolism is a writer's use of symbols. A **symbol** is a character, place, thing, or event in a literary work that stands for a larger idea. For example, a raven in a story might stand for death, or a doorway might stand for a new opportunity. To make a particular character or thing into a symbol, a writer may use these common strategies: (1) calling on traditional associations, such as a branching pathway that represents a choice in life; or (2) creating new associations, such as a character becoming more noble after choosing a path, which in turn helps the reader to understand that the path represents courage or bravery.

A story in which all characters and settings are clearly symbolic is called an **allegory.**

DIRECTIONS: *Complete the following chart. Explain what you think each symbol in "The Masque of the Red Death" represents and how it helps teach the lesson of the story.*

Symbol	What it represents	How it helps teach the lesson
Example: dreams	masqueraders, fantasies	Shows us that life is fleeting; forebodes the grim ending to the story
1. the masked visitor		
2. the black chamber		
3. the music		
4. the clock		

"The Masque of the Red Death" by Edgar Allan Poe
Reading: Identify Patterns to Draw Conclusions About Symbolism

When you **draw a conclusion,** you make a decision or form an opinion based on facts and details in a text. To draw a conclusion about the meaning of a symbol, **identify patterns** that suggest the nature of an object's greater importance.

DIRECTIONS: *List three details from the story that have to do with each symbol. Then identify a pattern created by these details in regard to the symbol. Finally, draw a conclusion about what the symbol means based on the pattern you discover.*

1. Symbol: the masked visitor
   Three details about this symbol:

   A. _____

   B. _____

   C. _____

   Pattern: _____

   _____

   Meaning: _____

   _____

   _____

2. Symbol: the black chamber
   Three details about this symbol:

   A. _____

   B. _____

   C. _____

   Pattern: _____

   _____

   Meaning: _____

   _____

   _____

Name _____ Date _____

"The Masque of the Red Death" by Edgar Allan Poe
Vocabulary Builder

Word List

august	impeded	cessation	disapprobation

A. DIRECTIONS: *In each of the following items, think about the meaning of the italicized word, and then answer the question.*

1. If a home has an *august* appearance, what kind of people would you assume live there? Why?

   _____

   _____

2. If Lindsey went to a baseball game and something *impeded* her view of the field, do you think she enjoyed the game? Why or why not?

   _____

   _____

3. If you hear the *cessation* of your air conditioner on an extremely hot day, how might you feel? Why?

   _____

   _____

4. A student reports to his parents on how he did on a major exam, and they look at him with *disapprobation:* How do you think he did on the exam? Why?

   _____

   _____

B. DIRECTIONS: *Choose the word that is most nearly the* opposite *of the word in CAPITAL LETTERS. Circle the letter of your choice.*

1. AUGUST
   A. grand
   B. humble
   C. royal
   D. awesome

2. IMPEDED
   A. blocked
   B. obstructed
   C. infected
   D. allowed

3. CESSATION
   A. continuation
   B. inaction
   C. interruption
   D. nervousness

4. DISAPPROBATION
   A. condemnation
   B. acceptance
   C. revelry
   D. disfavor

Name _____ Date _____

"The Masque of the Red Death" by Edgar Allan Poe
Support for Writing a Narrative

Use the graphic organizer below to help you write a brief narrative using an object as a symbol. To show what the object stands for, first describe it using vivid adjectives that suggest the qualities it symbolizes. Then provide information about its location and actions. Finally, plan how you will link it to important events in your story.

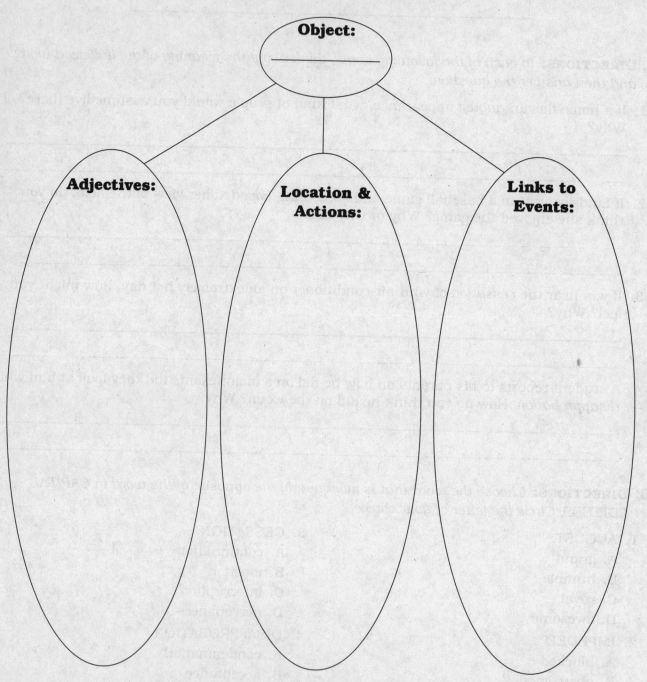

Now, use this graphic organizer to help you write your brief narrative using an object as a symbol.

"The Masque of the Red Death" by Edgar Allan Poe
Support for Extend Your Learning

Listening and Speaking

Though you cannot use a script or rehearse for your impromptu speech, you may take a few minutes to jot down some ideas before you speak. In your speech, you will describe one way people avoid facing their own limitations. Use the questions below to help you quickly brainstorm ideas for your speech.

1. What are three limitations people try to avoid facing?

   _____

   _____

   _____

2. Circle one of the limitations you listed above.

3. What is the way people have found to avoid this limitation?

   _____

   _____

   _____

Research and Technology

On the lines below, summarize important information about Poe's influence on either mysteries or on detective fiction. Circle any literary terms that you will need to define for your audience.

_____

_____

_____

_____

_____

_____

_____

_____

_____

_____

_____

_____

_____

"The Masque of the Red Death" by Edgar Allan Poe
Enrichment: Community Connections

In "The Masque of the Red Death," a plague is spreading outside the walls of the abbey in which Prince Prospero and his guests seek to hide. Though the Red Death is a fictional disease, there was a plague called the Black Death that caused a similar level of panic and death in the fourteenth and fifteenth-centuries.

In the modern world, plague is a rare threat. With medical improvements such as vaccinations and antibiotics, modern science has made incredible gains in the battle against disease. However, we are not completely immune to life-threatening illnesses. Epidemics such as AIDS and tuberculosis still present a serious threat. For example, certain strains of the tuberculosis virus have mutated and become resistant to medicines that once prevented them. Other viruses can mutate and reappear as a new disease.

Working with a group of classmates, come up with a plan for how people in your community can make a positive difference in preventing or curing disease. For example, you might come up with a plan to provide free or affordable vaccines to those who are at risk. Or you might think of a way to get people in your school or community involved in raising funds for medical research targeting a particular disease. Use the following chart to determine the steps you need to take to accomplish this community project. Present your project proposal to the class.

Project Title	
Goal Statement	
Task List to Reach Goal	
People Who Can Help	
Impact of Project on Community	

"The Masque of the Red Death" by Edgar Allan Poe
Selection Test A

Critical Reading *Identify the letter of the choice that best answers the question.*

____ 1. Why do Prince Prospero and his guests lock themselves in an abbey?
   A. to pray in seclusion
   B. to celebrate his birthday
   C. to escape an invading army
   D. to escape the Red Death

____ 2. The revelers' masks and costumes symbolize their attempt to hide from the Red Death. What detail from the story supports this interpretation?
   A. The music stops each time the ebony clock chimes.
   B. The uninvited guest has blood on his mask and costume.
   C. The revelers look like dreams moving from room to room.
   D. There are seven chambers, each decorated in a different color.

____ 3. Which of the following is the best description of the seven rooms in "The Masque of the Red Death"?
   A. grotesque and bizarre
   B. colorful and cheerful
   C. childish and disgusting
   D. elegant and bland

____ 4. Of the seven chambers in "The Masque of the Red Death," which room is the least popular and why?
   A. The white room because it is too plain.
   B. The orange room because it is too bright.
   C. The violet room because it is too cold.
   D. The black room because it is too frightening.

____ 5. What do the red windows in the last chamber symbolize in "The Masque of the Red Death"?
   A. blood and death
   B. love and hope
   C. jealousy and fear
   D. elegance and wealth

____ 6. Prince Prospero's guests seem happy and carefree, but they stop celebrating and get very quiet every time the clock chimes. What does this tell you about how they are really feeling?

A. They are annoyed that the clock keeps interrupting their fun.

B. They are happy about their flawless escape from the Red Death.

C. Under their happy exterior, they are still worried about the Red Death.

D. While they are quiet, they think about how much they dislike Prospero.

____ 7. Which of the following is a symbol that suggests that the revelers will not live long in "The Masque of the Red Death"?

A. the white room

B. the locked gates

C. the prince's dagger

D. the ebony clock

____ 8. Why does Prince Prospero become angry with the masked stranger?

A. Because the stranger refuses to answer Prospero's questions.

B. Because the stranger interrupts the music and refuses to dance.

C. Because the stranger is costumed as a victim of the Red Death.

D. Because the stranger was not invited to Prospero's masquerade.

____ 9. In "The Masque of the Red Death," what does the uninvited guest symbolize?

A. anger

B. wealth

C. celebration

D. death

____ 10. How does Prince Prospero die?

A. He is stabbed with a dagger.

B. He is stricken by the plague.

C. He is injured in a fall.

D. He is hanged from the battlements.

____ 11. The tripods' flames go out when the last of the revelers dies. Based on this detail, what might the tripods' flames symbolize in "The Masque of the Red Death"?

A. the revelers' lives

B. the peasants' revenge

C. that it was all a dream

D. Prince Prospero's wealth

____ 12. What message is Poe trying to convey in "The Masque of the Red Death"?

    A. God punishes sinners.

    B. Time passes slowly.

    C. Wealth cannot protect one from death.

    D. One should not attend parties uninvited.

Vocabulary and Grammar

____ 13. There is a _____ of the celebration when the clock chimes because the music stops and the guests are quiet for a few moments.

    A. lingering

    B. cessation

    C. continuation

    D. disapprobation

____ 14. Which of the following is the best antonym for the word *impeded?*

    A. obstructed

    B. unblocked

    C. disapproved

    D. enjoyed

____ 15. Which of the following sentences is written in passive voice?

    A. The guests avoid the black chamber.

    B. An uninvited stranger appears.

    C. Rage is felt by Prospero.

    D. Prospero attacks the stranger.

Essay

16. The setting and descriptive details of "The Masque of the Red Death" contain many symbols. Choose at least three symbols from the story, and in an essay, describe what each symbol stands for. Explain how the symbols give meaning to the story.

17. Think about the character of Prince Prospero. What kind of person is he? Is Prospero's attempt to escape death an act of unforgivable arrogance, or is it a normal human response to the inevitable? Consider the details given about Propero's personality and behavior. In an essay, support your opinion with examples from the story or from your own experience.

"The Masque of the Red Death" by Edgar Allan Poe

Selection Test B

Critical Reading *Identify the letter of the choice that best completes the statement or answers the question.*

_____ 1. In the "The Masque of the Red Death," whom does Prince Prospero invite to his abbey?
A. the plague victims of his land
B. a thousand healthy friends
C. a mysterious, masked guest
D. Edgar Allan Poe

_____ 2. Why does Prince Prospero decide to have a masquerade?
A. to show off his good decorating taste to his friends
B. to give the musicians and entertainers something to do
C. to distract himself and his guests from the boredom and fear of their seclusion
D. to taunt those outside the walls who are suffering and dying of the Red Death

_____ 3. In "The Masque of the Red Death," what do the dream-like costumes of the revelers symbolize?
A. repressed fears and desires
B. extreme tension and anxiety
C. youthful health and beauty
D. carefree glamour and luxury

_____ 4. The seven rooms of the masquerade are (in order) blue, purple, green, orange, white, violet, and black. What might this series of colors symbolize in "The Masque of the Red Death"?
A. Prospero's fascination with the bizarre
B. the progression through life toward death
C. the relative wealth and importance of Prospero's various guests
D. the fear and horror the guests are feeling throughout the masquerade

_____ 5. How do Prince Prospero's guests react to the black room?
A. They fear it and do not want to enter it.
B. They find it to be exciting and interesting.
C. They avoid it because it is too dark.
D. They are awed by its incredible beauty.

_____ 6. In "The Masque of the Red Death," the location of the black chamber at the western end of the suite
A. suggests the end of daylight and life.
B. indicates a fascination with the bizarre.
C. minimizes the presence of natural light.
D. suggests a mood of exploration and excitement.

_____ 7. What does the clock symbolize in "The Masque of the Red Death"?
A. the Red Death
B. Prince Prospero
C. that the guests do not have long to live
D. that it is time for the stranger to arrive

____ 8. What does the stranger symbolize in "The Masque of the Red Death"?
A. the Red Death
B. health and wealth
C. selfishness and arrogance
D. fear of the unknown

____ 9. Prince Prospero objects to the masked stranger because he
A. arrives uninvited.
B. is costumed as a victim of the Red Death.
C. interrupts the musicians.
D. might contaminate the abbey with the plague.

____ 10. The tripods' flames symbolize the lives of the revelers. What detail from "The Masque of the Red Death" gives evidence to support this interpretation?
A. The flames look frightening in the black room.
B. A group of revelers throw themselves on the stranger.
C. The flames are extinguished when the last of the revelers dies.
D. All the rooms except the black one are densely crowded with guests.

____ 11. Why is "The Masque of the Red Death" an allegory?
A. Everyone dies in the end.
B. The theme is ambiguous.
C. All of the characters and settings are symbolic.
D. The story teaches a lesson about good and evil.

____ 12. Which of the following best expresses the theme, or main point, of "The Masque of the Red Death"?
A. Beware of uninvited guests.
B. Death should be faced with courage.
C. Wealth offers no refuge from death.
D. Human beings are essentially selfish.

Vocabulary and Grammar

____ 13. The arrangement of the rooms at Prince Prospero's abbey _____ the guests' view of other chambers.
A. impeded
B. enhanced
C. forced
D. tantalized

____ 14. Which of the following situations would most likely result in a parent's disapprobation?
A. A child does not get a part in a play.
B. A child plays with neighborhood friends.
C. A child wins the science fair competition.
D. A child brings home a poor report card.

_____ 15. Which of the following sentences is written in active voice?
   A. Each chamber is decorated in a different color.
   B. In the last chamber, there stands a massive ebony clock.
   C. Prospero's guests celebrate their escape from the disease.
   D. The music is silenced every hour by the chiming of the clock.

_____ 16. Which of the following sentences is written in passive voice?
   A. Prospero angrily attacks the uninvited guest.
   B. Prince Prospero tries to escape the Red Death.
   C. The guests wander freely from room to room during the masquerade.
   D. The Red Death is characterized by bleeding from the pores of the skin.

Essay

17. Is Prince Prospero's attempt to escape death an act of unforgivable arrogance, or is it a normal human response to the inevitable? Consider the details given about Prospero's personality and behavior. In an essay, form an opinion about Prospero's actions. Support your opinion with examples from the story or from your own experience.

18. "The Masque of the Red Death" can be read as an allegory. In an essay, explain why the story is an allegory and what the characters, settings, and events symbolize. Think about patterns in the story to help you draw conclusions about the meanings of symbols.

19. In an essay, identify and explain the theme of "The Masque of the Red Death." How do mood and symbolism contribute to the story's message? Do you agree or disagree with what Poe is trying to say? Why?

Vocabulary Warm-up Word Lists

Study these words from "The Garden of Stubborn Cats." Then, complete the activities.

Word List A

distinction [di STINGK shuhn] *n.* clear difference between things
There was little <u>distinction</u> between the baby clothes for girls and boys.

domestic [duh MES tik] *adj.* living near or around humans; tame
Cats have been <u>domestic</u> animals for thousands of years.

futile [FYOO tuhl] *adj.* having no chance at being successful
It was <u>futile</u> to keep a secret from the inquisitive child.

luxurious [luhk ZHUHR ee us] *adj.* very comfortable, beautiful, and expensive
The <u>luxurious</u> hotel had a whirlpool bath in each room.

overrun [oh ver RUHN] *v.* to spread over a place quickly and in great numbers
The field was <u>overrun</u> with fans after the final out of the World Series.

reluctant [ri LUHK tuhnt] *adj.* unwilling and slow to do something
I was <u>reluctant</u> to share my favorite skirt with my sister.

riveted [RIV i tid] *v.* attracted and held by a strong interest
We were <u>riveted</u> to the television coverage of the Olympic gymnasts.

treacherous [TRECH ur us] *adj.* untrustworthy; not loyal
The <u>treacherous</u> officer revealed the battle plan to an enemy commander.

Word List B

infuriated [in FYOO ree ay tid] *adj.* very angry
The <u>infuriated</u> bees swarmed over the bear that pawed at their hive.

minimal [MIN uh muhl] *adj.* very small in degree or amount
It took a <u>minimal</u> effort to pull the toddler around in a wagon.

skyscraper [SKY skray pur] *n.* a very tall building in a city
The Empire State Building used to be the tallest <u>skyscraper</u> in New York.

surveillance [sur VAY luhns] *n.* the act of watching a particular person or place carefully, usually to prevent a crime or catch a criminal
The crime rate fell after hidden cameras began performing <u>surveillance</u>.

transformed [trans FORMD] *v.* having changed in appearance or character
The men were <u>transformed</u> by their new exercise routine.

unauthorized [uhn AW thuh rized] *adj.* done without official approval or permission
Civilians cannot have <u>unauthorized</u> access to a military base.

vibrant [VY bruhnt] *adj.* seeming to pulsate with energy
The <u>vibrant</u> colors seemed to make the image leap off the canvas.

voids [VOIDZ] *n.* empty spaces where nothing exists
The huge <u>voids</u> showed where buildings had stood before the earthquake.

Name _____ Date _____

"The Garden of Stubborn Cats" by Italo Calvino
Vocabulary Warm-up Exercises

Exercise A *Fill in each blank in the paragraph below with an appropriate word from Word List A. Use each word only once.*

While some may see little [1] _____ between African wild dogs that run in packs and [2] _____ dogs, there is a big difference between the two. While pet dogs often live in [3] _____ settings where they are well fed, wild dogs must hunt for their food. Ranches can be [4] _____ by wild dogs looking for prey. Animal researchers are [5] _____ by their observations of these dogs, who treat one another kindly. Unlike many other mammals, African wild dogs will not fight over their food, nor will a [6] _____ younger dog ever turn against a weaker member of the pack. If a person traps a wild dog, however, and escape seems [7] _____, a wild dog is not the least bit [8] _____ to attack a human.

Exercise B *Revise each sentence so that the underlined vocabulary word is used in a logical way. Be sure to keep the vocabulary word in your revision.*

Example: Given the many <u>voids</u> in the area, there was no room to build.
Given the many <u>voids</u> in the area, there was lots of room to build.

1. The painting was <u>vibrant</u> because the artist had used dull colors.
   _____

2. I tried to focus on many things as I kept the house under constant <u>surveillance</u>.
   _____

3. Since we were <u>unauthorized</u> to be there, they let us right in.
   _____

4. After the house was <u>transformed</u> by the decorator, it looked exactly the same.
   _____

5. I was barely out of breath after I ran up the stairs to the top of the <u>skyscraper</u>,
   _____

6. She used a <u>minimal</u> amount of red pepper in her sauce because she liked spicy foods.
   _____

7. The <u>infuriated</u> teacher praised her students for their excellent behavior.
   _____

"The Garden of Stubborn Cats" by Italo Calvino
Reading Warm-up A

Read the following passage. Pay special attention to the underlined words. Then, read it again, and complete the activities. Use a separate sheet of paper for your written answers.

Rome is a city that is famously <u>overrun</u> by cats. These animals are not like the <u>domestic</u> housecats seen in homes throughout the United States. Instead, they are often feral, or wild. They live outdoors, where the lucky ones are fed by people who love cats. They also hunt mice, lizards, and pigeons.

People have mixed feelings about the cats of Rome. Some people love them and are <u>reluctant</u> to remove the famous cats from their urban homes. In fact, cats living in three historic sites have been named part of Rome's "bio-heritage" by the city council. At these sites, there are cat sanctuaries where cat lovers can come to feed and care for the felines.

Other people, however, feel that the population of stray cats is a burden to the city. They worry that these scruffy animals might spread disease, and they see little <u>distinction</u> between the cats and common pests like rodents. Some <u>treacherous</u> people even leave poisoned food out for the wild cats.

Still, cats in Italy are supposed to be protected by laws, and legally, they cannot be killed if they are healthy. Perhaps the politicians realize that the cats attract people. Tourists have long been <u>riveted</u> by the sight of the cats prowling around the ancient Roman ruins. There is nothing <u>luxurious</u> or comfortable about these cats' lives, however. They have to scrounge for food and try to avoid the diseases that are common to outdoor cats. It is a hard life when there is so much competition from other cats, and there are no people to go home to.

Because of the great number of cats, it may seem <u>futile</u> to try to control their population. Nonetheless, volunteers at the sanctuaries have begun to spay and neuter the cats so that the population won't continue to grow. They also try to find owners for the cats. Eventually, they hope to make the beloved cats of Rome as healthy and well cared for as they can be.

1. Circle the word that tells what has <u>overrun</u> Rome. Explain what **overrun** means.

2. Underline the phrase that tells where some <u>domestic</u> cats live. Then use **domestic** in a sentence.

3. Circle the phrase that tells what some people are <u>reluctant</u> to do. Then tell what **reluctant** means.

4. Underline the words that explain why some people might see little <u>distinction</u> between the cats and other pests. Give a synonym for **distinction**.

5. Underline the phrase that tells how <u>treacherous</u> people treat the cats. Then explain what makes these people **treacherous**.

6. Underline the sight that has <u>riveted</u> the attention of tourists. Write a sentence about something that has **riveted** your attention.

7. Circle the word that is similar in meaning to <u>luxurious</u>. Then use the word **luxurious** in a sentence.

8. Underline the phrase that tells why it might seem <u>futile</u> to control the cat population. Then tell what **futile** means.

"The Garden of Stubborn Cats" by Italo Calvino
Reading Warm-up B

Read the following passage. Pay special attention to the underlined words. Then, read it again, and complete the activities. Use a separate sheet of paper for your written answers.

When Jerry and the crew began to work on the new housing project, the bare lots looked like just so many voids in the urban landscape. As bulldozers began to level the earth, however, the crew saw that there was actually an extraordinary amount of wildlife on the ground. They were surprised that there could be such active communities of living things right in the shadow of the neighboring skyscraper. There were insects, spiders, and worms, of course. There were also cats that prowled about, and moles with elaborate underground tunnels. On nearby trees, pigeons seemed to be keeping surveillance on the project.

One evening at dusk, vibrant colors filled the sky. As Jerry looked toward the horizon, something caught his eye. A parade of rats scurried by, apparently looking for dinner. Jerry knew that city rats often live on garbage, so he took the minimal precaution of closing the dumpster with a bungee cord.

While the rest of the animals might have to head to another lot, Jerry knew that these unauthorized tenants would be hard to remove. Jerry hoped that his crew would help him set humane traps and relocate the rodents to the open fields outside the city. When, instead, they threatened to poison the rats and be done with it, Jerry became infuriated.

"Think about how this will be transformed," Jerry said to the crew. "Instead of tiny animals and weeds, this place will be swarming with people. I'm not sure that's an improvement."

"What do you think will happen to all of these living things?" asked Ed, one of the carpenters. Jerry predicted that the pigeons would stay nearby. Unless the developers hired an exterminator, the rodents would also keep their nests, though they could be startled by the changes in their environment. The crew had to agree—it was amazing to consider all of the life that existed in a city that, at first glance, seemed to be only for humans.

1. Underline the phrase that tells what made voids in the urban landscape. Then tell what *voids* are.

2. Write a sentence about a skyscraper that you've seen.

3. Write a sentence describing how pigeons might look as they keep surveillance.

4. Circle the words that tell what was vibrant. Underline the words that name the time of day. In your own words, define *vibrant*.

5. Underline the minimal precaution Jerry took. Give an example of when it is not okay to take *minimal* precautions.

6. What is the author describing with the phrase "unauthorized tenants?" What does *unauthorized* mean?

7. Underline the way in which the crew infuriated Jerry. Write about something that makes you feel *infuriated*.

8. Write a sentence about something you have seen transformed over time. Define *transformed*.

"The Gden of Stubborn Cats" by Italo Calvino
Literary Analysis: Symbolism

Symbolism is a writer's use of symbols. A **symbol** is a character, place, thing, or event in a literary work that stands for a larger idea. For example, a raven in a story might stand for death, or a doorway might stand for a new opportunity. To make a particular character or thing into a symbol, a writer may use these common strategies: (1) calling on traditional associations, such as a branching pathway that represents a choice in life; or (2) creating new associations, such as a character becoming more noble after choosing a path, which in turn helps the reader to understand that the path represents courage or bravery.

A story in which all characters and settings are clearly symbolic is called an **allegory**.

DIRECTIONS: *Complete the following chart. Explain what you think each symbol in "The Garden of Stubborn Cats" represents and how it helps teach the lesson of the story.*

Symbol	What it represents	How it helps teach the lesson
Example: cats	mischief and mystery	Shows us that cats are clever and adaptable creatures; their society is mysterious to humans and has its own rules
1. the fish Marcovaldo catches		
2. the garden		
3. the cat lovers		
4. those who dislike the cat garden		

"The Garden of Stubborn Cats" by Italo Calvino
Reading: Identify Patterns to Draw Conclusions About Symbolism

When you **draw a conclusion,** you make a decision or form an opinion based on facts and details in a text. To draw a conclusion about the meaning of a symbol, **identify patterns** that suggest the nature of an object's greater importance.

DIRECTIONS: *List three details from the story that have to do with each symbol. Then identify a pattern created by these details in regard to the symbol. Finally, draw a conclusion about what the symbol means based on the pattern you discover.*

1. Symbol: the "city of cats"
   Three details about this symbol:

   A. _____

   B. _____

   C. _____

   Pattern: _____

   _____

   Meaning: _____

   _____

   _____

2. Symbol: the Marchesa
   Three details about this symbol:

   A. _____

   B. _____

   C. _____

   Pattern: _____

   _____

   Meaning: _____

   _____

   _____

"The Garden of Stubborn Cats" by Italo Calvino
Vocabulary Builder

Word List

itinerary	intrigues	solemn	indigence

A. DIRECTIONS: *In each of the following items, think about the meaning of the italicized word, and then answer the question.*

1. If you went on a vacation to a foreign country, would you be likely to see more sights with or without an *itinerary*? Why?

   _____

   _____

2. What kind of person might be involved in *intrigues*? In what kinds of intrigues might such a person participate?

   _____

   _____

3. Are guests at a child's birthday party usually *solemn*? Why or why not?

   _____

   _____

4. If the national economy is improving, is the level of *indigence* likely to increase? Why or why not?

   _____

   _____

B. DIRECTIONS: *Choose the word that is the best synonym for the word in CAPITAL LETTERS. Circle the letter of your choice.*

1. ITINERARY
   A. stubborn
   B. metallic
   C. employment
   D. schedule

2. INTRIGUES
   A. schemes
   B. pathways
   C. robberies
   D. disagreements

3. SOLEMN
   A. exuberant
   B. somber
   C. confused
   D. grieving

4. INDIGENCE
   A. tenacity
   B. privilege
   C. poverty
   D. cleverness

"The Garden of Stubborn Cats" by Italo Calvino
Support for Writing a Narrative

Use the graphic organizer below to help you come up with an animal to use as a symbol in your narrative. To show what the animal stands for, first describe it using vivid adjectives that suggest the qualities it symbolizes. Then provide information about its situation and actions. Give it a name that hints at what it represents.

Finally, plan how you will link it to important events in your story.

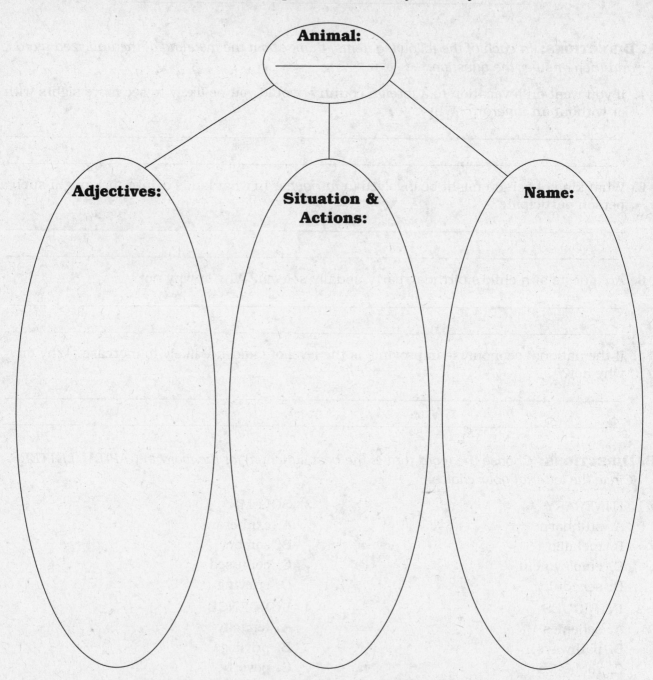

Now, use this graphic organizer to help you write your brief narrative using an animal as a symbol.

"The Garden of Stubborn Cats" by Italo Calvino
Support for Extend Your Learning

Listening and Speaking

Though you cannot use a script or rehearse for your impromptu speech, you may take a few minutes to jot down some ideas before you speak. In your speech, you will describe one way people adapt places to new uses. Use the questions below to help you quickly brainstorm ideas for your speech.

1. What is one place that people adapt to new uses?

   _____

2. What is the intended use for the place you chose?

   _____

3. What is the new way people have found to use this place?

   _____

   _____

   _____

Research and Technology

On the lines below, summarize important information about the structure(s) you chose to research. Circle any technical terms that you will need to define for your audience. If possible, show the class a photo or diagram of the structure(s) as you speak.

_____

_____

_____

_____

_____

_____

_____

_____

_____

_____

_____

_____

_____

_____

"The Garden of Stubborn Cats" by Italo Calvino
Enrichment: Community Connections

In "The Garden of Stubborn Cats," the cats retreat into the Marchesa's garden because there are fewer and fewer places for them to safely be in the "city of men." Some of the people in the neighborhood love the cats and praise the Marchesa for letting the animals live in her garden. Others think the cats are an annoyance and possibly even a health hazard.

As cities continue to grow and expand all over the world, animals have found ways to adapt and survive in them. However, animals in or near cities sometimes need help from humans, and other times they are dangerous to humans. How does your community deal with stray animals and pet overpopulation? How can individuals help animals in your community? Find out more about animal populations in your area and what public policies affect them. Look into policies that are meant to control animal populations and policies that are meant to protect animal populations. Then, working with a group of classmates, come up with a plan for how young people can make a positive difference in how people interact with animals in your community. Use the following chart to determine the steps you need to take to accomplish this community project. Present your project proposal to the class.

Project Title	
Goal Statement	
Task List to Reach Goal	
People Who Can Help	
Impact of Project on Community	

"The Masque of the Red Death" by Edgar Allan Poe
"The Garden of Stubborn Cats" by Italo Calvino

Build Language Skills: Vocabulary

Etymology

The word *predominant* has the Latin root, *-dom-*, which means "rule." Therefore, *predominant* means "ruling before all others" or "superior." Other words containing the root *-dom-* will also refer to the idea of ruling or mastering, such as *dominion, dominate,* and *freedom.*

A. DIRECTIONS: *Choose any word with the Latin root -dom-, meaning "rule," and write it in the word map below. Then, fill in the rest of the word map.*

	Synonym:
Word:	**Example sentence:**
	Antonym:

Academic Vocabulary Practice

consequently	predominant	comprehend	coincide	infer

B. DIRECTIONS: *For each sentence, explain whether it makes sense, given the meaning of the underlined word. If it does not make sense, write a new sentence using the word correctly.*

> **Examples:** *People were able to return to their homes when* <u>consequently</u> *the plague ended.* [does not make sense; people returning to their homes did not end the plague]
> *The plague ended; consequently, people were able to return to their homes.*

1. The Marchesa's <u>predominant</u> feeling toward the cats is one of resentment.

   _____

2. Marcovaldo likes to <u>comprehend</u> cats along their pathways during his lunch break.

   _____

3. The chimes of the clock <u>coincide</u> with pauses in the guests' merriment, implying that the clock chimes make the revelers feel worried and uncomfortable.

   _____

4. The uninvited guest's bloody costume and mask <u>infer</u> that he is dressed as the Red Death.

   _____

"The Masque of the Red Death" by Edgar Allan Poe
"The Garden of Stubborn Cats" by Italo Calvino
Build Language Skills: Grammar

Active and Passive Voice

A verb is in the **active voice** when the subject performs the action. A verb is in the **passive voice** when the action is performed on the subject. Verbs in the passive voice consist of a form of *be* used as a helping verb followed by the past participle of the main verb. Passive voice is used when the writer wants to emphasize the recipient of the action. Passive voice is also used when the subject performing the action is unknown. However, you should choose the active voice whenever possible because it is more direct and less wordy than passive voice.

Active voice:	Marcovaldo *followed* the tabby.
Passive voice:	The tabby was *followed* by Marcovaldo.
Active voice:	The Red Death *frightened* Prince Prospero.
Passive voice:	Prince Prospero *was frightened* of the Red Death.

A. PRACTICE: *Identify each verb or verb phrase as active or passive by writing AV or PV on the line before each sentence.*

Example:

_PV_ Prospero's guests were given a safe place to stay.

____ 1. A fish *was caught* by Marcovaldo.

____ 2. Marcovaldo *followed* the fishing line to the Marchesa's garden.

____ 3. The Marchesa *was cooking* the fish.

____ 4. An elaborate masquerade *was thrown* by Prospero for his guests.

B. Writing Application: *Rewrite each sentence below, changing it from passive to active voice.*

1. Marcovaldo was told that the cats were never fed by the Marchesa.

_____

2. Construction is stopped by the mischievous cats.

_____

3. The Red Death is characterized by bleeding from the pores.

_____

4. The Red Death, though a fictitious disease, is based on the real Black Death of the 1300s.

_____

"The Garden of Stubborn Cats" by Italo Calvino
Selection Test A

Critical Reading *Identify the letter of the choice that best answers the question.*

____ 1. In "The Garden of Stubborn Cats," why has the city of men become almost uninhabitable by cats?
   A. People abuse and kill the cats.
   B. Marcovaldo blocks the cats' pathways.
   C. The Marchesa and her neighbors do not like them.
   D. Cars are dangerous to cats and there are few gardens.

____ 2. Where does Marcovaldo catch a fish?
   A. in the aquarium of a fancy restaurant
   B. in a pond in the Marchesa's garden
   C. in a stream near where he works
   D. in a public fountain in the park

____ 3. What happens to the fish that Marcovaldo catches?
   A. Marcovaldo throws it back.
   B. The tabby steals it and eats it.
   C. Marcovaldo eats it for his lunch.
   D. The Marchesa cooks it and eats it.

____ 4. How does Marcovaldo find the Marchesa's garden?
   A. He stumbles upon it one day while wandering during his lunch break.
   B. He hears about it from his coworkers and finds it on a map of the city.
   C. He follows a fishing line that was dragged by the tabby who stole his fish.
   D. The Marchesa's neighbors, who know he is a cat-lover, tell him how to find it.

____ 5. What does the garden of cats symbolize?
   A. resistance to urban development
   B. the inevitability of death
   C. harmony between cats and humans
   D. conflict between cats and frogs

____ 6. Which of the following details is part of the pattern that helps readers to determine what the animals in the garden symbolize?
   A. Marcovaldo follows the tabby to the Marchesa's garden.
   B. Marcovaldo likes to explore with cats during his lunch break.
   C. The cats are rarely seen during the winter, until the day the Marchesa dies.
   D. The cats knock things over and jump on the backs of the construction workers.

_____ 7. In the story, two groups of people argue about the character and intentions of the Marchesa. What are their opposing points of view?

    A. she is crazy or she is sane

    B. she protects the cats or she hates the cats

    C. she is on vacation or she has died

    D. she stole the fish or she did not steal it

_____ 8. What does the disagreement between the Marchesa's neighbors symbolize?

    A. the "negative city"

    B. the Marchesa's death

    C. the conflict between the Marchesa and Marcovaldo over the fish

    D. the conflict between the desire to modernize and the desire to preserve natural areas

_____ 9. In "The Garden of Stubborn Cats," why does the Marchesa feel like a prisoner in her home?

    A. She is too ill and weak to leave her home.

    B. There are bars on her windows and doors.

    C. She is afraid to leave her home because her neighbors hate her.

    D. She believes the cats will not let her sell her house and the garden lot.

_____ 10. Based on evidence from the story, what will most likely happen to the garden after the Marchesa dies?

    A. The cats will block the redevelopment of the property.

    B. The cats will disappear from the garden and never return.

    C. The neighbors will buy the lot and preserve it as a public garden.

    D. A skyscraper will be built on the lot where the garden once stood.

_____ 11. What do the construction workers symbolize in "The Garden of Stubborn Cats"?

    A. human progress

    B. hatred of animals

    C. love of nature

    D. fear of technology

_____ 12. There are two main opposing forces at work in "The Garden of Stubborn Cats." The forces are not named directly, but rather are implied by symbolism. If one of the forces is urban development, what is the other force?

    A. nature

    B. death

    C. the Marchesa

    D. human progress

Vocabulary and Grammar

_____ 13. Which of the following is the best synonym for the word *itinerary*?
   A. purpose
   B. destiny
   C. lifestyle
   D. route

_____ 14. Which of the following situations would most likely be described as *solemn?*
   A. a vacation
   B. a funeral
   C. baking a cake
   D. catching a fish

_____ 15. Which of the following sentences is written in passive voice?
   A. Marcovaldo follows a tabby.
   B. Marcovaldo is led to a secret garden.
   C. The Marchesa feels trapped.
   D. The Marchesa dies the next winter.

Essay

16. An allegory is a story in which all characters and settings are clearly symbolic. In an essay, explain why "The Garden of Stubborn Cats" can be read as an allegory. List some examples of what various characters, settings, and events in the story symbolize. Think about patterns in the story to help you draw conclusions about the meanings of symbols.

17. In an essay, explain why the Marchesa felt trapped in "The Garden of Stubborn Cats." Was she really trapped? Could she have freed herself? If so, how? Do you think she wanted to live as she did? What does her situation symbolize in the story?

"The Garden of Stubborn Cats" by Italo Calvino
Selection Test B

Critical Reading *Identify the letter of the choice that best completes the statement or answers the question.*

_____ 1. In "The Garden of Stubborn Cats," what is the "city of cats"?
A. the Marchesa's garden
B. an underground system of tunnels
C. alleys, wells, air conduits, yards, and rooftops
D. streets, parking lots, condominiums, and skyscrapers

_____ 2. In "The Garden of Stubborn Cats," why do cats choose to live in the "negative city"?
A. It is the only way to get to the Marchesa's garden.
B. The light is dim there, and cats can see well in the dark.
C. It is safer for them because it is away from human traffic.
D. They feel more secure because dogs cannot chase them there.

_____ 3. The setting of "The Garden of Stubborn Cats" is
A. New York.
B. Turin, Italy.
C. an ancient city of fable.
D. an unnamed modern city.

_____ 4. Which of the following passages from "The Garden of Stubborn Cats" is a clue that the cats symbolize resistance to order?
A. "Following his tabby friend, Marcovaldo had started looking at places as if through the round eyes of a cat. . . ."
B. "On the other hand, from the cat city there opened unsuspected peepholes onto the city of men. . . ."
C. "Marcovaldo realized that with regard to the old Marchesa opinions were sharply divided: some saw her as an angelic being, others as an egoist and a miser."
D. "Cats walked along all the planks, they made bricks fall and upset buckets of mortar, they fought in the midst of the piles of sand."

_____ 5. How does Marcovaldo find the Marchesa's garden?
A. He stumbles upon it one day while wandering during his lunch break.
B. He hears about it from his coworkers and finds it on a map of the city.
C. He follows a fishing line that was dragged by the tabby who stole his fish.
D. The Marchesa's neighbors, who know he is a cat-lover, tell him how to find it.

_____ 6. In the story, two groups of people argue about the character and intentions of the Marchesa. One side believes she is an angel who protects the animals by giving them a safe haven in her garden. The other side thinks she is a selfish miser who hates cats. Who is correct?
A. both
B. neither
C. those who think she is protecting the cats
D. those who believe she hates the cats

_____ 7. What does the disagreement between the Marchesa's neighbors symbolize in "The Garden of Stubborn Cats"?
   A. the "negative city"
   B. the Marchesa's death
   C. the conflict between the desire to modernize and the desire to maintain natural areas in the city
   D. the conflict between the animals who live in the garden and the construction workers who want to build there

_____ 8. What does the Marchesa's situation in "The Garden of Stubborn Cats" symbolize?
   A. the nobility of caring for animals
   B. the conflict between humans and nature
   C. the achievements of human progress
   D. the inevitability of aging and dying

_____ 9. In "The Garden of Stubborn Cats," after the Marchesa's death, it is implied that
   A. the cats had caused the Marchesa's death.
   B. the neighbors understood the Marchesa's actions.
   C. the cats block the redevelopment of the property.
   D. Marcovaldo assumes responsibility for the cats and the garden.

_____ 10. Which of the following details is NOT part of the pattern that helps readers to determine what the animals in the garden symbolize in "The Garden of Stubborn Cats"?
   A. The cats are rarely seen during the winter, until the day the Marchesa dies.
   B. The birds nest in the trestles and the cab of the construction workers' crane.
   C. The cats knock things over and jump on the backs of the construction workers.
   D. The workers cannot dip up a bucket of water without getting a bucket full of frogs.

_____ 11. What are the two main opposing forces at work in "The Garden of Stubborn Cats"?
   A. cat lovers and cat haters
   B. urban development and nature
   C. the Marchesa and her neighbors
   D. the construction workers and the animals

_____ 12. Why is "The Garden of Stubborn Cats" an allegory?
   A. There are animals in the story.
   B. The theme is ambiguous.
   C. All of the characters and settings are symbolic.
   D. The story teaches a lesson about good and evil.

Vocabulary and Grammar

_____ 13. Which of the following words is the best synonym for *indigence*?
   A. outrage
   B. inactivity
   C. poverty
   D. foolishness

_____ 14. Which of the following people would be most likely to be involved in *intrigues*?
   A. an international spy
   B. a sales clerk at a clothing store
   C. a computer programmer
   D. a musician in a rock band

_____ 15. Which of the following sentences is written in active voice?
   A. The city of cats exists inside the city of men.
   B. The well-fed tabby is followed by Marcovaldo.
   C. The garden is filled with cats and other animals.
   D. A restaurant is found on one of their expeditions.

_____ 16. Which of the following sentences is written in passive voice?
   A. Neighbors argue about the garden.
   B. The Marchesa feels trapped by the cats.
   C. The Marchesa dies during the winter.
   D. The lot is finally sold for development.

Essay

17. "The Garden of Stubborn Cats" can be read as an allegory. In an essay, explain why the story is an allegory and what various characters, settings, and events symbolize. Think about patterns in the story to help you draw conclusions about the meanings of symbols.

18. Do you feel the garden of cats should remain as it is, or do you feel that developers should be free to build over it? In an essay, explain and support your position using examples from "The Garden of Stubborn Cats" or from your own experience.

19. In an essay, identify the two opposing forces at work in "The Garden of Stubborn Cats" and how you know what they are. Use symbolism from the story to help you identify the opposing forces. Then explain which force you think prevails and why.

Vocabulary Warm-up Word Lists

Study these words from the selections. Then, complete the activities that follow.

Word List A

absolute [AB suh loot] *adj.* unlimited; complete
  The witness stated with <u>absolute</u> certainty that he had seen the suspect.

critics [KRI tiks] *n.* people who express judgments or find faults
  The movie <u>critics</u> are all raving about the new animated film.

distraction [dis TRAK shuhn] *n.* something that takes your attention away
  The siren was a <u>distraction</u> while we were taking the exam.

frank [FRANGK] *adj.* honest
  Don't worry about my feelings; give me your <u>frank</u> opinion of my poem.

sabotage [SAB uh tahzh] *v.* to destroy intentionally
  He tried to <u>sabotage</u> their business by passing documents to the competition.

scheming [SKEEM ing] *v.* plotting; making secret or underhanded plans
  The thief is <u>scheming</u> to steal the jewels.

scrawled [SKRAWLD] *v.* written hastily or sloppily
  I <u>scrawled</u> my name quickly at the bottom of the note.

unique [yoo NEEK] *adj.* one of a kind; unlike any other
  Everyone has a <u>unique</u> set of fingerprints.

Word List B

anticipated [an TIS uh pay tid] *v.* looked forward to; expected
  We correctly <u>anticipated</u> that the score would be close.

assailed [uh SAYLD] *v.* overwhelmed; attacked
  The politician was <u>assailed</u> by shouts from protesters.

attentive [uh TEN tiv] *adj.* paying attention; noticing
  A good nurse is <u>attentive</u> to the patient's needs.

censorship [SEN ser ship] *n.* acts limiting what people can communicate
  Banning a film is one example of <u>censorship</u>.

confidential [kahn fuh DEN shuhl] *adj.* private; secret
  This information is <u>confidential</u>, so you must not share it with anyone.

electronic [ee lek TRON ik] *adj.* using electricity controlled by special circuits
  The new <u>electronic</u> signs can blink in a variety of patterns.

fulfilled [ful FILD] *v.* carried out; completed
  My brother finally <u>fulfilled</u> the requirements for graduation.

masterpiece [MAS ter pees] *n.* greatest work done by a person
  She painted her <u>masterpiece</u> the year before she died.

"Like the Sun" by R. K. Narayan
"The Censors" by Luisa Valenzuela
Vocabulary Warm-up Exercises

Exercise A *Fill in each blank in the paragraph below with an appropriate word from Word List A. Use each word only once.*

Because she was jealous, my little sister wanted to [1] _____ my violin concert. She was [2] _____ for weeks, thinking up new tricks. First, she [3] _____ her name all over my sheet music. Then she began to play her drums whenever I practiced. The pounding beat of her drums was a terrible [4] _____. Finally, I decided the only thing to do was to have a [5] _____ and open discussion with her. Together, we came up with a [6] _____ solution. We decided that she would be my page-turner. She promised to sit in [7] _____ silence while I played. My sister was finally happy because she was involved. The concert turned out to be a big success. Even the [8] _____ said that they enjoyed the evening.

Exercise B *Decide whether each statement below is true or false. Explain your answers.*

1. If you <u>anticipated</u> the ending of a book, you weren't surprised when you read it.
   T / F _____

2. Antique collectors often hunt for rare <u>electronic</u> equipment.
   T / F _____

3. Magazine articles are a powerful form of <u>censorship</u>.
   T / F _____

4. A writer's <u>masterpiece</u> is always his or her first book.
   T / F _____

5. It is possible to feel <u>assailed</u> by the noise at a rock concert.
   T / F _____

6. Someone who loves to gossip can be trusted with <u>confidential</u> information.
   T / F _____

7. An <u>attentive</u> listener is bored and easily distracted.
   T / F _____

8. If you have <u>fulfilled</u> a goal, you still have a lot of work to do.
   T / F _____

"Like the Sun" by R. K. Narayan
"The Censors" by Luisa Valenzuela

Reading Warm-up A

Read the following passage. Pay special attention to the underlined words. Then, read it again, and complete the activities. Use a separate sheet of paper for your written answers.

Polygraphs are sometimes called "lie detectors," but this nickname is inaccurate. These machines do not test the truth of a statement. Instead, they measure changes in someone's body as they answer questions. These changes may suggest that the person is lying. However, the polygraph does not provide an <u>absolute</u> judgment.

A polygraph test is usually given in a quiet room, away from any possible <u>distraction</u>. Only the polygraph operator and the test subject are present. Sensors are attached to the test subject, who then responds to questions. The tool records changes in blood pressure, pulse, respiration, and sweat levels. The results are then analyzed to determine which are <u>frank</u> and which are dishonest. In older polygraph machines, the results were <u>scrawled</u> on scrolling paper by a set of moving pens. Today, most polygraphs produce a digital display.

The test operator must be alert for attempts to fool the polygraph machine. Subjects could be secretly <u>scheming</u> to throw off the test results. For example, they might take a calming drug in an attempt to reduce body changes that occur during lying. Some might bite their tongue or cheek, or even place tacks inside their shoes. These strategies can <u>sabotage</u> the results by overpowering the body's natural response to each question.

Many <u>critics</u> of these tests insist that they do not provide clear proof that someone is lying. Only rarely do courts allow polygraph evidence to be used during criminal or civil cases. Even those who administer the tests agree that they are not literally testing for truth.

Nevertheless, investigators believe the polygraph is a <u>unique</u> tool for evaluating people's responses. Although the results may not be foolproof, the polygraph remains the most reliable tool we currently have.

1. Underline the sentence that tells why a polygraph cannot provide an <u>absolute</u> judgment. Then, tell what *absolute* means.

2. Underline the words that explain what is done to avoid <u>distraction</u>. Then, describe a *distraction* you have experienced.

3. Circle the antonym for <u>frank</u>. Then, tell what *frank* means.

4. Underline the words that describe how the results were <u>scrawled</u>. Then, tell what *scrawled* means.

5. Underline the words that tell what subjects could be <u>scheming</u> to do. Then, tell what *scheming* means.

6. Underline two ways that subjects can <u>sabotage</u> a polygraph. Describe a project that someone might try to *sabotage*.

7. Underline the words that explain what <u>critics</u> insist. Then, tell something else that *critics* might judge.

8. Underline the words that explain why the polygraph is <u>unique</u>. Then, describe another *unique* tool.

"Like the Sun" by R. K. Narayan
"The Censors" by Luisa Valenzuela
Reading Warm-up B

Read the following passage. Pay special attention to the underlined words. Then, read it again, and complete the activities. Use a separate sheet of paper for your written answers.

George Orwell depicts the frightening world of Big Brother in his stunning success *1984*. This science-fiction <u>masterpiece</u> depicts a government that controls its citizens through fear, lies, and punishment.

The novel is set in the fictional world of Oceania. Characters living there are constantly observed by a mysterious government known only as the Party. The head of the Party is Big Brother, whose handsome face is seen on posters throughout Oceania along with the head-line "Big Brother Is Watching You." Citizens are also <u>assailed</u> by an endless repetition of three Party slogans: "War Is Peace," "Freedom Is Slavery," and "Ignorance Is Strength." These seemingly absurd statements numb people's ability to oppose the government.

In this world of constant observation, no one can keep secrets or information <u>confidential</u>. Party officials are constantly on the lookout for anyone who voices any dis-agreement with the Party. These highly <u>attentive</u> spies watch other citizens through viewing screens and other <u>electronic</u> devices.

The novel is written in the form of Winston Smith's secret diary. The very act of keeping a diary is dangerous in this world of strict government control, where the <u>censorship</u> of opposing ideas is a basic part of the gov-ernment's operations.

Orwell may not have <u>anticipated</u> how popular the name Big Brother would become. Today, the phrase is used to mean any government surveillance, or monitor-ing. It has also become the title of several "reality televi-sion" programs filmed around the world. If a writer's goal is to create a lasting impression, Orwell certainly <u>fulfilled</u> this aim. However, the use of Big Brother for entertain-ment misses the serious point that Orwell makes in his chilling novel.

1. Circle the two words that support the assertion that 1984 is a <u>masterpiece</u>. Then, give an example of another writer's *masterpiece*.

2. Underline the words that tell what <u>assailed</u> citizens. Then, tell what *assailed* means.

3. Circle the synonym for <u>confidential</u>. Then, tell why it is difficult to keep information *confidential*.

4. Underline the words that tell what the <u>attentive</u> spies do. Then, tell what *attentive* means.

5. Describe one *electronic* device that was invented after Orwell wrote 1984 in 1948.

6. Circle the words that tell the focus of <u>censorship</u> in Oceania. Then, tell what *censorship* means.

7. Underline the words that tell what Orwell may not have <u>anticipated</u>. Then, tell some-thing you *anticipated* that actually happened.

8. Circle the word that says what Orwell <u>fulfilled</u>. Then, tell what *fulfilled* means.

"Like the Sun" by R. K. Narayan
"The Censors" by Luisa Valenzuela

Literary Analysis: Irony and Paradox

Irony is the effect created when a writer makes a forceful contrast between words or expectations and reality.

- In **situational irony,** something happens that directly contradicts strong expectations. For example, if you go through a door expecting a surprise party and instead find an empty room, you actually *will* be surprised.
- In **verbal irony,** words are used to "say" the opposite. If it starts to rain, and you say, "Oh, this is *great*" to mean "Oh, this is *awful*," you are using verbal irony.
- In **dramatic irony,** the reader or audience knows something that a character or speaker does not. In "Like the Sun," for example, the reader knows about Sekhar's experiment, but the headmaster does not.

Another kind of contrast writers use is **paradox.** A paradox expresses two contradictory ideas and yet also reveals a truth. "You must sometimes be cruel to be kind" is one example of a paradox.

A. DIRECTIONS: *Explain what is ironic in each of the following passages from "Like the Sun" and "The Censors." Then identify the type of irony in each passage.*

"Like the Sun"

1. "No. I want it immediately—your frank opinion. Was it good?" "No, sir . . ." Sekhar replied.

   _____

   _____

   Type of irony: _____

"The Censors"

2. He was about to congratulate himself . . . when his letter to Mariana reached his hands. Naturally, he censored it without regret. And just as naturally, he couldn't stop them from executing him . . . .

   _____

   _____

   Type of irony: _____

B. DIRECTIONS: *Explain how each paradox is illustrated in "Like the Sun" or "The Censors."*

"Like the Sun"

1. "You have to be cruel to be kind." _____

   _____

"The Censors"

2. "Because he was loyal, he was seen as a traitor." _____

   _____

"**Like the Sun**" by R. K. Narayan
"**The Censors**" by Luisa Valenzuela
Vocabulary Builder

Word List

tempering	ingratiating	stupefied	scrutinized
irreproachable	ulterior	staidness	conniving

A. DIRECTIONS: *Write a complete sentence to answer each question. For each item, use a word from the Word List in place of the underlined word(s) with a similar meaning.*

Example: What might you be <u>stunned</u> to see?

Answer: I might be <u>stupefied</u> to see an elephant walking down the street.

1. What motive <u>beyond</u> kindness might a person have for doing a good deed?

   _____

2. Two children with water balloons might be <u>conspiring</u> to do what?

   _____

3. When can <u>softening</u> your tone come in handy?

   _____

4. Why might a person who is <u>blameless</u> make a poor leader?

   _____

5. In what kind of situation would a <u>state of seriousness or somberness</u> be appropriate?

   _____

6. Why might a person's signature be <u>closely examined</u>?

   _____

7. Why do many people find behavior <u>intended to win someone's favor</u> annoying?

   _____

B. DIRECTIONS: *On the line, write the letter of the word that is most nearly* opposite *in meaning to the word in CAPITAL LETTERS.*

____ 1. SCRUTINIZED:
   A. punished   B. celebrated   C. purchased   D. ignored

____ 2. STAIDNESS:
   A. restlessness   B. weakness   C. oddness   D. gentleness

____ 3. IRREPROACHABLE:
   A. distant   B. guilty   C. harmless   D. calm

____ 4. INGRATIATING:
   A. civilized   B. thankful   C. disrespectful   D. soothing

Name _____ Date _____

"**Like the Sun**" by R. K. Narayan
"**The Censors**" by Luisa Valenzuela
Support for Writing a Comparison-and-Contrast Essay

Before you draft your essay comparing and contrasting the ideas of honesty and deception in these two stories, complete the graphic organizer below.

	"Like the Sun"	"The Censors"
Examples of a character's honesty or deception		
How a character's attitude toward honesty or deception changes		
Resulting ironies or paradoxes		
Important idea(s) the author wants to convey		

Now, use your notes to write an essay comparing and contrasting the authors' ideas about honesty and deception. In your essay, examine how each author uses irony or paradox to express these ideas.

"Like the Sun" by R. K. Narayan
"The Censors" by Luisa Valenzuela
Selection Test A

Critical Reading *Identify the letter of the choice that best answers the question.*

____ 1. In "Like the Sun," what experiment does Sekhar conduct?
A. observing how anger affects different people
B. keeping the ungraded papers a secret for ten days
C. studying the effects of sunlight
D. telling the truth for one day

____ 2. In "Like the Sun," Sekhar makes a comment about breakfast to his wife. What is the result of this comment?
A. He has a bad day at work.
B. She prepares another meal.
C. Her feelings are hurt.
D. He gets another helping.

____ 3. In "Like the Sun," how does Sekhar feel when he is asked to critique the head-master's singing?
A. excited
B. uneasy
C. angry
D. pleased

____ 4. In "Like the Sun," Sekhar fears that because of his actions, he may lose his friends and his job. Why does he fear these things?
A. because he is wasting time on his experiment
B. because people do not want Sekhar to improve himself
C. because people are generally against change
D. because hearing the truth can be painful for people

____ 5. Which is an ironic event in "Like the Sun"?
A. Sekhar has an idea for an experiment.
B. Sekhar goes to the headmaster's house for dinner.
C. The headmaster sings traditional Indian songs.
D. The headmaster thanks Sekhar for his opinion.

____ 6. In "The Censors," why does Juan take a job as a censor?

    A. to retrieve his own letter

    B. to serve the government

    C. to find Mariana

    D. to please his mother

____ 7. In "The Censors," why does Juan make a good censor?

    A. because he believes censorship is good

    B. because he helps people in need

    C. because he is focused

    D. because he is a good manager

____ 8. At the end of "The Censors," which event leads to Juan's death?

    A. He quits.

    B. He turns himself in.

    C. His boss finds his letter.

    D. He becomes ill.

____ 9. In "The Censors," Juan gets a job as a censor. Why is this ironic?

    A. because Mariana lives in France

    B. because Juan is against censorship

    C. because the Censorship Division is full

    D. because Juan has no skills

____ 10. Which idea is explored in both "Like the Sun" and "The Censors"?

    A. death

    B. greed

    C. honesty

    D. affection

____ 11. How are Sekhar in "Like the Sun" and Juan in "The Censors" alike?

    A. They both have a clear goal.

    B. They are both musicians.

    C. They both lose their jobs.

    D. They are both kind to others.

____ 12. What is a paradox?

    A. a statement that expresses contradictory ideas, but is true

    B. a clue to the outcome of the story

    C. a person, place, or thing that stands for something other than itself

    D. a conflict between a character and his or her surroundings

___ **13.** Which message is expressed in both "Like the Sun" and "The Censors"?

    A. Love is rare.

    B. Love leads to lies.

    C. Avoid the truth at all costs.

    D. The truth can hurt.

Vocabulary

___ **14.** What might a *conniving* person do?

    A. forgive a friend   **C.** make a secret deal

    B. welcome a stranger   **D.** watch too much TV

___ **15.** Which is the most likely to be *scrutinized*?

    A. dirty dishes   **C.** a nursery rhyme

    B. a crime scene   **D.** a cold drink

Essay

16. Both Juan in "The Censors" and Sekhar in "Like the Sun" have a mission. In a brief essay, identify each character's mission. Does it succeed or does it fail? Why? Be sure to include examples from the stories to support what you say.

17. In an essay, identify two moments of irony in "Like the Sun" and two moments of irony in "The Censors." Then explain how these ironic moments help the author express a certain message about truth or deception.

"Like the Sun" by R. K. Narayan
"The Censors" by Luisa Valenzuela
Selection Test B

Critical Reading *Identify the letter of the choice that best completes the statement or answers the question.*

____ 1. In "Like the Sun," what reason does Sekhar give for his experiment?
   A. It will be amusing to see people's reactions.
   B. Without truth, life is meaningless.
   C. Pleasing people has become tedious.
   D. The sun shines, but not forever.

____ 2. In "Like the Sun," how is Sekhar's response to his wife's cooking ironic?
   A. She spent hours preparing a special meal.
   B. He usually enjoys breakfast.
   C. She knew he would not like the meal.
   D. She did not expect him to be so honest.

____ 3. In "Like the Sun," what becomes the most difficult test of Sekhar's vow?
   A. being honest with his co-workers
   B. telling the truth about the headmaster's singing
   C. listening to music he does not typically enjoy
   D. grading one hundred test papers in a single night

____ 4. In "Like the Sun," what is ironic about the headmaster's response to Sekhar the day after Sekhar visits his home?
   A. The headmaster is openly angry with Sekhar.
   B. The headmaster refuses to speak to Sekhar.
   C. The headmaster has accepted Sekhar's opinion.
   D. The headmaster rewards Sekhar for telling the truth.

____ 5. In "Like the Sun," what does Sekhar's firm commitment to his experiment say about his character?
   A. He wants to become an honest person.
   B. He does not truly value his friends and loved ones.
   C. He wants to be considerate at all costs.
   D. He enjoys hurting people's feelings.

____ 6. In "Like the Sun," what does Sekhar mean when he says telling the truth is a "luxury"?
   A. Being honest at all times is a challenge.
   B. The experiment has proved to be a waste of time.
   C. Only people who do not need to succeed or be liked can practice total honesty.
   D. It is expensive to be honest and so should only be practiced by the very wealthy.

____ 7. In "The Censors," why does Juan take a job with the Censorship Division?
   A. to climb the career ladder as a censor
   B. to better serve the government
   C. to locate Mariana in France
   D. to disrupt the process of censorship

____ 8. In "The Censors," why does Juan report the co-worker who tries to organize a strike?
   A. He thinks it will serve his own best interests.
   B. He believes strikes are illegal.
   C. He disagrees with the man's reasons for the strike.
   D. He believes the man is a traitor.

____ 9. In "The Censors," what character trait makes Juan a good censor?
   A. disobedience
   B. diligence
   C. patience
   D. generosity

____ 10. Which event in "The Censors" is ironic?
   A. Juan is troubled that Mariana might be in danger.
   B. Juan is transferred to Section E of the Censorship Division.
   C. Juan begins to see innocent letters as dangerous.
   D. Juan's letter to Mariana reaches his hands.

____ 11. At the end of "The Censors," why is Juan put to death?
   A. He stops performing his job.
   B. He censors his own letter.
   C. He is discovered to be a fake.
   D. He is betrayed by Mariana.

____ 12. Which sentence best describes a paradox in "The Censors"?
   A. Juan tries to save Mariana, but can't.
   B. Censorship ruins people's lives.
   C. Some letters contain dangerous ideas; others do not.
   D. Juan becomes the very thing he fears.

____ 13. Both "Like the Sun" and "The Censors" explore themes related to
   A. betrayal and death.
   B. greed and power.
   C. honesty and deception.
   D. knowledge and ignorance.

____ 14. How are Sekhar in "Like the Sun" and Juan in "The Censors" alike?
   A. Both have a "noble mission."
   B. Both experiment with telling the truth.
   C. Both lose their jobs.
   D. Both betray themselves.

____ 15. Which occurs when the reader knows something that a character or speaker does not?
   A. situational irony
   B. verbal irony
   C. dramatic irony
   D. paradox

____ 16. Which quality is shared by Sekhar in "Like the Sun" and Juan in "The Censors"?
   A. determination
   B. sensitivity
   C. ambition
   D. self-deception

____ 17. Which message is expressed in both "Like the Sun" and "The Censors"?
   A. If one is honest, love will prevail.
   B. Deceptive behavior will always result in punishment.
   C. Love is an action, not a feeling.
   D. One's actions can have unintended consequences.

Vocabulary

____ 18. In "The Censors," Juan has an *ulterior* motive for getting a job as a censor because
   A. he lies about his skills.
   B. he does not state why he really wants the job.
   C. it is his last chance.
   D. he disapproves of the censorship process.

____ 19. When the headmaster tells Sekhar to *scrutinize* the students' papers in "Like the Sun," what does he want Sekhar to do?
   A. throw the papers away   C. give the papers to him
   B. examine the papers closely   D. glance at the papers

____ 20. Which of these might be considered *ingratiating*?
   A. a shriek   C. flattery
   B. a critical comment   D. an unusual request

Essay

21. Both "Like the Sun" and "The Censors" make use of situational irony. In an essay, explain how. For each story, identify at least two events that violate the expectations either of the reader or of characters in the story. What specific ideas do these moments of irony help each author express?

22. The main characters in both "Like the Sun" and "The Censors" challenge a certain system, or accepted way of doing things. In an essay, identify the system each character challenges; how he does so; and what his reasons are. In your opinion, is either character successful? Why?

23. The title of each of these selections—"Like the Sun" and "The Censors"—contains a measure of paradox, or contradiction. In an essay, explain how this is so. As you consider the title "Like the Sun," think about Sekhar's comment that "Truth is like the sun." In what ways *is* it like the sun? In what ways is it *not*? As you consider the title "The Censors," ask yourself who the censors are. Who did you understand them to be at the beginning of the story? the middle? the end?

Writing Workshop—Unit 2, Part 2
Exposition: Problem-and-Solution Essay

Prewriting: Narrowing Your Topic

Use the following chart to help you narrow the problems you are considering for your essay. Identify one aspect of the problem for each category.

World	Nation	State	Town	School

Drafting: Shaping Your Writing

Use the following graphic organizer to help you figure out how best to structure the information and reasoning you want to present in your essay.

Thesis Statement (including a statement of the problem):
Possible Solution:
Possible Solution:
Possible Solution:
Closing (including your personal evaluation of the problem):

Writing Workshop—Unit 2, Part 2
Problem-and-Solution Essay: Integrating Grammar Skills

Revising Subject-Verb Agreement

For a subject and verb to agree, both must be singular or plural. A phrase or clause between the subject and verb does not change the number. A compound subject (joined by *and*) is plural in number and requires a plural verb.

The indefinite pronouns *each* and *one*, as well as those ending in *-body* and *-one* (such as *somebody* and *everyone*), are always singular. The indefinite pronouns *both*, *few*, *many*, *others*, and *several* are always plural. The indefinite pronouns *all*, *any*, *more*, *most*, *none*, and *some* may be singular or plural, depending on the nouns to which they refer.

Identifying Correct Subject-Verb Agreement

A. DIRECTIONS: *Complete each sentence by circling the verb that agrees with the subject.*

1. A statue or two (stands, stand) in front of city hall.
2. Most of the paintings inside city hall (is, are) the work of local talent.
3. Most of the artwork (honors, honor) the past.
4. Each of the work's inscriptions (gives, give) information on the subject.

Fixing Errors in Subject-Verb Agreement

B. DIRECTIONS: *On the lines provided, rewrite these sentences so that they use correct subject-verb agreement. If a sentence is correct as presented, write* correct.

1. Donations to the library system buys new books and other media.

   _____

2. Most of the city's tax revenue pay for equipment and grounds maintenance.

   _____

3. An endowment that two benefactors left the community covers all salaries.

   _____

4. Each of the two children's librarians work just twenty-five hours a week.

   _____

Name _____ Date _____

Unusual Vowel Combinations

To spell some words correctly, you must be on the lookout for **unusual vowel combinations.** Often, as in *toupée,* two vowels are used to spell a single sound, or the sound is spelled by letters you do not expect. Make note of troublesome parts of this type—or other tricky parts—in the words in this list.

Word List

acquiesce	distinguished	pseudonym	sleuth
bureaucracy	matinee	sergeant	surveillance

A. DIRECTIONS: *Write the word from the Word List that matches each clue.*

1. rank above private   _____

2. give in   _____

3. not one's real name   _____

4. afternoon performance   _____

5. noteworthy or well-known   _____

6. groups helping run a government   _____

7. close watch   _____

8. detective   _____

B. DIRECTIONS: *Write two or three related sentences using each group of words.*

1. sleuth   pseudonym   surveillance _____

_____

_____

_____

2. sergeant   bureaucracy   distinguished

_____

_____

_____

3. acquiesce   distinguished   matinee

_____

_____

_____

Communications Workshop—Unit 2
Viewing and Evaluating a Speech

After viewing a speech, fill out the following chart to help you evaluate the presentation.

Topic of presentation: _____

What is the purpose of the speech?
What facts or quotations from trustworthy sources are used?
What are the supporting details that the speaker uses to support the argument?
What emotionally charged words are used?
How did the speaker's body language, eye contact, and vocal tone impact his or her message?

For Further Reading—Unit 2

The Fall of the House of Usher and Other Writings by Edgar Allen Poe

Discussion What are some of the elements that Poe uses in his stories to create the feeling of horror in the reader? Consider subject, pacing, and sound as part of your discussion.

Connections—Literature Circle Why do you think some people love to fly in planes and some people hate it? Why do some people love hiking alone in the mountains and others detest solitude? Think about the difference in our individual fears and whether there are universal fears.

41 Stories by O. Henry by O. Henry

Discussion O. Henry provides the reader with clues to the ending throughout a story. Choose one story that your group particularly liked. Find and list the clues in the story. Discuss why the reader does not follow these clues during the first reading of the story.

Connections—Literature Circle How might using your skills to find clues in literature help you in real life?

The Joy Luck Club by Amy Tan

Discussion Generations are shaped by the cultural, social, and political environment of the time. Discuss how the different background of each mother might have influenced how she raised her daughter. Why do you think that each daughter had a difficult time understanding her mother?

Connections—Literature Circle As a group, identify and discuss three major events that have occurred during your lifetime. How have these events shaped you as a person?

Anton Chekov: The Selected Stories by Anton Chekov

Discussion In "The Nincompoop," the governess is humiliated by her employer. Why do you think she felt that she could not say anything when he tried to cheat her out of her wages? Do you think this was a fair way to try to teach her a lesson? Why?

Connections—Literature Circle In "The Confession," what do you think that Chekov is saying about how money affects people? Use examples from the text to discuss how money becomes central for both the cashier and the people around him. Choose three people, including the cashier, and discuss what each person uses the money to gain.

Unit 2: Short Stories
Part 2 Benchmark Test 4

MULTIPLE CHOICE

Literary Analysis *Read the selection. Then, answer the questions that follow.*

Guinivere laughed quietly as she rocked the cradle with her foot. It had been so simple in the end! All she had needed was faith: faith in her husband, faith in her beliefs, and above all faith in herself. "I did it! I really, really did it!" she crowed under her breath.

1. What is the theme of a selection?
   A. its ideas
   B. its underlying meaning
   C. its overall plot
   D. its dialogue

2. What is the theme of this selection?
   A. Faith is all we need.
   B. Believe in yourself.
   C. Faith is nothing without determination.
   D. Beliefs are nothing without faith.

3. How is the theme of this selection revealed?
   A. The author states the theme.
   B. The plot transmits the theme.
   C. A character reveals the theme.
   D. The dialogue expresses the theme.

Read the selection. Then, answer the questions that follow.

Nostrils flaring and eyes flashing, Great White Horse reared, shaking the great balance scales it carried on its back. The Horse had brought order to the village. Its judgments and rules were etched on the tablets of truth for all time. Yet for how long would the people remember?

4. This selection is an example of which of the following?
   A. myth
   B. allegory
   C. paradox
   D. irony

5. Why do good writers use symbols in their work?
   A. to make their work relevant
   B. to provide a comprehension challenge for readers
   C. to show how educated they are
   D. to transmit important ideas to readers

6. Of the following choices, which is the Horse likeliest to symbolize?
   A. the power of law and order
   B. delight in cruelty
   C. the effects of fear
   D. the triumph of nature over civilization

7. Which of the following describes dramatic irony?
   A. Two contradictory statements reveal the truth.
   B. The reader or audience knows or understands something that the character does not.
   C. The truth is indicated by stating the opposite.
   D. Something happens that directly contradicts the reader's strong expectations.

8. What is the literary term for two contradictory statements that reveal a truth?
   A. situational irony
   B. dramatic irony
   C. verbal irony
   D. paradox

9. Which literary term describes the following?

   "Looks don't matter in this contest," Emily said, as she applied still more mascara and blush.

   A. situational hyperbole
   B. dramatic irony
   C. verbal irony
   D. paradox

10. Which literary term applies to the following?

    The politician who opposed funding an early-warning hurricane system was killed in a hurricane.

    A. situational irony
    B. verbal irony
    C. situational paradox
    D. verbal paradox

Reading Skills *Read the selection. Then, answer the questions that follow.*

The quilt had been in Ana's family for generations. Now her mother handed it to Ana. "You're nearly 21, Ana, and I know you are ready to care for it," Ana's mother said stroking the quilt, her voice cracking. Tears dripped down Ana's cheeks as she accepted the treasured keepsake.

11. What conclusion can you draw about the importance of the quilt in Ana's family?
    A. The quilt is unimportant.
    B. The quilt is not very important.
    C. The quilt is somewhat important.
    D. The quilt is very important.

12. What is the most logical conclusion to draw about Ana's feelings on receiving the quilt?
    A. She is unaffected.
    B. She is annoyed.
    C. She is moved.
    D. She is jubilant.

13. Which detail hints at Ana's feelings?
    A. She is nearly 21.
    B. She is crying.
    C. She accepts the quilt.
    D. She doesn't say anything.

14. What helps a reader draw valid conclusions?
    A. the reader's opinions
    B. the reader's point of view
    C. facts and details in the text
    D. opinions and arguments in the text

15. What is the most logical conclusion to draw about the symbolic meaning of the quilt?
    A. It symbolizes Ana's adulthood.
    B. It symbolizes the artistic abilities of the women in Ana's family.
    C. It symbolizes the cultural heritage of Ana's family.
    D. It symbolizes the importance of hard work to Ana's family.

16. What is the best way to draw a conclusion about what an item in a selection might symbolize?
    A. identify patterns that suggest a larger meaning
    B. recall what the item symbolized in another selection
    C. think about how the item makes you feel when you read about it
    D. pay close attention to what the characters say about the item

Read the review. Then, answer the questions that follow.

   Georgia on Our Mind is a great example of the best of the new Southern writing, and, believe me, I have read most of it! Devin McLeod has a fabulous ear, and his use of Southern dialect of all classes and types of Southerners is pitch perfect. What reader will ever forget the character of Miz Roberts?

17. What is strength of this review?
    A. It is written in an objective style.
    B. It clearly states the reviewer's opinion.
    C. It eschews irrelevant information.
    D. It summarizes the selection.

18. What is a weakness of this review?
    A. It is predictable and boring.
    B. It does not describe all the characters and summarize the story completely.
    C. It appeals to an overly limited audience.
    D. It does not give enough support for the reviewer's opinion.

Vocabulary: Word Etymology

19. What is the etymology of a word?
    A. the word's definition
    B. the word's pronunciation
    C. the word's history
    D. the word's spelling

20. Based on your knowledge of the origins of the word *sequence*, what is the meaning of the word *sequel*?
    A. an original movie
    B. the second part of a book series
    C. an original text
    D. the first part of a book series

21. Based on your knowledge of the origins of the word *predominant*, what is the meaning of the word *dominate*?
    A. rule over
    B. authorize
    C. instruct
    D. make fun of

22. Which word best completes the following sentence?

    There are usually _____ when a person makes a bad decision.

    A. inconsequent
    B. consequences
    C. sequences
    D. inconsequential

23. Which word best completes the following sentence?

    Lilly had the habit of always _____ the conversation.

    A. predominance
    B. predominant
    C. dominant
    D. dominating

Grammar

24. Which of these sentences has a linking verb?
    A. When she says jump, he jumps.
    B. The contract clearly states the penalty for noncompliance.
    C. Claudia has been living here for forty years.
    D. Whenever possible, I like to walk instead of drive.

25. Which of these sentences has an action verb?
    A. Let's run to the next marker.
    B. Dan will be sixteen next week.
    C. My middle name is Claudia.
    D. Little sisters can be really annoying.

26. Which type of verb appears in the following sentence?

    George is an excellent rugby player.

    A. action
    B. linking
    C. past tense
    D. passive

27. Which type of verb appears in the following sentence?

    Demetria trained each day to prepare for the state track meet.

    A. gerund
    B. linking
    C. infinitive
    D. action

28. How would the following sentence be written if it were in the passive voice?

    Nick grills hamburgers and hot dogs every Sunday throughout the summer.

    A. Every Sunday throughout the summer, Nick had been grilling hamburgers and hot dogs.
    B. The hamburgers and hot dogs are grilled by Nick every Sunday throughout the summer.
    C. Every Sunday throughout the summer, Nick grills hamburgers and hot dogs.
    D. Nick has been grilling hamburgers and hot dogs every Sunday through the summer.

29. How would the following sentence be written if it were in the passive voice?

    The teacher gave the students the math exam on the last day of school.

    A. The teacher had given the math exam to the students on the last day of school.
    B. On the last day of school, the teacher gave the students the math exam.
    C. The students were given the math exam by the teacher on the last day of school.
    D. The teacher, on the last day of school, gave the students the math exam.

30. Why is the following sentence incorrect?

The decision handed down by the esteemed panel of judges are final.

   A. The plural subject requires a singular verb.
   B. The singular subject requires a plural verb.
   C. The plural subject requires a plural verb.
   D. The singular subject requires a singular verb.

31. Which of the following indefinite pronouns is plural?
   A. each
   B. everybody
   C. something
   D. few

Spelling

32. Which of these sentences contains an incorrectly spelled word?
   A. The counterfeit painting was sold for millions.
   B. He always played the villane in movies.
   C. He became a second lieutenant when he graduated.
   D. Our department acts as a liaison between the athletes and the coaches.

33. Which of these sentences contains an incorrectly spelled word?
   A. The store sells both porecelin and stoneware.
   B. Jenny orders her clothes from an online catalogue.
   C. The fawn was nearly invisible, so effective was its camouflage.
   D. He acts as a liaison between the faculty and students.

ESSAY

34. Write a brief narrative in which you use symbolism to express a closely held opinion, idea, or belief. Challenge yourself to make your symbols interesting and neither overly obvious nor obscure.

35. Analyze a memorable character from a novel you have read. Explain the character's importance to the plot and describe the character's most important traits. Use specific examples from the text, and consider using dialogue or other quotations.

36. What national or local problem would you most like to see resolved? Write a problem-and-solution essay on that topic. Describe both the problem and the solution thoroughly, clearly, specifically, and persuasively.

ANSWERS

"The Threads of Time" by C. J. Cherryh

Vocabulary Warm-up Exercises, p. 2

A.
1. evolved
2. acquired
3. warp
4. melancholy
5. alterations
6. random
7. arrival
8. transfer

B. Sample Answers
1. You have a lot of challenges ahead if you are <u>beset</u> by problems.
2. A stand-up comic probably has a harder time being funny if the audience is <u>somber</u>.
3. If the coupon is <u>valid</u>, the grocery store will accept it.
4. Shaking your head back and forth is a nonverbal way of <u>contradicting</u> what someone is saying.
5. If someone is <u>overseeing</u> a project, he or she tells team members what to do.
6. Parachute-diving and riding a bicycle without a helmet are two <u>hazardous</u> activities.
7. If the plot of a movie is hard to follow and has a lot of confusing twists, the audience will probably be <u>perplexed</u>.

Reading Warm-up A, p. 3

Sample Answers
1. <u>forward or backward in time</u>; It might be difficult to *transfer* to a new school because changing your environment can be stressful.
2. (in medieval times); My uncle's *arrival* from Puerto Rico was a big event for our family.
3. (carefully selects); I might make a *random* choice on a test when I do not have a clue about the right answer.
4. <u>The genre of time travel fiction</u>; *Evolved* means "grown or developed gradually over time."
5. (changes); I would like to make several *alterations* in my room, including a new paint color and a new rug.
6. <u>the flow of time bends or changes shape</u>; If a shelf has a *warp* in it, it is not completely flat.
7. (feeling sadness); An abandoned ghost town might make people feel *melancholy*.
8. <u>a taste for reading about characters who break out of the here and now</u>; I recently *acquired* a new portable music player.

Reading Warm-up B, p. 4

Sample Answers
1. (nonsense); You can decide if a statement is *valid* by checking the facts in a reliable reference source.
2. <u>weird characters and events</u>; *Beset* means "attacked on all sides by."

3. <u>the logic of our world</u>; I was *contradicting* my sister when she was insisting that we should go to Canada for our vacation.
4. (humorous); The mood at the courthouse was very *somber*.
5. <u>because they know nothing about the history or culture there</u>; I was *perplexed* when I tried to follow the instructions for building the new bookcase.
6. <u>what happens in every universe, watching and perhaps guiding events and actions</u>; *Overseeing* means "supervising."
7. (leading to severe results); Skateboarding without a helmet on is an extremely *hazardous* activity.
8. <u>the truth as we know it</u>; *Violate* means "breaks."

C. J. Cherryh

Listening and Viewing, p. 5

Segment 1. C. J. Cherryh likes to draw, sculpt, ice skate, travel overseas, and study archaeology. Students may answer that practicing other art forms can encourage creativity, skating provides a break from sitting at her computer, and traveling overseas to archaeological sites allows her to meet new people, share and listen to ideas, and discover new information that she can use in her writing.

Segment 2. Fantasy stories are usually about moral issues such as making the right choices whereas science-fiction stories are often about power and having the ability to do something. Students may answer that short stories are condensed and aim to have an impact on the reader by making him or her think.

Segment 3. C. J. Cherryh believes that revising is the most important step in the writing process, so she advises students to get anything down on paper and then spend time revising—adding foreshadowing, details to plot, and so on—until the work is brilliant. Students may agree that revising allows one to build on the draft, or they may feel that other steps in the writing process such as researching, brainstorming, outlining, and drafting are just as important.

Segment 4. Science-fiction stories have been around since early times and often discuss the idea of adventure and voyage, both of which are still universal themes today. Students may suggest that it is important to write for today's audience but that it is also important to consider future readers, who will use the writing of our lifetimes to determine the characteristics and issues of our culture and society.

Learning About Short Stories, p. 6

1. direct characterization
2. external conflict
3. setting
4. stated theme
5. indirect characterization
6. internal conflict
7. setting

8. indirect characterization
9. external conflict
10. setting

from "*The Threads of Time*" by C. J. Cherryh

Model Selection: Short Story, p. 7

A. Conflict: external, between time and the qhal; Climax: Alhir notices the potsherd is missing, and Harrh begins to realize that time is falling apart; Resolution: Harrh forgets everything; Main Character: Harrh, a time-mender who wants to quit and stay in the present with his family; Setting: another planet in another time

B. Sample Answers

The theme of the story is that the abuse or lack of understanding of science can be very dangerous. The theme is implied; the author points out that time-travelers are changing the past and illustrates the dangers by showing the changes in, and the eventual destruction of, the present.

Selection Test A, p. 8

Critical Thinking

1. ANS: C	DIF: Easy	OBJ: Literary Analysis
2. ANS: B	DIF: Easy	OBJ: Literary Analysis
3. ANS: D	DIF: Easy	OBJ: Literary Analysis
4. ANS: A	DIF: Easy	OBJ: Literary Analysis
5. ANS: C	DIF: Easy	OBJ: Literary Analysis

Critical Reading

6. ANS: B	DIF: Easy	OBJ: Literary Analysis
7. ANS: B	DIF: Easy	OBJ: Comprehension
8. ANS: A	DIF: Easy	OBJ: Comprehension
9. ANS: A	DIF: Easy	OBJ: Comprehension
10. ANS: D	DIF: Easy	OBJ: Literary Analysis
11. ANS: A	DIF: Easy	OBJ: Comprehension
12. ANS: A	DIF: Easy	OBJ: Interpretation
13. ANS: C	DIF: Easy	OBJ: Comprehension
14. ANS: A	DIF: Easy	OBJ: Literary Analysis
15. ANS: D	DIF: Easy	OBJ: Interpretation

Essay

16. Answers will vary. Students may note that qhal seem very human in most of their characteristics. They may feel that the author made her characters non-human to give the story a fantastic quality but that she made them very nearly human to give readers the sense that the story could have a message for humans.
Difficulty: *Easy*
Objective: *Essay*

17. Students may state that a theme of the story is the potential danger of science that is badly used or poorly understood. They should support the theme with examples and details.
Difficulty: *Easy*
Objective: *Essay*

Selection Test B, p. 11

Critical Thinking

1. ANS: A	DIF: Average	OBJ: Literary Analysis
2. ANS: D	DIF: Average	OBJ: Literary Analysis
3. ANS: C	DIF: Average	OBJ: Literary Analysis
4. ANS: D	DIF: Average	OBJ: Literary Analysis
5. ANS: B	DIF: Challenging	OBJ: Literary Analysis
6. ANS: C	DIF: Challenging	OBJ: Literary Analysis

Critical Reading

7. ANS: B	DIF: Challenging	OBJ: Interpretation
8. ANS: C	DIF: Challenging	OBJ: Literary Analysis
9. ANS: B	DIF: Challenging	OBJ: Interpretation
10. ANS: C	DIF: Challenging	OBJ: Literary Analysis
11. ANS: C	DIF: Challenging	OBJ: Interpretation
12. ANS: B	DIF: Average	OBJ: Comprehension
13. ANS: D	DIF: Challenging	OBJ: Interpretation
14. ANS: A	DIF: Average	OBJ: Comprehension
15. ANS: C	DIF: Average	OBJ: Literary Analysis
16. ANS: B	DIF: Challenging	OBJ: Interpretation
17. ANS: D	DIF: Average	OBJ: Comprehension
18. ANS: C	DIF: Average	OBJ: Comprehension
19. ANS: B	DIF: Average	OBJ: Comprehension
20. ANS: A	DIF: Average	OBJ: Comprehension

Essay

21. Answers will vary but should be supported by details from the story. Students should point out that those who do go beyond disappear, so no one knows what happens to them.
Difficulty: *Average*
Objective: *Essay*

22. Answers will vary, but students should refer to the dangers of backtiming and the implication that it can change the present. Students may feel that someone has changed the past so greatly that the events that shaped Harrh's memory no longer exist.
Difficulty: *Average*
Objective: *Essay*

23. Students may note that the paradox of backtiming is the idea that if you change the past, the present also changes. You, your past, and your present are all

changed. In addition, the instant that you backtime, the past is changed, thus creating a cycle of change that cannot exist. Students should point to the various changes that take place in the story that make no sense, indicating that the paradox is taking place.

Difficulty: *Challenging*

Objective: *Essay*

Unit 2, Part 1 Answers

Diagnostic Test 3, p. 15

MULTIPLE CHOICE

1. ANS: A
2. ANS: D
3. ANS: B
4. ANS: D
5. ANS: B
6. ANS: A
7. ANS: C
8. ANS: D
9. ANS: B
10. ANS: B
11. ANS: C
12. ANS: A
13. ANS: D
14. ANS: A
15. ANS: C

"A Visit to Grandmother"
by William Melvin Kelley

Vocabulary Warm-up Exercises, p. 19

A.
1. engaging
2. discussion
3. additional
4. swapped
5. ventured
6. injured
7. absence
8. reunion

B. Sample Answers

1. The case was *quickly solved* because the detective's suspicion turned out to be true.
2. You could see Mai's uncertainty because she *hesitated and shuffled her feet.*
3. A particularly interesting story is one that is probably *full of surprises.*
4. Our picnic was rather meager so we were all *still hungry* afterward.

5. She had *never been in a play before*, so she performed timidly onstage.
6. Someone who is an exception will always *stand out from* the crowd.
7. *Running water* is a potentially useful source of energy for electricity.

Reading Warm-up A, p. 20

Sample Answers

1. a big, friendly gathering of relatives; Relatives who have not seen one another in a long time might come to a *reunion.*
2. (talent show) (games) (crafts); *Additional* means "extra."
3. (conversation); My family might have a *discussion* about whether to get a dog.
4. If the invitation list leaves someone out; *Injured* means "hurt."
5. (participants); I *ventured* a great distance when my family drove across the country.
6. some relatives cannot attend; *Absence* means "not being there."
7. make time for storytelling; I think a science fiction book group would be very *engaging.*
8. (exchanged); Baseball cards could be *swapped* for toy cars.

Reading Warm-up B, p. 21

Sample Answers

1. learning would lead to disobedience and rebellion; *Suspicion* means "the thought that something is wrong without having proof."
2. Few existing schools would accept former slaves as students. Meager means "not plentiful."
3. No one could predict the effects of this enormous change to society's structure. The period before the United States entered World War II was also a period of *uncertainty.*
4. The period of the Vietnam War was *particularly* important.
5. (better future); *Potentially* means "possibly."
6. (boldly); *Timidly* means "shyly."
7. (graduating students); Our high school awards *diplomas* every June.
8. (standard); Our mayor is an *exception* because she works for no salary.

"A Visit to Grandmother"
by William Melvin Kelley

Literary Analysis: Characterization, p. 22

A. Sample Answers

1. Direct—Doctor Charles Dunford cared about people. Indirect—Charles has an ugly look in his eyes when he kisses his mother; Mama reveals that it has been a very long time since he has seen his mother; his voice cracks when he speaks to Mama.

2. Direct—Chig is seventeen years old. The author does not directly describe his personality because the story is told from his point of view. Indirect—Mama says Chig looks like his mother; he speaks very politely and correctly to Mama; he promises to be honest.

3. Direct—The author does not directly describe Mama's personality, probably because it is more interesting to reveal her character through her appearance, actions, and dialogue. Indirect—Mama has white hair and wears thick glasses; she has ten children; Mama is proud and does not want people to help her and do things for her; she treats her children differently, according to what she believes they need from her.

B. Students who say they prefer direct characterization will probably mention the ease with which they can know a character. Students who prefer indirect characterization will mention that it helps a reader visualize a character and know him or her through his or her feelings, actions, and thoughts.

Reading: Relate Characters and Events to Your Own Experiences to Make Inferences, p. 23

Sample Answers

1. Personal experience—I never know how to act or feel when I visit my great-grandma in the nursing home. She does not know who I am. I feel guilty about it, but I have to try hard not to make a face when she asks for a kiss. Inference—Charles does not see his mother much and does not want to see her now. He is uncomfortable kissing her.

2. Personal experience—My mother is always trying to get me to eat more. She thinks I am too skinny. Inference—Rose thinks Chig is too skinny, or she assumes that a teenage boy wants to eat a lot. Chig's weak protest means he really does not mind her giving him more food.

3. Personal experience—I had a friend who told a story she thought was funny, but I did not think it was. Inference—Charles did not think the horse story was funny. He seems mad at Mama.

4. Personal experience—I do not know anyone like GL, but I have seen grown men and women before who seem happy, but do not have much common sense. Inference—GL is not very smart or mature, but his friendly smile makes people like him anyway.

Vocabulary Builder, p. 24

A. 1. C; 2. A; 3. B

B. **Sample Answers**

1. I treat my nephew with <u>indulgence</u> and let him get away with a little bad behavior now and then. My sister wishes I would not <u>indulge</u> her son because he continues to behave badly when she comes to pick him up.

2. <u>Grimacing</u> in pain, I limped to the nurse's office to get my ankle wrapped. She <u>grimaced</u> as well when she saw how badly swollen it was already.

3. Not even a <u>trace</u> of a smile crossed his face, and I knew he was really upset. I could still see <u>traces</u> of crayon marks on the wall behind him and knew my little sister was in trouble.

Enrichment: Connecting to the Performing Arts Through Storytelling, p. 27

A. **Sample Answers**

1. The use of interesting, vivid details, a clear speaking voice, changes in the loudness or softness of a voice, and body language are all important qualities in the art of storytelling.

2. She shares a story about GL conning a man into giving him a horse for an old chair, then riding in a buggy being pulled by the horse. The horse begins to run, and she is forced to jump on the horse's back to pull it to a stop.

3. She gives a number of vivid, interesting details at each point in the story. She also changes her voice to reflect exciting parts in the story. She talks about her reaction when GL first brings the horse home, how she feels when she is riding through town in the buggy, and she describes the excitement of being caught in the buggy when the horse begins to run. She raises her voice when she describes scolding GL. She inserts her own unique perspective in the following ways: She refers to GL as a "swindler" and shares her doubts about the deal he made. She also talks about feeling "elegant like a fine lady" when she first gets into the buggy and then describes how she scolds GL when the horse first begins to run.

B. Students should try to tell their stories using interesting details, body language, and strong, clear voices. Their performances should show that they spent time rehearsing and thinking about storytelling techniques. Students should give one another constructive criticism.

Selection Test A, p. 28

Critical Reading

1. ANS: C	**DIF:** Easy	**OBJ:** Comprehension
2. ANS: B	**DIF:** Easy	**OBJ:** Comprehension
3. ANS: A	**DIF:** Easy	**OBJ:** Interpretation
4. ANS: C	**DIF:** Easy	**OBJ:** Reading
5. ANS: D	**DIF:** Easy	**OBJ:** Literary Analysis
6. ANS: A	**DIF:** Easy	**OBJ:** Interpretation
7. ANS: A	**DIF:** Easy	**OBJ:** Literary Analysis
8. ANS: D	**DIF:** Easy	**OBJ:** Literary Analysis
9. ANS: C	**DIF:** Easy	**OBJ:** Comprehension

10. ANS: D	DIF: Easy	OBJ: Reading	13. ANS: B	DIF: Average	OBJ: Interpretation
11. ANS: B	DIF: Easy	OBJ: Interpretation	14. ANS: C	DIF: Challenging	OBJ: Interpretation
12. ANS: C	DIF: Easy	OBJ: Interpretation	15. ANS: B	DIF: Average	OBJ: Interpretation

Vocabulary and Grammar

13. ANS: C	DIF: Easy	OBJ: Vocabulary
14. ANS: B	DIF: Easy	OBJ: Vocabulary
15. ANS: B	DIF: Easy	OBJ: Grammar

Vocabulary and Grammar

16. ANS: C	DIF: Average	OBJ: Vocabulary
17. ANS: B	DIF: Average	OBJ: Vocabulary
18. ANS: B	DIF: Average	OBJ: Vocabulary
19. ANS: A	DIF: Average	OBJ: Grammar

Essay

16. Students should describe how Kelley characterizes Mama through both direct and indirect characterization. He describes how she looks. She is tiny, brown, and very wrinkled. Her hair is pure white. The author characterizes Mama through indirect characterization through what she says. She says she does not need any help and can do things for herself. This reveals that she is a strong and proud woman. She later says that she gave each of her children what she thought they needed most. This shows that she thought Charles was mature and did not need her as much as GL.

Difficulty: *Easy*

Objective: *Essay*

17. Students may respond that Mama gave each of her children what she thought they needed. Charles was smart and mature, so she didn't think he needed much attention from her. GL was not very smart and was always getting in trouble. Mama gave him lots of attention. She was worried he would end up getting hanged if she didn't. Students should tell whether or not they think her approach was a good one and use examples from the story and real life to support their opinion.

Difficulty: *Easy*

Objective: *Essay*

Selection Test B, p. 31

Critical Reading

1. ANS: A	DIF: Challenging	OBJ: Reading
2. ANS: C	DIF: Average	OBJ: Comprehension
3. ANS: C	DIF: Average	OBJ: Comprehension
4. ANS: C	DIF: Average	OBJ: Reading
5. ANS: C	DIF: Average	OBJ: Interpretation
6. ANS: B	DIF: Challenging	OBJ: Literary Analysis
7. ANS: D	DIF: Average	OBJ: Literary Analysis
8. ANS: D	DIF: Challenging	OBJ: Literary Analysis
9. ANS: C	DIF: Average	OBJ: Interpretation
10. ANS: A	DIF: Average	OBJ: Comprehension
11. ANS: A	DIF: Challenging	OBJ: Literary Analysis
12. ANS: D	DIF: Average	OBJ: Reading

Essay

20. Students should state that Charles has been angry at his mother and brother for many years because he thinks that GL is his mother's favorite. He thinks she likes GL better because she rarely punished GL as a child and always punished Charles. He also thinks that Mama likes GL better because he has good hair and looks almost white. Mama says she gave each of her ten children what they needed. She paid special attention to GL because she was worried he would end up being hanged if she didn't. She didn't think Charles needed as much attention because he was very smart and mature. She does not understand why Charles would be jealous of GL, who is simple-minded and always gets in trouble.

Difficulty: *Average*

Objective: *Essay*

21. Students should explain that Charles feels fear because he has not faced his mother and his bad feelings about home in many years. He feels uncertainty because he does not know how Mama will react. He feels sadness for all the years he has lost with his mother and the rest of his family. He feels a little bit of hatred because he believes his mother does not love him and never did. Charles has all these negative feelings toward his family because he thinks his mother never loved him. He has always been convinced that GL is her favorite son. Students may feel that he wants his mother to admit that she treated GL better than she did Charles. Some small part of him might hope that he can mend things with his family and make everything better.

Difficulty: *Challenging*

Objective: *Essay*

"A Problem" by Anton Chekhov

Vocabulary Warm-up Exercises, p. 35

A. 1. disagreeable
2. philosophy
3. guarantee
4. commit

5. motives
6. sufficiently
7. signature
8. awaiting

B. Sample Answers

1. T; Baby food is *blandly* spiced because a baby's sense of taste is still developing.
2. F; Even with experience, a teacher might make a mistake and lead a class *astray*.
3. T; If you are lazy, one possible *consequence* is that you will not seek out new information, and you will be ignorant as a result.
4. F; An *emphatic* speaker will probably make an audience feel energized.
5. F; *Asserted* facts are not always true.
6. T; Performers usually prefer a crowd that is responsive rather than one that is *indifferent*.
7. T; If you are *initiated* into a club, you are a member, so it is likely that you will have to follow the club rules.
8. T; Schools often ask *distinguished* people to speak at graduation ceremonies in order to inspire the graduating class.

Reading Warm-up A, p. 36

Sample Answers

1. that they will pay back the money; *Guarantee* means "promise."
2. (buying a car) (starting a business); Two other *motives* for borrowing money are buying a house or going to college.
3. (satisfactorily); *Sufficiently* means "adequately."
4. (forms must be satisfactorily filled out); I find taking out the trash *disagreeable*.
5. (an answer); I am *awaiting* the arrival of spring.
6. the signer's legal promise to repay the loan; I placed my *signature* on my student ID.
7. The cardholder is the borrower. The credit card company is the lender; The *philosophy* behind shaking hands is to show that you will be peaceful.
8. (the crime of fraud); *Commit* means "to do something."

Reading Warm-up B, p. 37

Sample Answers

1. she didn't care how long she was kept waiting; I am *indifferent* to most team sports.
2. (forceful); *Emphatic* means "with strong emphasis."
3. she will not be allowed to participate in this weekend's competition; Failing is a possible *consequence* of not studying for a test.
4. You can tell if someone is trying to lead you *astray* if he or she makes promises that seem too good to be true.

5. (swim team); I could be *initiated* into the school cheerleading squad.
6. Our local librarian is quite *distinguished* in her field.
7. trying to show no expression at all; *Blandly* means "mildly."
8. You're right.; I *asserted* to my parents that I have the right to choose my own clothes.

"A Problem" by Anton Chekhov

Literary Analysis: Characterization, p. 38

A. Sample Answers

1. Direct—Sasha is in debt and has no money of his own; he is sick of life and finds it insufferably hard; he feels empty inside; he detests his family. Indirect—Sasha thoughts reveal that he totally does not understand why what he did is a crime; he demands money from Ivan at the end, proving that he did not learn a lesson; he behaves, thinks, and speaks in a very immature way.
2. Direct—The Colonel is Sasha's paternal uncle; he is opposed to paying Sasha's debt for him. Indirect—He has a metallic voice and speaks his views forcefully. He leaves the study in such a way that he does not have to look at Sasha.
3. Direct—The author states that Ivan Markovitch is kind-hearted. Indirect—Chekhov describes his voice as bland, suave, subdued, weeping, and muttering; Markovitch seems therefore to be quite persuasive and to genuinely believe the uncles should help Sasha. He is honestly shocked and horrified when Sasha demands money and leaves him behind.

B. Students who say they prefer direct characterization will probably mention the ease with which they can know a character. Students who prefer indirect characterization will mention that it helps a reader visualize a character and know him or her through his or her feelings, actions, and thoughts.

Reading: Relate Characters and Events to Your Own Experiences to Make Inferences, p. 39

Sample Answers

1. Personal experience—I have had teachers who feel it is best to immediately punish kids who break the rules and other teachers who give kids several chances. Inference—Ivan Markovitch must hope that paying Sasha's debt will make Sasha feel grateful and want to straighten up on his own without having to go to court.
2. Personal experience—Sometimes when I get in trouble with my parents, I get really mad, too. I have to fight against the urge to say or do something that will make things worse. Inference—Sasha is very angry, but he doesn't want to make things worse by actually yelling at his uncle.

3. Personal experience—I have a friend who is always concerned about what other people will think of her. She always wants to be part of the "in" crowd. Inference—Sasha wants to be part of the "in" crowd, so he is embarrassed to be out of money.

4. Personal experience—Many people in our society today have debt, too. I know it is not good to be in debt. Inference—Sasha thinks that because everyone does it, it is not a crime and there is nothing wrong with it.

Vocabulary Builder, p. 40

A. 1. C; 2. B; 3. A

B. Sample Answers

1. My brother is very <u>candid</u> about his political beliefs and never worries about whether or not he's offending anyone. My sister, on the other hand, does not like to reveal her political beliefs to others and rarely speaks <u>candidly</u> about it.

2. My best friend in middle school was <u>taciturn</u> around other people, but he talked all the time when it was just him and me. People never understood why a talkative person like me would choose such a <u>taciturn</u> best friend.

3. Everyone was worried about Grandma being in the hospital, so the mood around the dinner table was <u>subdued</u>. When we spoke to the doctor the next day, her voice was <u>subdued</u> but somewhat optimistic about Grandma's improvement.

C. 1. A; 2. D

Enrichment: Connecting to the Humanities by Examining Personal Honor, p. 43

Sample Responses

Definition of honor—A family's honor depends upon the honorable actions of each family member.

1. Ivan Markovitch defends his nephew. It is honorable because Sasha does not have his parents to teach him and defend him.

2. Sasha's behavior is dishonorable. He forged a promissory note; he has a bad attitude toward his family; and he demands more money from the uncle who had helped him out of a bad situation.

3. The Colonel's desire to let Sasha deal with the consequences of his actions is honorable. He believes it would be in Sasha's best interest in the long run because he thinks Sasha will be more likely to learn his lesson if he has to go to trial.

4. The official of the Treasury's desire to keep the story out of the papers is honorable. It is honorable because he does not want other members of the family to suffer for Sasha's mistake.

5. It was dishonorable when Sasha's friend Handrikov did not give Sasha the money he said he'd lend him. It would have been honorable for Handrikov to keep his promise and for Sasha's friends to be understanding about his lack of money.

"A Visit to Grandmother"
by William Melvin Kelley
"A Problem" by Anton Chekhov

Build Language Skills: Vocabulary, p. 44

Sample Answers

A. synonym—compose; antonym—demolish; root word—*forma*; definition—express in a fixed or definite way; example: My family formulated a travel plan for our annual vacation.

B. 1. From my <u>perspective</u>, she should have waited before buying a new computer. Watching John at his job gave me a whole new <u>perspective</u> on what it is like to work hard.

2. We don't <u>anticipate</u> having a chance to visit our family again for a very long time. I am <u>anticipating</u> seeing my grandmother, who has not been well lately.

3. I will <u>indicate</u> when it is your turn to speak by calling your name. He <u>indicated</u> his understanding with a nod of his head.

4. His uncle could easily <u>discern</u> that he would not learn his lesson. The boy had trouble <u>discerning</u> right from wrong.

Build Language Skills: Grammar, p. 45

A. 1. present participle
2. past participle
3. past
4. present
5. past
6. past participle

B. Sample Answers

1. We <u>had talked</u> many times on the phone, but had not yet met in person.

2. Most students <u>agree</u> that Tyrone should be class president.

3. My parents <u>are deciding</u> whether or not I can go on the camping trip this weekend.

4. Kim <u>laughed</u> when she saw how silly I looked in my costume.

"A Problem" by Anton Chekhov

Selection Test A, p. 46

Critical Reading

1. ANS: B	DIF: Easy	OBJ: Reading
2. ANS: A	DIF: Easy	OBJ: Interpretation
3. ANS: B	DIF: Easy	OBJ: Comprehension
4. ANS: B	DIF: Easy	OBJ: Comprehension
5. ANS: D	DIF: Easy	OBJ: Reading
6. ANS: C	DIF: Easy	OBJ: Comprehension
7. ANS: A	DIF: Easy	OBJ: Interpretation

8. ANS: C	DIF: Easy	OBJ: Literary Analysis
9. ANS: D	DIF: Easy	OBJ: Literary Analysis
10. ANS: C	DIF: Easy	OBJ: Literary Analysis
11. ANS: B	DIF: Easy	OBJ: Interpretation

Vocabulary and Grammar

12. ANS: B	DIF: Easy	OBJ: Vocabulary
13. ANS: B	DIF: Easy	OBJ: Vocabulary
14. ANS: D	DIF: Easy	OBJ: Vocabulary
15. ANS: B	DIF: Easy	OBJ: Grammar

Essay

16. Students may respond that they would have made Sasha go to court and take his punishment. They may feel that is the only way he would have learned his lesson. He obviously does not care about making his family look bad. He also does not understand why forging a note at the bank was wrong. They may note that if nothing bad happens to people when they do something bad, they will just do it again.
    Difficulty: *Easy*
    Objective: *Essay*

17. Students may predict that Sasha will get into more debt. He will probably get as much money as he can out of Ivan and will cash another fake note at the bank. They may also predict that when he gets caught a second time, his uncles will not help him. The Colonel will not help him again because he will have proof that Sasha is not going to change. Paying his debt again will only make things worse.
    Difficulty: *Easy*
    Objective: *Essay*

Selection Test B, p. 49

Critical Reading

1. ANS: D	DIF: Average	OBJ: Reading
2. ANS: C	DIF: Average	OBJ: Comprehension
3. ANS: C	DIF: Challenging	OBJ: Interpretation
4. ANS: B	DIF: Average	OBJ: Comprehension
5. ANS: D	DIF: Average	OBJ: Literary Analysis
6. ANS: D	DIF: Average	OBJ: Reading
7. ANS: A	DIF: Challenging	OBJ: Interpretation
8. ANS: C	DIF: Average	OBJ: Interpretation
9. ANS: D	DIF: Average	OBJ: Interpretation
10. ANS: C	DIF: Challenging	OBJ: Reading
11. ANS: B	DIF: Challenging	OBJ: Literary Analysis
12. ANS: B	DIF: Challenging	OBJ: Literary Analysis
13. ANS: D	DIF: Average	OBJ: Literary Analysis
14. ANS: C	DIF: Challenging	OBJ: Interpretation

Vocabulary and Grammar

15. ANS: D	DIF: Average	OBJ: Vocabulary
16. ANS: C	DIF: Average	OBJ: Vocabulary
17. ANS: A	DIF: Average	OBJ: Vocabulary
18. ANS: A	DIF: Challenging	OBJ: Grammar
19. ANS: B	DIF: Average	OBJ: Grammar

Essay

20. Students should state that Sasha cashes a false promissory note at the bank. If news of this gets out, the Uskov's will be very embarrassed. It will damage their family honor. Students should explain that at first, Sasha does not care. Then, he gets angry at the Colonel for calling him a criminal. He thinks he has not done anything so terribly wrong. One uncle, the Treasury official, thinks they should pay Sasha's debt so the story won't get out in the papers. Another uncle, the Colonel, thinks they should not pay the debt because Sasha will just do it again. The third uncle, Ivan Markovitch, thinks they should pay the debt to help Sasha. After hours of arguing, Ivan wins and the uncles agree to pay Sasha's debt.
    Difficulty: *Average*
    Objective: *Essay*

21. Students may predict that Sasha will get into more debt. He will probably get as much money as he can out of Ivan. Then, he will cash another fake note at the bank. Students may respond that when he gets caught a second time, though, his uncles will not help him. The Colonel will not help him again because it will be obvious that Sasha is not going to change. Paying his debt again will only make things worse. Some students may predict that Sasha is likely to end up in Siberia or run away when he knows he can't get away with it anymore.
    Difficulty: *Average*
    Objective: *Essay*

"The Streets of the Cañon" by Josephina Niggli

Vocabulary Warm-up Exercises, p. 53

A. 1. mottled
  2. historian
  3. humanity
  4. interruption
  5. apprehension
  6. prominent
  7. assurance
  8. decisively

B. Sample Answers
  1. Sally should not be worried about Jim's getting lost because *doubtless* means "certain."

2. You can trust her with your best belongings because *virtuous* means "good."

3. If a wall is *whitewashed*, the result should be light and bright.

4. There would be only one road because *merged* means "joined together."

5. It would probably be hard to get through because *intricate* means "complicated."

6. The guests were probably much younger than 25 because a *chaperone* accompanies children or young adults.

7. I wouldn't describe them as sweet because *pungent* means "sharp or bitter."

Reading Warm-up A, p. 54

Sample Answers

1. <u>treating them as if they weren't people like themselves.</u> *Humanity* means human beings.

2. (without hesitation); The paramedic acted *decisively* to save the child's life by performing CPR.

3. (non-Indians); *Apprehension* means "worry or fear."

4. (begin planting); An *interruption* in my daily routine might happen if I got sick and had to stay home from school.

5. <u>Winged ants mottled the sunlight</u>; *Prominent* means obvious.

6. (the sunlight); Sunlight that is *mottled* by winged ants might look as if it were covered by lace.

7. <u>that they could win</u>; *Assurance* is a commitment that is meant to give confidence to another.

8. (Mexico's past and this struggle); A <u>historian</u> might study the history of First People from North and South America.

Reading Warm-up B, p. 55

Sample Answers

1. (complex); A spider web is *intricate*.

2. <u>her intelligence and beauty</u>; *Doubtless* means certain.

3. A *chaperone* goes with young people while they socialize to be sure they follow rules.

4. My mother, my sister, and my father are all *virtuous*, because they are concerned with being good people and doing the right thing.

5. <u>the challenge of their cultural differences</u>; *Merged* means "joined with."

6. If she sat *humbly*, then Lupe sat modestly, not calling attention to herself.

7. (home); *Whitewashed* means "having applied a substance similar to paint to whiten walls."

8. Three foods that have a *pungent* flavor are goat cheese, cilantro, and tamarind.

"The Street of the Cañon" by Josephina Niggli

Literary Analysis: Setting, p. 56

A. Sample Answers

Overall Time: Setting—probably during the early 1800s; Evidence—there are references to cowboys and the frontier; Impact—transportation and communication between villages is not quick or easy, so the conflict is likely to go on longer than it would today

Overall Place: Setting—the village of San Juan Iglesias in the Valley of the Three Marys in Mexico; Evidence—the first sentence states the name and location of the village; Impact—the story takes place in a small, isolated community

Specific Time: Setting—an evening in May; Evidence—the first paragraph states that it is May and describes the moonlit night; Impact—the darkness helps to hide Pepe's arrival and departure

Specific Place: Setting—a party at Don Roméo Calderón's home; Evidence—stated in the first paragraph; Impact—the party provides an opportunity for a stranger to be welcomed without question

B. Students' summaries should include descriptions of a setting in their own region that incorporates a rivalry between two communities. Their storylines should feature a person from one community who attends incognito an event in the other.

Reading: Make Inferences and Read on to Find Additional Support, p. 57

Sample Answers

1. Inference—She is signaling that she wants him to ask her to dance. Detail—He later goes to her and dances with her.

2. Inference—The stranger is trying to charm the old chaperone so that she will let him dance with Sarita. Detail—The chaperone is amused and allows the stranger to dance with Sarita.

3. Inference—The stranger knows Pepe Gonzalez. Detail—At the end of the story, Sarita suspects the stranger is Pepe Gonzalez.

4. Inference—The cheese is made in Hidalgo; they used to have it in San Juan before the feud began. Detail—Tío Daniel states that the cheese is made in Hidalgo.

Vocabulary Builder, p. 58

A. 1. A; 2. C; 3. B

B. Sample Answers

1. The wealthy and arrogant guests <u>imperiously</u> demanded their dinner.

2. Due to the <u>plausibility</u> of his story, everyone believed him without question.

3. Accustomed to getting good grades, she glanced <u>nonchalantly</u> at the A+ she had expected to receive on her research paper.

C. 1. B; 2. B; 3. D

Enrichment: Connecting to Cultures, p. 61

Sample Answers

1. The dancing sets the mood of the story. The fluid dance movements contrast with the fact that the two are supposed to be feuding and hateful. The reader can tell how the two feel about each other by images of the dance at key moments in the conversation. For example, Pepe grips Sarita's arm more tightly when she speaks angrily about Hidalgo. When she calls him a dangerous man he holds her closer; and at the end of the story she remembers having her arm looped in his.

2. Pepe might be looking for a way to connect with his enemies in a certain way. He is hoping to prove that under normal, relaxed circumstances, they are all human.

3. Students might talk about the social aspects of dance as well as the fun and relaxation dancing provides. Students should describe dances they have seen at parties or on television.

Selection Test A, p. 62

Critical Reading

1. ANS: B	DIF: Easy	OBJ: Literary Analysis
2. ANS: C	DIF: Easy	OBJ: Reading
3. ANS: C	DIF: Easy	OBJ: Interpretation
4. ANS: B	DIF: Easy	OBJ: Interpretation
5. ANS: C	DIF: Easy	OBJ: Interpretation
6. ANS: A	DIF: Easy	OBJ: Comprehension
7. ANS: B	DIF: Easy	OBJ: Comprehension
8. ANS: C	DIF: Easy	OBJ: Reading
9. ANS: D	DIF: Easy	OBJ: Reading
10. ANS: D	DIF: Easy	OBJ: Literary Analysis
11. ANS: A	DIF: Easy	OBJ: Literary Analysis

Vocabulary and Grammar

12. ANS: C	DIF: Easy	OBJ: Vocabulary
13. ANS: C	DIF: Easy	OBJ: Vocabulary
14. ANS: C	DIF: Easy	OBJ: Grammar

Essay

15. Students should explain that Sarita suspects the stranger is Pepe Gonzalez because of the cheese. Daniel says that the cheese is from Hidalgo. He goes on to say that the cheese is made by Pepe Gonzalez's father. Another clue students should identify is while they were dancing, she was talking about some men from Hidalgo who came to her village to steal some bones. He wanted to know if the men were young. He wants her to talk more about the leader, Pepe. Later, Sarita probably realizes that he was so interested because he is Pepe.

Difficulty: *Easy*

Objective: *Essay*

16. Students' should note that Pepe is in danger because the people of San Juan Iglesias hate the people of Hidalgo. Possible dangers he may encounter if they find out that he is from Hidalgo include jail or even death. Students should provide an explanation for whether they believe Pepe Gonzalez would encounter these dangers in another setting.

Difficulty: *Easy*

Objective: *Essay*

Selection Test B, p. 65

Critical Reading

1. ANS: D	DIF: Average	OBJ: Literary Analysis
2. ANS: D	DIF: Average	OBJ: Reading
3. ANS: C	DIF: Challenging	OBJ: Interpretation
4. ANS: B	DIF: Average	OBJ: Interpretation
5. ANS: A	DIF: Average	OBJ: Comprehension
6. ANS: C	DIF: Average	OBJ: Comprehension
7. ANS: C	DIF: Average	OBJ: Reading
8. ANS: D	DIF: Challenging	OBJ: Interpretation
9. ANS: B	DIF: Challenging	OBJ: Interpretation
10. ANS: D	DIF: Challenging	OBJ: Interpretation
11. ANS: D	DIF: Average	OBJ: Reading
12. ANS: A	DIF: Average	OBJ: Comprehension
13. ANS: A	DIF: Challenging	OBJ: Reading
14. ANS: B	DIF: Average	OBJ: Interpretation
15. ANS: C	DIF: Challenging	OBJ: Literary Analysis

Vocabulary and Grammar

16. ANS: D	DIF: Average	OBJ: Vocabulary
17. ANS: C	DIF: Average	OBJ: Vocabulary
18. ANS: B	DIF: Average	OBJ: Grammar
19. ANS: C	DIF: Average	OBJ: Grammar

Essay

20. Students may identify several possible reasons that the party is a good setting for Pepe to play his prank. First, people would be less likely to be suspicious of a stranger at a big party. Everyone would assume that he was there to wish Sarita a happy birthday. Second, a birthday party is a good reason for him to be carrying a package. Third, pretty much everyone in town is at the party, so Pepe's prank will get the biggest reaction when

everyone figures it out at the same time. The party is at night and everyone is off the streets of the village, so Pepe could escape back to his village without being seen.

Difficulty: *Average*

Objective: *Essay*

21. Students should describe what would happen a week later into the story and provide details to support their prediction. Some students may predict that Pepe will return to the village in order to walk with Sarita. Another possible prediction is that the romance between Pepe and Sarita will end the feud between the villages.

Difficulty: *Average*

Objective: *Essay*

"There Will Come Soft Rains" by Ray Bradbury

Vocabulary Warm-up Exercises, p. 69

A.
1. radioactive
2. wavered
3. preference
4. quenching
5. reveal
6. linoleum
7. tragic
8. hysterically

B. Sample Answers
1. The circuits could be switched off at the breaker.
2. The nails served as reinforcements to the glue that held the boards together.
3. The chef's current preoccupation is Jamaican food.
4. The birds moved in a frenzy to get the seeds that Kim had scattered.
5. The froth on my hot chocolate tasted warm and sweet.
6. The cluttered shelves were full of jumbled toys.
7. The toddler ejected the video when she pressed the button.

Reading Warm-up A, p. 70

Sample Answers
1. (her invention); *Reveal* means "to show or make known."
2. the look and durability; *Linoleum* is a material used for floors that has a strong, shiny surface.
3. (athletes' thirst); *Quenching* means "satisfying a thirst."
4. They had not been able to decide whether to build on someone else's innovation or to hold out for a truly unique idea. *Wavered* means "felt uncertain."
5. for inventions that could truly help the world. *Preferences* are those things that we like better than other things.
6. it could be dangerous to keep the high-level waste stored in the containers that were currently available

7. In fact, some believed the use of the current containers could lead to *terrible* results.
8. she saw one of the workshop advisors browsing through the directory on her computer; Someone who reacts almost *hysterically* might scream and shout or cry.

Reading Warm-up B, p. 71

Sample Answers
1. are networked so that they can communicate with one another. *Circuits* are paths for electricity.
2. When we wrapped presents for the party, there was a *frenzy* of activity.
3. (milk); *Froth* means "bubbles on the surface of a liquid."
4. The systems would provide *reinforcements* when there was an electric outage.
5. (kitchen); *Preoccupation* means "something that you give all your attention to."
6. You might find appliances, dishes, and cookbooks on top of *cluttered* counters.
7. Items being *ejected* from a refrigerator might look like toast popping out of a toaster.
8. (overcooked); *Charred* means "blackened by cooking or fire."

"There Will Come Soft Rains" by Ray Bradbury

Literary Analysis: Setting, p. 72

A. Sample Answers

Overall Time: Setting—August 4, 2026; Evidence—stated in the third paragraph; Impact—lets readers know the story is set in the future

Overall Place: Setting—Allendale, California; Evidence—stated in the third paragraph; Impact—implies that this is an average American city

Specific Time: Setting—story begins at 7:00 a.m.; Evidence—stated in the first paragraph; Impact—shows that the events take place over the course of one day

Specific Place: Setting—the McClellan family's home; Evidence—the house asks Mrs. McClellan which poem she would like to hear; Impact—gives a name to the family that had owned the house, which makes it a bit more personal for the reader

B. Students' summaries will vary, but should include descriptions of the new setting, and a description of a story that is similar to "There Will Come Soft Rains."

Reading: Make Inferences and Read on to Find Additional Support, p. 73

Sample Answers
1. Inference—Based on the numbers and types of food and drink being served, there seem to be four people in the family: two adults and two children. Detail—The paint silhouettes on the side of the house confirm that there were two adults and two children in the family.

2. Inference—The family had been outside when they were killed in a nuclear blast. Detail—The family does not reappear throughout the story, so they must have died.

3. Inference—The dog is suffering from starvation and sickness. It will probably die without its human family's help. Detail—The dog dies and the cleaning mice incinerate its remains.

Vocabulary Builder, p. 74

A. 1. C; 2. A; 3. B

B. Sample Answers

1. The leaves on the tree in the front yard <u>fluttered</u> in the afternoon breeze.

2. Her voice was soft and <u>tremulous</u> as she nervously gave the worst speech of her life.

3. The giant meteorite made a <u>titanic</u> splash as it struck the surface of the ocean.

C. 1. A; 2. B; 3. C

Enrichment: Connecting to Technology, p. 77

Sample Answers

Automatic sprinkler systems: keeps lawns around homes and businesses green and attractive; often wasteful because systems water lawns even when it is raining

Digital recording devices: compact, durable, high-quality audio and video recordings; makes it very easy for people to steal songs, movies, and so on.

Cellular telephones: instant communication, emergency help; hazardous driving, intrusive calling

Online shopping: ease of shopping, can find almost anything; isolation, junk mail, credit card security risk

Central air conditioning: constant and controlled temperature, saves lives in severe heat; cost of energy, environmental risk

Online banking: convenience, control; loss of privacy

Electronic surveillance: increased security; increased fear, loss of privacy

Cable television: instant access to news and entertainment; loss of interaction with real life, junk television

"The Street of the Cañon" by Josephina Niggli
"There Will Come Soft Rains" by Ray Bradbury

Build Language Skills: Vocabulary, p. 78
Sample Answers

A. 1. <u>Perspective</u> is how one sees things. This relates to the root word -*spec*-, which has to do with looking or seeing.

2. <u>Inspect</u> means "to look closely at something," which also clearly has to do with looking or seeing.

3. The prefix <u>retro</u>- means "backward," and the word root -<u>spec</u>- means "to look." So <u>retrospect</u> means "looking back or thinking about something in the past."

4. A <u>suspect</u> is someone who might have done something wrong, so police look closely at the person to see if there is evidence that he or she committed a crime.

B. 1. True—It would be the job of a prom committee to come up with plans for the event.

2. False—The reader would only understand one character's point of view.

3. False—*Anticipate* means "to look forward to something that has yet to happen." Therefore, one can not anticipate something that has already happened.

4. True—Nodding is one way of showing understanding.

5. True—It is hard to perceive or recognize clues if a crime scene is very clean.

Build Language Skills: Vocabulary p. 79

A. 1. past
2. past participle
3. present participle
4. past
5. past participle
6. present

B. Sample Answers

1. The sweaters <u>have shrunk</u> since she put them in the dryer.

2. I <u>will freeze</u> some popsicles for the children to eat after school.

3. He <u>is bursting</u> with excitement about winning first place at the science fair.

4. I <u>caught</u> your cold after you sneezed on me.

"There Will Come Soft Rains" by Ray Bradbury

Selection Test A, p. 80
Critical Reading

1. ANS: C	DIF: Easy	OBJ: Literary Analysis
2. ANS: B	DIF: Easy	OBJ: Literary Analysis
3. ANS: C	DIF: Easy	OBJ: Interpretation
4. ANS: C	DIF: Easy	OBJ: Reading
5. ANS: D	DIF: Easy	OBJ: Reading
6. ANS: B	DIF: Easy	OBJ: Comprehension
7. ANS: A	DIF: Easy	OBJ: Reading
8. ANS: A	DIF: Easy	OBJ: Interpretation
9. ANS: C	DIF: Easy	OBJ: Interpretation
10. ANS: C	DIF: Easy	OBJ: Comprehension
11. ANS: D	DIF: Easy	OBJ: Literary Analysis

Vocabulary and Grammar

12. ANS: B	DIF: Easy	OBJ: Vocabulary
13. ANS: A	DIF: Easy	OBJ: Vocabulary
14. ANS: B	DIF: Easy	OBJ: Grammar

Essay

15. Students should explain how well they think Bradbury predicted twenty-first century houses. They may say that Bradbury was right about much of the technology he thought about. Today, most people can not afford to have the kinds of machines Bradbury wrote about, but many of them do exist. There are high-tech houses now that are programmed to do all kinds of things. They can turn lights on and off, change the temperature, and lots more. There are even vacuum cleaners that are like little robots that clean up all by themselves.

Difficulty: *Easy*

Objective: *Essay*

16. Students should describe how Bradbury uses personification over and over in "There Will Come Soft Rains." Details they might cite include the following: the house is paranoid about protecting itself, the mechanical mice are annoyed with the dog when it tracks mud in the house, Bradbury describes the fire as clever, and the house dies. They may reason that he does this because there are no humans in the story to show emotions. Therefore, Bradbury puts the emotions he wants to show in the house, the machines, and the fire.

Difficulty: *Easy*

Objective: *Essay*

Selection Test B, p. 83

Critical Reading

1. ANS: B	DIF: Average	OBJ: Interpretation
2. ANS: A	DIF: Average	OBJ: Reading
3. ANS: D	DIF: Average	OBJ: Reading
4. ANS: C	DIF: Average	OBJ: Interpretation
5. ANS: D	DIF: Challenging	OBJ: Literary Analysis
6. ANS: C	DIF: Challenging	OBJ: Literary Analysis
7. ANS: D	DIF: Challenging	OBJ: Interpretation
8. ANS: A	DIF: Average	OBJ: Reading
9. ANS: B	DIF: Average	OBJ: Comprehension
10. ANS: C	DIF: Challenging	OBJ: Interpretation
11. ANS: A	DIF: Average	OBJ: Reading
12. ANS: A	DIF: Average	OBJ: Literary Analysis
13. ANS: C	DIF: Challenging	OBJ: Interpretation
14. ANS: D	DIF: Average	OBJ: Comprehension
15. ANS: A	DIF: Average	OBJ: Comprehension

Vocabulary and Grammar

16. ANS: D	DIF: Average	OBJ: Vocabulary
17. ANS: B	DIF: Average	OBJ: Vocabulary
18. ANS: C	DIF: Average	OBJ: Grammar
19. ANS: A	DIF: Average	OBJ: Grammar

Essay

20. Students should explain ways in which technology is both helpful and dangerous. When describing technology as dangerous, students may say that in "There Will Come Soft Rains," all the people are gone. They were destroyed by their own technology, a nuclear bomb. For ways technology is helpful, they may cite the ways the house was made to help humans. It cooks the meals and cleans up. It waters the lawn and reads poetry. But in the end the house "dies" because it can not make decisions for itself. It just does things mindlessly because it is programmed to do them.

Difficulty: *Average*

Objective: *Essay*

21. Students should describe whether or not they find Bradbury's vision of the future to be realistic. Students should use examples from the story and from real life to support their opinions. Students who find the story realistic may cite the there really are high-tech houses that are programmed to do all kinds of things such as turn lights on and off and change the temperature. Students who do not find the story realistic may state that kitchens can not cook and clean up without human help.

Difficulty: *Average*

Objective: *Essay*

22. Students should note that Teasdale's poem is about how humans could disappear entirely and nature would not care. The world would go on. In Bradbury's short story, it is the technology created by humans that does not care. The house just goes on as usual. Students may describe the gloomy, depressing effect the poem has on the story.

Difficulty: *Challenging*

Objective: *Essay*

"One Thousand Dollars" by O. Henry
"By the Waters of Babylon"
by Stephen Vincent Benét

Vocabulary Warm-up Exercises, p. 87

A. 1. eternal
2. sequestered
3. Moreover

4. restless
5. heirs
6. offensive
7. qualifications
8. render

B. Sample Answers

1. I know you are happy; <u>nevertheless</u>, I feel sad.
2. She gave me a <u>trifling</u> amount of money, so I didn't become rich.
3. The winning team got a <u>trophy</u>, and the losing team got nothing.
4. Drivers drove <u>chariots</u> pulled by teams of horses.
5. I was relaxed after my <u>leisurely</u> walk.
6. There were lots of pebbles <u>underfoot</u>.
7. The information was in the <u>writings</u>, so anyone could find it if he or she looked.

Reading Warm-up A, p. 88

Sample Answers

1. (four hundred); *Heirs* are people who legally receive the money of a person who has died.
2. <u>in the Desert Inn in Las Vegas</u>; *Sequestered* means "put away or shut off from other people."
3. (so that he could stay put); It feels hard to keep still when I'm *restless*.
4. (clear instructions); *Render* means "to give or yield something."
5. *Besides that,* instead of close friends, he had a staff of people who gave him food and medication.
6. <u>Dummar said it was because he once gave Hughes a ride in his car</u>; My *qualifications* are that I'm punctual, dependable, and trained.
7. (everlasting) She has my *eternal* friendship.
8. (distasteful); Dummar found talk of forgery *offensive* because it insulted him to suggest that he was dishonest.

Reading Warm-up B, p. 89

Sample Answers

1. <u>any of the countless descriptive writings</u>; I have read *writings* on Roman mythology.
2. (the Colosseum); A house is usually *professionally* designed by an architect.
3. If people were knocked down by a large, unruly crowd, they could be trampled *underfoot*.
4. <u>carried on litters by their slaves or servants</u>; *Leisurely* means "moving in a relaxed way," which is how you would moved if carried by others.
5. (The most prominent gladiators); *Chariots* were also used in races and battles.
6. The combat was no *trifling* matter because one of the gladiators would lose his life.

7. *However*, it was the emperor who had the final word.
8. <u>he was occasionally granted his freedom</u>; A *trophy* is a prize, such as a cup, awarded for winning a competition

"One Thousand Dollars" by O. Henry
"By the Waters of Babylon"
by Stephen Vincent Benét

Literary Analysis: Point of View, p. 90

1. because the narrator is not a character in the story; because the narrator refers to the characters as *he, him, she, her,* and *they*
2. Gillian and the reader know that Gillian wants Miriam Hayden to have the $50,000, and that is why he ripped up the statement of his account (which would have secured the money for himself).
3. It implies that the lawyers believe Gillian to have committed a selfish act, when in fact, his actions have been selfless and loving.
4. Possible answer: Yes, it makes me less willing to judge people harshly.
5. A. Possible answer: "My father is a priest; I am the son of a priest."
   B. *My* and *I* should be circled.
6. John knows the dangers posed by the Forest People and the customs and beliefs of the People of the Hills.
7. The reader knows that the gods are humans, that the Place of the Gods is a city, and that the "magic" items are simply machines.
8. The story's dramatic irony creates a suspenseful, mysterious mood.

Vocabulary Builder, p. 91

A. 1. yes, because lake water may be unclean
2. no, because it is not safe to rollerblade without a helmet; It was prudent of James to rollerblade with a helmet.
3. no, because a person would not want to go to bed in spite of being sleepy; Greta is sleepy; nevertheless, she wants to stay up.
4. yes, because entry forms often specify certain rules or conditions for contests

B. 1. prudent; 2. nevertheless; 3. purified; 4. stipulates

Selection Test A, p. 93

Critical Reading

1. ANS: B	DIF: Easy	OBJ: Comprehension
2. ANS: A	DIF: Easy	OBJ: Interpretation
3. ANS: C	DIF: Easy	OBJ: Interpretation
4. ANS: D	DIF: Easy	OBJ: Comprehension
5. ANS: C	DIF: Easy	OBJ: Literary Analysis

6. ANS: A	DIF: Easy	OBJ: Interpretation
7. ANS: B	DIF: Easy	OBJ: Comprehension
8. ANS: B	DIF: Easy	OBJ: Interpretation
9. ANS: D	DIF: Easy	OBJ: Comprehension
10. ANS: D	DIF: Easy	OBJ: Literary Analysis
11. ANS: A	DIF: Easy	OBJ: Literary Analysis
12. ANS: C	DIF: Easy	OBJ: Comprehension
13. ANS: A	DIF: Easy	OBJ: Interpretation

Vocabulary

| 14. ANS: B | DIF: Easy | OBJ: Vocabulary |
| 15. ANS: C | DIF: Easy | OBJ: Vocabulary |

Essay

16. Students should identify the point of view of "One Thousand Dollars" as third-person point of view. They should note that the narrator is outside the story and that this narrator tells the story by focusing on the actions and experiences of Gillian. This narrator knows exactly what the reader knows. Neither the narrator nor the reader knows what the characters are thinking or feeling; instead, they know only what the characters do and say. Students should identify the point of view of "By the Waters of Babylon" as first-person point of view. The story's narrator is John, the son of a priest in a future society. This narrator knows more about some things than the reader does, and less about other things. For example, he knows more about his own society, its laws, and its practices. On the other hand, he knows less about New York City and the "gods" of the past than the reader does.

Difficulty: *Easy*
Objective: *Essay*

17. Students may respond that "One Thousand Dollars" invites its readers to see people themselves in a new way and to be less judgmental about people's motives and actions. It does this by first portraying Gillian in a negative light and then revealing him to be a loving, generous person. Students may respond that "By the Waters of Babylon" invites its readers to see modern civilization in a new way and to recognize that our way of life is temporary. It does this by showing us the ruins of New York City through the eyes of a person who lives long after the city's destruction.

Difficulty: *Easy*
Objective: *Essay*

Selection Test B, p. 96

Critical Reading

1. ANS: B	DIF: Average	OBJ: Comprehension
2. ANS: D	DIF: Average	OBJ: Interpretation
3. ANS: A	DIF: Challenging	OBJ: Interpretation
4. ANS: A	DIF: Average	OBJ: Comprehension

5. ANS: C	DIF: Average	OBJ: Literary Analysis
6. ANS: C	DIF: Challenging	OBJ: Literary Analysis
7. ANS: D	DIF: Challenging	OBJ: Comprehension
8. ANS: B	DIF: Average	OBJ: Interpretation
9. ANS: A	DIF: Average	OBJ: Interpretation
10. ANS: B	DIF: Challenging	OBJ: Comprehension
11. ANS: C	DIF: Average	OBJ: Literary Analysis
12. ANS: D	DIF: Challenging	OBJ: Literary Analysis
13. ANS: D	DIF: Challenging	OBJ: Literary Analysis
14. ANS: A	DIF: Challenging	OBJ: Interpretation
15. ANS: B	DIF: Average	OBJ: Literary Analysis
16. ANS: C	DIF: Average	OBJ: Comprehension
17. ANS: A	DIF: Average	OBJ: Interpretation
18. ANS: C	DIF: Average	OBJ: Interpretation

Vocabulary

| 19. ANS: D | DIF: Average | OBJ: Vocabulary |
| 20. ANS: B | DIF: Average | OBJ: Vocabulary |

Essay

21. Students' responses should be logical and consistent with the stories' characters and plots. For example, if students choose first-person point of view as an alternate point of view for "One Thousand Dollars," they might conclude that the story would lose some of its suspense and irony, insofar as the reader would sooner know Gillian's feelings toward Miss Hayden and therefore the source of his discomfort with the inheritance. Likewise, if students choose third-person limited point of view for "By the Waters of Babylon," they might conclude that the story would lose much of its interest, insofar as the reader would not be allowed to see the ruins of New York City through new eyes.

Difficulty: *Average*
Objective: *Essay*

22. Students will likely respond that they experienced a mix of pity and admiration for Gillian's silent sacrifice at the end "One Thousand Dollars." The dramatic irony is rooted in the fact that everyone sees Gillian as selfish and immature, even at the moment when he makes a sacrifice for love. Students should note that the ending shows Gillian in a new light as someone capable of deep feeling and serious action.

Some students may respond that they felt pity for John throughout "By the Waters of Babylon" because of his fear of what he does not understand. The dramatic irony here is that John takes for magic what the reader understands to be the artifacts of our everyday technology. Some students may note that the felt pity at the end for the gods, who are revealed to be fallible human beings despite their wondrous technology. The dramatic irony here is rooted in the fact that it is the naive narrator who turns out to be in a position to pass judgment on the gods. Other students may note a sensation of discomfort reading the ending: The ending shows that we, the readers, are foolishly complacent about our advanced technology. Though the reader has known more than John for much of the story, the end of the story traps the reader into accepting John's judgments on the reader's own world.

Difficulty: *Average*

Objective: *Essay*

23. The point of view used in "One Thousand Dollars" is third-person point of view. Students may or may not specify that the narrator is a limited third-person narrator but should note that the narrator tells the story by focusing on the actions and experiences of Gillian. The point of view creates dramatic irony as the reader observes Gillian taking actions that will redirect his fortune to Miss Hayden, while the lawyers believe he has spent the money foolishly. The point of view used in "By the Waters of Babylon" is first-person point of view. The story is told by John, and his experiences are seen by the reader through his eyes. This point of view creates dramatic irony as John describes the ruins of New York City without prior knowledge of its history or inhabitants—a knowledge the reader fully possesses.

Difficulty: *Challenging*

Objective: *Essay*

Writing Workshop—Unit 2, Part 1

Short Stories: Integrating Grammar Skills, p. 100

A. 1. will arrive; 2. came; 3. had reached; 4. has fallen

B. Last week, my sister Pat and I attended a football game. Pat <u>had purchased</u> the tickets weeks ago. We <u>walked</u> to the corner and <u>boarded</u> a special bus to the stadium. By the time we <u>arrived</u>, people <u>had filled</u> most of the good seats. We <u>hunted</u> for seats for some time. Finally, we <u>discovered</u> two seats on the highest bleacher. Next time, we <u>will get</u> reserved seats.

Unit 2, Part 1 Answers

Benchmark Test 3, p. 101

MULTIPLE CHOICE

1. ANS: A
2. ANS: B
3. ANS: A
4. ANS: D
5. ANS: B
6. ANS: D
7. ANS: A
8. ANS: D
9. ANS: A
10. ANS: C

11. ANS: B
12. ANS: A
13. ANS: A
14. ANS: C
15. ANS: C
16. ANS: B
17. ANS: C
18. ANS: A
19. ANS: D
20. ANS: C
21. ANS: B
22. ANS: A
23. ANS: D
24. ANS: C
25. ANS: C
26. ANS: B
27. ANS: C
28. ANS: D
29. ANS: A
30. ANS: D
31. ANS: D
32. ANS: D
33. ANS: C

ESSAY

34. Retellings should be in a person different from the original stories.

35. Reviews should include summaries, and opinions should be supported.

36. Short stories should have characters unlike the writers and historical or futuristic settings.

Unit 2, Part 2 Answers

Diagnostic Test 4, p. 108

MULTIPLE CHOICE

1. ANS: D
2. ANS: B
3. ANS: D
4. ANS: A
5. ANS: B
6. ANS: C
7. ANS: D
8. ANS: A
9. ANS: B
10. ANS: D
11. ANS: B

12. ANS: C
13. ANS: B
14. ANS: C
15. ANS: A

"How Much Land Does a Man Need?"
by Leo Tolstoy

Vocabulary Warm-up Exercises, p. 112

A. 1. wooded
2. interpreter
3. civilly
4. bargaining
5. blundered
6. remainder
7. quarreled
8. hazy

B. Sample Answers
1. Yes, I think that people would enjoy sharing a *communal* garden.
2. Watching television might make you *envious* because you might start wanting the things that people on television have.
3. Pop quizzes have *recurred* in our history class.
4. We all know the *proverb* "Haste makes waste."
5. *Burdening* a bicycle with extra weight might make it difficult to ride.
6. I think that the land around our school was *formerly* a forest.
7. Crops are *sowed* at different times because they have different growing seasons.

Reading Warm-up A, p. 113

Sample Answers
1. he thinks I will tolerate this kind of disrespect; *Blundered* means "made a bad mistake."
2. knew how to speak the neighbor's language; People need an *interpreter* if they do not speak each other's language.
3. (the fence); *Quarreled* means "had a strong disagreement."
4. making a demand; When you *bargain* with someone you can reach a peaceful agreement.
5. the farmer did not see the neighbor until he bumped into the man; *Hazy* means "smoky."
6. A *wooded* patch would be an area planted with many trees.
7. (rudely); *Civilly* means "politely."
8. In the *remainder* of today I will have the rest of my classes, go to band practice, and then go home and study for tomorrow's test. The *remainder* is what's left of something.

Reading Warm-up B, p. 114

Sample Answers
1. Variety is the spice of life.; A *proverb* is a short, popular saying.
2. The nutrients in the soil were exhausted, and the land soon became infertile.; *Burdening* is "loading heavily."
3. (rye) (winter wheat); Alfalfa, soybeans, and corn might also be *sowed*.
4. I could start *afresh* on a story that I stopped writing last year.
5. (infertile); *Formerly* means "in the past."
6. in which ownership is shared by a group of people. A *communal* park would be owned and shared by the public.
7. (problems with pests); The yearly band concert has *recurred* without fail every spring.
8. the plentiful results of modern research; A modern farmer might be *envious* of a neighbor's farm that produces more crops.

"How Much Land Does a Man Need?"
by Leo Tolstoy

Literary Analysis: Theme, p. 115

Sample Answers

A. **Philosophical assumption:** People should remember that they are mortal and should not waste their lives on trivial things.

First event: Pahom was happy when he first became a landowner, but he became unhappy because his neighbors trespassed. He wasted his happiness on being upset about little problems with his neighbors.

Second event: He makes an even better life for himself across the Volga, but again becomes unhappy over small things. He wants more and more land and becomes jealous of others.

Third event: Pahom dies because he tried to mark off too much land. He was more concerned with his greed for more land than his health.

Theme: Reaching for too much can result in the loss of everything.

B. Students may state that many people in the United States today are unhappy with what they have and always want more. They want bigger houses, newer cars, and nicer clothes. People may think it makes them happy to have many possessions, but usually it just makes them want more stuff.

Reading: Recognize Key Details to Draw Conclusions About Theme, p. 116

Sample Answers

Theme: Reaching for too much can result in the loss of everything.

1. Owning land did make Pahom happy. In fact, it made him even less happy.

2. Pahom might have been content with his land purchase in his second home. But again he got greedy for more.

3. Tolstoy reminds readers that Pahom's greed is the Devil's way of using him for evil.

4. Even when he is getting more land than he ever dreamed of owning, Pahom's greed leads him to mark off just a little too much.

5. The answer to the question in the story's title is that a man needs only enough land to be buried in. People can not take material possessions with them when they die.

Vocabulary Builder, p. 117

A. Sample Answers

1. syn.—irritated; ant.—pleased; ex.—She was piqued when she found out her sister had borrowed her sweater without permission.

2. syn.—belittled; ant.—complimented; ex.—The wealthy man disparaged the restaurant's chef for cooking a meal he did not like.

3. syn.—refrained; ant.—indulged; ex.—The upset student forbore from saying anything he would regret to his teacher.

4. syn.—wronged; ant.—comforted; ex.—He was aggrieved by what he felt were unfair student council election results.

B. 1. D; 2. C; 3. B; 4. A

Enrichment: Connecting to Social Studies, p. 120

Sample Responses

1. Pahom would probably not have liked the idea of communism. He wanted more than his neighbors, which is not a communist way of thinking. He was not happy in the second place he lived, which was a community that used communist ideas like shared land.

2. Many free peasants could not do well economically because they could not afford land of their own, or they were crushed by taxes.

3. Pahom and others have trouble paying fines. Good farmland is crowded and it is difficult for peasants to expand their farms. Peasants fight among themselves over land and feel resentful of landowners. Those who do not own land do not get to keep the crops they grow.

Selection Test A, p. 121

Critical Reading

1. ANS: A	DIF: Easy	OBJ: Comprehension
2. ANS: A	DIF: Easy	OBJ: Comprehension
3. ANS: C	DIF: Easy	OBJ: Comprehension
4. ANS: C	DIF: Easy	OBJ: Literary Analysis
5. ANS: D	DIF: Easy	OBJ: Interpretation
6. ANS: C	DIF: Easy	OBJ: Reading
7. ANS: B	DIF: Easy	OBJ: Comprehension
8. ANS: D	DIF: Easy	OBJ: Interpretation
9. ANS: D	DIF: Easy	OBJ: Literary Analysis
10. ANS: B	DIF: Easy	OBJ: Literary Analysis
11. ANS: D	DIF: Easy	OBJ: Literary Analysis

Vocabulary and Grammar

12. ANS: C	DIF: Easy	OBJ: Vocabulary
13. ANS: B	DIF: Easy	OBJ: Vocabulary
14. ANS: B	DIF: Easy	OBJ: Grammar
15. ANS: C	DIF: Easy	OBJ: Grammar

Essay

16. Students' essays should establish and support an opinion about whether or not Pahom deserves what happens to him. Some might say that Pahom gets an appropriate punishment for his greed. They might mention the effects of Pahom's quest for more land on his family and neighbors. Others might say that Pahom does not deserve his fate. They might support this opinion by pointing out that Pahom was only acting the way many people would. Many people want to own property and feel happy about having property of their own.

Difficulty: *Easy*

Objective: *Essay*

17. Students' essays should identify Tolstoy's theme and list details that helped them figure it out. Several interpretations of the story's message are valid, including the following: reaching for too much can result in the loss of everything; land ownership leads to greed and selfishness; people should not waste their lives on unimportant things; or material possessions do not matter when one dies. Examples of details from the story that support one or more of these interpretations include the fact that the Devil is glad that he has found a way to gain power over Pahom; Pahom is happy at first, but becomes unhappy very soon after buying his land; Pahom dies trying to get more land; and all the land Pahom really needs in the end is six feet in which to bury him.

Difficulty: *Easy*

Objective: *Essay*

Selection Test B, p. 124

Critical Reading

1. ANS: A	DIF: Average	OBJ: Comprehension
2. ANS: D	DIF: Challenging	OBJ: Interpretation
3. ANS: B	DIF: Average	OBJ: Comprehension

4. ANS: A	DIF: Average	OBJ: Comprehension
5. ANS: C	DIF: Challenging	OBJ: Reading
6. ANS: D	DIF: Average	OBJ: Interpretation
7. ANS: B	DIF: Average	OBJ: Reading
8. ANS: C	DIF: Average	OBJ: Literary Analysis
9. ANS: B	DIF: Average	OBJ: Literary Analysis
10. ANS: C	DIF: Challenging	OBJ: Reading
11. ANS: A	DIF: Challenging	OBJ: Literary Analysis
12. ANS: C	DIF: Average	OBJ: Comprehension

Vocabulary and Grammar

13. ANS: C	DIF: Average	OBJ: Vocabulary
14. ANS: A	DIF: Average	OBJ: Vocabulary
15. ANS: B	DIF: Average	OBJ: Grammar
16. ANS: C	DIF: Challenging	OBJ: Grammar

Essay

17. Students' essays should explain Tolstoy's answer to the title's question. The last line of the story shows that Tolstoy believes a man only needs enough land to bury him in. Students should then either support or refute Tolstoy's position. To support his position, they might point out that one cannot take material positions beyond death. Therefore, struggling for land and goods is a useless task in the end. To refute his position, students might mention that one must gain property to prosper in life, and that property ownership does lead to happiness for many people.

Difficulty: *Average*

Objective: *Essay*

18. Students' essays should establish how they feel about Pahom and why. They should also explain how Pahom's characteristics influence the theme and outcome of the story. Pahom is a flat character, so his characteristics are simple and do not vary. He is greedy and not very insightful. He is jealous of those who have more land than he does. He seems unable to understand the consequences of his actions until it is too late. Because of these characteristics, the ending for Pahom is inevitable. He loses everything because he cannot be satisfied with what he has.

Difficulty: *Average*

Objective: *Essay*

"Civil Peace" by Chinua Achebe

Vocabulary Warm-up Exercises, p. 128

A. 1. rickety
2. collapse
3. commandeered
4. assortment
5. immediate
6. continuously
7. paralyzed
8. agony

B. Sample Answers

1. No, many *heroic* actions require other qualities, such as courage, loyalty, or determination.
2. People who get a *windfall* might be very excited or numb with astonishment.
3. If I have *accumulated* papers, I might collect them in a binder or a box.
4. I would rather work for a *corporation* because it would provide good benefits.
5. Yes, the book should arrive within a *fortnight*, because shipping takes two weeks.
6. I might plan an *extraordinarily* unusual menu by finding recipes from other regions.
7. Drink water if your mouth feels *parched*.
8. No, if a counselor were *imperious*, he or she would probably not be able to connect well with clients.

Reading Warm-up A, p. 129

Sample Answers

1. was almost certain to fall apart; *Rickety* means "likely to fall apart."
2. the dream of a peaceful and unified nation; A building might *collapse*.
3. (money) (supplies) (housing); *Commandeering* means "taking something for use by the government or military."
4. (an economic blockade); An *immediate* action is one that happens right away.
5. (the flow of resources); *Paralyzed* means "stopped movement completely."
6. conditions; Test scores have improved *continuously* in our school district.
7. (suffering); *Agony* means "extreme pain or suffering."
8. Nigeria might have passed an *assortment* of laws because the complicated situation could not be fixed with only one law.

Reading Warm-up B, p. 130

Sample Answers

1. the hot air sucked the night's moisture from the tall man's body; *Parched* means "very hot and dry."
2. (fourteen days); In a *fortnight*, I will visit my grandparents.
3. One *corporation* in our city works to clean up industrial waste.
4. (arrogant); *Imperious* means "haughty" or "arrogant."
5. (rejection after rejection); I have *accumulated* a collection of comic books.
6. you could hear the sound of each man holding his breath; It is *extraordinarily* interesting that scientists have been able to map our genetic code.

7. I would like to receive a *windfall* of a million dollars.
8. (patience) (good nature); *Heroic* means "having the qualities of a hero."

"Civil Peace" by Chinua Achebe

Literary Analysis: Theme, p. 131

Sample Answers

A. Philosophical assumption: In order to survive, we must be able to let go of what we have lost.

First event: Jonathan is thankful that he, his wife, and three of their four children survived the war. He does not dwell on all that he lost.

Second event: Jonathan is overjoyed that his house is still standing. Again, his perspective is that anything beyond survival is a bonus. He is not bothered by the poor condition of his home or the surrounding village.

Third event: After the thieves steal what little money Jonathan had, he does not seem bothered. He survived without the *egg-rasher* before he got it, and knows he will continue to survive without it. If he had fought the thieves, he and his family would be dead, and he would have lost everything.

Theme: One should be thankful for what one has and not worry about what is lost.

B. Students may state that many people in the United States today tend to take survival for granted. However, sometimes we are faced with situations that change our point of view and make us more thankful for what we have. For example, if a person gets cancer and then overcomes it, she may realize that nothing is as valuable or as important to her as her health.

Reading: Recognize Key Details to Draw Conclusions About Theme, p. 132

Sample Answers

Theme: One should be thankful for what one has and not worry about what is lost.

1. Jonathan's joy in finding his house still standing shows that he considers anything beyond being alive to be a bonus. He is not bothered by the poor condition of his house and is very grateful that it is still there.

2. Jonathan and Maria find ways to survive and are thankful that they can do so. They realize that others are not so fortunate.

3. He does not see the money as his by right. He sees it as a gift. Again, the money is just a bonus. He does not value it more than his and his family's survival.

4. Jonathan knows that if he fights the thieves they will kill him and his family. Then he would lose everything. The money is not as important as survival.

5. Jonathan knows what he values most, and it is the survival of his family. Because of this, he is able to let go of the money without a problem.

Vocabulary Builder, p. 133

A. Sample Answers

1. syn.—disgraceful; ant.—honorable; ex.—The <u>disreputable</u> car salesman sold them a car with many hidden problems.

2. syn.—responsive; ant.—disagreeable; ex.—Most of the members of the band were <u>amenable</u> to the idea of marching in the city's holiday parade.

3. syn.—impoverished; ant.—prosperous; ex.—Many were left <u>destitute</u> when the stock market crashed in 1929.

4. syn.—sympathize; ant.—oppose; ex.—My mother will always <u>commiserate</u> with me when I lose a tennis match.

B. 1. B; 2. A; 3. D; 4. C

Enrichment: Connecting to Geography, p. 136

Students' books should include accurate information about Nigeria's landforms, bodies of water, climate, population, culture, government, economy, and history. Books should also include illustrations to help convey the information about Nigeria's geography. Text and illustrations should all be appropriate for the target age group (elementary age students). If possible, allow groups to share their books with younger students in your school district. Assess students' work based on accuracy of the information presented, neatness, writing, presentation, and group participation.

"How Much Land Does a Man Need?" by Leo Tolstoy
"Civil Peace" by Chinua Achebe

Build Language Skills: Vocabulary, p. 137

Sample Answers

A. 1. sequel: definition—a story that continues a previous story

Because -*sequi*- has to do with following, a sequel is a story that follows another story.

2. sequence: definition—a continuous connected series

A sequence is a series of events that follow each other and are connected somehow, which again clearly makes use of the meaning of -*sequi*-, which means "follow."

3. non sequitur: definition—a statement that does not follow logically from anything that was previously said

Because -*sequi*- has to do with following, and *non* means "not," a non sequitur must be something that does not follow something else.

B. 1. synonym: main; sentence: The <u>main</u> reaction in the waiting room was one of relief when the doctor said she would recover.

2. synonym: understand; sentence: It would be difficult for some people to <u>understand</u> why a man would risk his life for a piece of land.

3. synonym: happen at the same time; sentence: This year, the prom and my family reunion will <u>happen at the same time</u> so I will have to decide which to attend.

4. synonym: deduce; It was easy for the teacher to <u>deduce</u> which students had studied and which had not based on their answers to the essay question.

Build Language Skills: Grammar, p. 138

A. 1. LV; 2. AV; 3. LV; 4. LV; 5. AV; 6. AV

B. Responses will vary. Students should circle verbs and label them as action verbs (AV) or linking verbs (LV).

"Civil Peace" by Chinua Achebe

Selection Test A, p. 139

Critical Reading

1. ANS: D	DIF: Easy	OBJ: Interpretation
2. ANS: C	DIF: Easy	OBJ: Interpretation
3. ANS: C	DIF: Easy	OBJ: Comprehension
4. ANS: B	DIF: Easy	OBJ: Literary Analysis
5. ANS: C	DIF: Easy	OBJ: Comprehension
6. ANS: B	DIF: Easy	OBJ: Comprehension
7. ANS: D	DIF: Easy	OBJ: Interpretation
8. ANS: B	DIF: Easy	OBJ: Reading
9. ANS: D	DIF: Easy	OBJ: Comprehension
10. ANS: A	DIF: Easy	OBJ: Reading
11. ANS: C	DIF: Easy	OBJ: Literary Analysis
12. ANS: C	DIF: Easy	OBJ: Literary Analysis

Vocabulary and Grammar

13. ANS: C	DIF: Easy	OBJ: Vocabulary
14. ANS: A	DIF: Easy	OBJ: Vocabulary
15. ANS: A	DIF: Easy	OBJ: Grammar

Essay

16. Students should identify the story's theme, which should be something similar to, "Where there is life there is hope." To support this theme, they might mention how Jonathan always has a positive attitude. He is always pleasantly surprised when something good happens. He lets go of the things that are lost and focuses on survival. As long as he and his family continue to survive, he is content. They might also point out that Achebe probably believes that money and possessions are not as important as the lives of one's family and oneself.

Difficulty: *Easy*
Objective: *Essay*

17. Students' essays should describe the character of Jonathan Iwegbu. He is an optimistic person who feels grateful for anything good that happens in his life. He lets go of what is lost and focuses on surviving. His and his family's safety is what matters most to him. Students might note that most people in the United States today would be unlikely to be as optimistic after losing a child, finding themselves in poverty, and being robbed of the only money they had.

Difficulty: *Easy*
Objective: *Essay*

Selection Test B, p. 142

Critical Reading

1. ANS: D	DIF: Average	OBJ: Interpretation
2. ANS: D	DIF: Average	OBJ: Reading
3. ANS: A	DIF: Average	OBJ: Comprehension
4. ANS: A	DIF: Challenging	OBJ: Interpretation
5. ANS: B	DIF: Average	OBJ: Interpretation
6. ANS: A	DIF: Challenging	OBJ: Interpretation
7. ANS: B	DIF: Average	OBJ: Comprehension
8. ANS: D	DIF: Average	OBJ: Comprehension
9. ANS: C	DIF: Average	OBJ: Reading
10. ANS: B	DIF: Challenging	OBJ: Reading
11. ANS: C	DIF: Average	OBJ: Literary Analysis
12. ANS: C	DIF: Average	OBJ: Literary Analysis
13. ANS: A	DIF: Average	OBJ: Literary Analysis

Vocabulary and Grammar

14. ANS: D	DIF: Challenging	OBJ: Vocabulary
15. ANS: B	DIF: Average	OBJ: Vocabulary
16. ANS: A	DIF: Average	OBJ: Grammar
17. ANS: C	DIF: Challenging	OBJ: Grammar

Essay

18. Students should note that Jonathan relies on the proverb in good times and in bad. It applies when he receives the *egg-rasher* as well as when it is stolen from him. Rather than providing an easy explanation for events, the proverb is a source of spiritual strength. It helps Jonathan deal with losing a child, most of his possessions, and the only money he has. It means that he trusts in the plan God has for him.

Difficulty: *Average*
Objective: *Essay*

19. Students might point out that the story begins and ends with examples of Jonathan's optimism. In the beginning, he feels lucky even though one of his children died

in the war and his family is destitute. At the end, he points out he survived without the egg-rasher before and can continue to survive without it. Jonathan feels optimistic because the war has made him value his and his family's survival above all else. As long as they are alive, he has hope.

Difficulty: *Average*

Objective: *Essay*

20. Students' essays should identify Achebe's philosophical assumption, which is that survival is the most important thing in life. They might describe how Jonathan takes each piece of good fortune—such as regaining his bike, finding his house intact, and getting the *egg-rasher*—as a miracle. But when he loses the money, he does not dwell on it. It is far more important to him that he and his family lived through the confrontation with the thieves. The theme of the story is that there is hope as long as there is life. Achebe's philosophical assumption that survival is the most important thing in life clearly influences this theme.

Difficulty: *Challenging*

Objective: *Essay*

"The Masque of the Red Death"
by Edgar Allan Poe

Vocabulary Warm-up Exercises, p. 146

A. 1. suite
2. acknowledged
3. sustain
4. revelers
5. throng
6. unlimited
7. expressive
8. bizarre

B. Sample Answers

1. You won't feel hungry, because *indulge* means "to let yourself have something."
2. He would be proud, because *attained* means "having reached a place or goal."
3. Nan didn't reject the teacher's ideas, because *embraced* means "taken in and included."
4. Juan won't see many people, because *seclusion* means "being away from other people."
5. It's unlikely that she would be asked, because *cowardice* means "a lack of bravery," and a leader should be brave, not fearful.
6. It would make people shudder, because *grotesque* means "ugly in a way that is frightening."
7. I wouldn't be surprised, because *emphasis* means "special importance."

Sample Answers

1. costumes weren't necessarily popular with everyone. *Acknowledged* means "accepted or admitted that something is true."
2. (distaste); *Expressive* means "showing what someone is thinking or feeling."
3. (strange); People's faces looked bizarre under the orange lights.
4. (party); *Revelers* are "people who are noisily enjoying festivities."
5. The options seemed *endless*.
6. (the entire backyard at Sandy's house); A *suite* of rooms would be nice because the setting would be elegant and spacious.
7. a mood of outlandish fun; *Sustain* means "to make something continue to exist."
8. friends costumed as characters from horror movies standing alongside others dressed as favorite characters from their preschool years; A *throng* of people gathered to protest the new city rules.

Reading Warm-up B, p. 148

Sample Answers

1. enjoy reading a ripping horror story; *Fear* is a synonym for *cowardice*.
2. who leave people shuddering at their sight; *Grotesque* means "ugly or strange in a way that is unpleasant or frightening."
3. If critics have *disregarded* the genre, they have ignored it.
4. If people have *embraced* horror stories, they have eagerly accepted them; *rejected* is an antonym for *embraced*
5. (fame); *Attained* means "to have reached a goal."
6. what will scare the reader; Writers of humor place an *emphasis* on what will make people laugh.
7. I like to *indulge* my taste for salty snacks.
8. Reading a horror story in *seclusion* might be scary because I'd be all alone and might start imagining scary things.

"The Masque of the Red Death"
by Edgar Allan Poe

Literary Analysis: Symbolism, p. 149

Sample Answers

1. death, or the disease called the Red Death; shows how death comes "like a thief in the night," uninvited and unwelcome, but unavoidable

2. represents the grave, forebodes death; shows that death is the final resting place

3. life, revelry; guests are happy while the music plays and experience fear every time the music stops

4. passage of time, inevitability of death; shows how, under their seemingly happy surface, the guests remain very afraid of death; implies that they are living on borrowed time and gives a sense of impending doom

Reading: Identify Patterns to Draw Conclusions About Symbolism, p. 150

Sample Answers

1. A. He enters without being noticed.
   B. His costume includes a corpse-like face and blood-red robes.
   C. Everyone dies after he appears.

Pattern: The masked visitor has all the same characteristics as the disease called the Red Death.

Meaning: The masked visitor symbolizes the Red Death.

2. A. The black chamber has blood-red windows and looks ghastly.
   B. None of the guests want to enter the black chamber.
   C. The final confrontation with the masked visitor happens in this chamber.

Pattern: The chamber causes fear and resembles death.

Meaning: The black chamber symbolizes fear and death.

Vocabulary Builder, p. 151

Sample Answers

A. 1. I would assume that wealthy and powerful people live there because an august home would be a grand and impressive one.

2. Lindsey probably did not enjoy the game because something was in her way and kept her from being able to see the field.

3. I might be worried that the air conditioner has broken.

4. He probably did poorly on the exam because his parents looked at him with disapproval.

B. 1. B; 2. D; 3. A; 4. B

Enrichment: Connecting to the Community, p. 154

Students' project proposals should address a specific issue related to disease prevention, such as making vaccinations available to those who need them, funding medical research, promoting public awareness of sanitation and how diseases are spread, etc. Whatever topic they choose to address, students should come up with a clear goal, steps to accomplish the goal, a list of people who might contribute to the effort, and a clear understanding of how their project will impact the community.

Selection Test A, p. 155

Critical Reading

1. ANS: D	DIF: Easy	OBJ: Comprehension
2. ANS: C	DIF: Easy	OBJ: Reading
3. ANS: A	DIF: Easy	OBJ: Comprehension
4. ANS: D	DIF: Easy	OBJ: Comprehension
5. ANS: A	DIF: Easy	OBJ: Literary Analysis
6. ANS: C	DIF: Easy	OBJ: Interpretation
7. ANS: D	DIF: Easy	OBJ: Literary Analysis
8. ANS: C	DIF: Easy	OBJ: Interpretation
9. ANS: D	DIF: Easy	OBJ: Literary Analysis
10. ANS: B	DIF: Easy	OBJ: Comprehension
11. ANS: A	DIF: Easy	OBJ: Reading
12. ANS: C	DIF: Easy	OBJ: Interpretation

Vocabulary and Grammar

13. ANS: B	DIF: Easy	OBJ: Vocabulary
14. ANS: B	DIF: Easy	OBJ: Vocabulary
15. ANS: C	DIF: Easy	OBJ: Grammar

Essay

16. Students might list major symbols such as the costumes, which represent dreams or an attempt to escape from reality; the clock, which represents the limited time the guests have to live; the stranger, who symbolizes death or the Red Death; the seven chambers, which stand for the progression of life toward inevitable death.

Difficulty: *Easy*

Objective: *Essay*

17. Students should state their opinions on Prospero's character and support their responses with examples from the story or real life. Students might criticize Prospero for leaving most of his people outside the walls of the abbey to suffer and die. Students might defend Prospero's actions by recognizing their own desire to avoid death.

Difficulty: *Easy*

Objective: *Essay*

Selection Test B, p. 158

Critical Reading

1. ANS: B	DIF: Average	OBJ: Comprehension
2. ANS: C	DIF: Average	OBJ: Interpretation
3. ANS: A	DIF: Challenging	OBJ: Literary Analysis
4. ANS: B	DIF: Challenging	OBJ: Reading
5. ANS: A	DIF: Average	OBJ: Comprehension
6. ANS: A	DIF: Challenging	OBJ: Literary Analysis

7. ANS: C	DIF: Average	OBJ: Literary Analysis
8. ANS: A	DIF: Average	OBJ: Literary Analysis
9. ANS: B	DIF: Average	OBJ: Interpretation
10. ANS: C	DIF: Average	OBJ: Reading
11. ANS: C	DIF: Average	OBJ: Literary Analysis
12. ANS: C	DIF: Challenging	OBJ: Interpretation

Vocabulary and Grammar

13. ANS: A	DIF: Average	OBJ: Vocabulary
14. ANS: D	DIF: Average	OBJ: Vocabulary
15. ANS: C	DIF: Challenging	OBJ: Grammar
16. ANS: D	DIF: Average	OBJ: Grammar

Essay

17. Students should state clear opinions about Prospero's behavior and support their responses with well-reasoned explanations. Students might criticize Prospero's actions on the grounds of class—wealthy Prospero invites his friends to join him in safety after "his dominions were half depopulated." Students might defend Prospero's actions by recognizing in themselves a desire to avoid death; Prospero's actions cannot be condemned simply because they are unusual.

Difficulty: *Average*

Objective: *Essay*

18. Students should explain that the story is an allegory because most or all of the characters, settings, and events can be considered symbolic. They might list major symbols such as the costumes, which represent dreams or an attempt to escape from reality; the clock, which represents the limited time the guests have to live; the stranger, who symbolizes death or the Red Death; the seven chambers, which might stand for the unpredictability of life or the progression of life toward inevitable death.

Difficulty: *Average*

Objective: *Essay*

19. Students should identify a theme that is similar to the following: Wealth provides no refuge from death. They should support this interpretation by pointing out that the mood is one of unavoidable doom thinly covered by a "mask" of revelry. Prospero and his guests desperately try to forget about the Red Death and hide from it by participating in a masquerade. They leave the common people outside the walls to suffer and die. But death comes to everyone, regardless of social status.

Difficulty: *Challenging*

Objective: *Essay*

"The Garden of Stubborn Cats"
by Italo Calvino

Vocabulary Warm-up Exercises, p. 162

A. 1. distinction
2. domestic
3. luxurious
4. overrun
5. riveted
6. treacherous
7. futile
8. reluctant

B. Sample Answers

1. The painting was vibrant because the artist had used vivid colors.
2. I tried to focus on the entrance as I kept the house under constant surveillance.
3. Since we were unauthorized to be there, they would not let us in.
4. After the house was transformed by the decorator, it looked completely different.
5. I was totally out of breath after I ran up the stairs to the top of the skyscraper.
6. She used a minimal amount of red pepper in her sauce because she did not like spicy foods.
7. The infuriated teacher reprimanded her students for their poor behavior.

Reading Warm-up A, p. 163

Sample Answers

1. (cats); *Overrun* means "to spread over a place quickly and in great numbers."
2. in homes throughout the United States; *Domestic* cats make great pets for apartment dwellers.
3. (to remove the famous cats from their urban homes); *Reluctant* means "unwilling or slow to do something."
4. They worry that these scruffy animals might spread disease; A synonym for *distinction* is *difference*.
5. leave poisoned food out; They are *treacherous* because they appear to be doing something kind but actually wish to harm the cats.
6. cats prowling around the ancient Roman ruins; The tense World Series' playoffs kept my attention *riveted* to the television screen.
7. (comfortable) The *luxurious* car had fine leather seats.
8. because of the great number of cats; *Futile* means "having no chance at being successful."

Reading Warm-up B, p. 164

Sample Answers

1. the bare lots; *Voids* are "empty spaces where nothing exists."
2. My favorite *skyscraper* is the Chrysler Building in New York City.
3. Pigeons keeping *surveillance* would watch the area from their perch without moving.
4. (colors) at dusk; *Vibrant* means "vivid," or, in this case, rich with color.
5. closing the dumpster with a bungee cord; It's not okay to take minimal precaution before a hurricane hits, for example. If people are not prepared for a hurricane, they might get badly injured or killed.
6. the rats; *Unauthorized* means "without permission."
7. they threatened to poison the rats and be done with it; I feel *infuriated* when my brother scratches my favorite CD.
8. The desert in southern California has been *transformed* by development. *Transformed* means "changed beyond recognition."

"The Garden of Stubborn Cats" by Italo Calvino

Literary Analysis: Symbolism, p. 165

Sample Answers

1. a prize, or the conflict between humans and nature (cats); shows how there are no natural fishing places in the city, so Marcovaldo must go "fishing" in a restaurant's tank; also shows that humans and cats are sometimes in conflict for food and other means of survival
2. a tiny slice of nature; shows that animals and nature find a way to adapt and survive in human cities
3. valuing animals and nature; shows that there are two types of people with regard to the garden and the Marchesa
4. valuing human progress; shows that there are people who feel the garden and the animals are a health hazard and an eyesore

Reading: Identify Patterns to Draw Conclusions About Symbolism, p. 166

Sample Answers

1. A. It exists inside the city of men, but it is not the same city.
   B. The city of cats was once the same as the city of men.
   C. It is made up of the spaces between buildings: alleys, courtyards, gardens, and roofs.

Pattern: The city of cats is shrinking—imprisoned and diminished by the city of men.

Meaning: The city of cats symbolizes how nature is diminishing because of technology and development. It represents the conflict between humans and their environment.

2. A. Some people believe she represents a noble effort to save a small piece of nature from developers.
   B. Those who dislike the garden think she represents selfish disregard for the animals and her neighbors alike.
   C. The Marchesa is afraid of the cats and feels imprisoned by them.

Pattern: The Marchesa's relationship with the people and animals of her neighborhood shows that she is the center of a conflict between humans and animals.

Meaning: The Marchesa symbolizes the conflict between humans and nature.

3. A. The cats knock things over and jump on the backs of the workers.
   B. The birds nest in the trestles and the cab of the crane.
   C. The workers cannot dip up a bucket of water without getting a bucket full of frogs.

Pattern: The animals are making it difficult for the workers to construct a building where the garden used to be.

Meaning: The animals' behavior symbolizes nature's fight to survive in the face of urban development.

Vocabulary Builder, p. 167

A. Sample Answers

1. I would see more sights with an itinerary. If I had an itinerary, I would have a plan for what I want to see.
2. A spy might be involved in intrigues. He or she might be involved in plots or schemes to steal national secrets.
3. No, guests at a birthday party are not usually solemn. Children at a birthday party would be the opposite of solemn; they would be happy and excited.
4. No, the level of indigence would decrease if the national economy is improving. Indigence is poverty, and fewer people would be in poverty in a good economy.

B. 1. D; 2. A; 3. B; 4. C

Enrichment: Connecting to the Community, p. 170

Students' project proposals should address a specific issue or issues related to animal populations in their area. For example, they might address how the community encourages pet owners to spay or neuter their pets to control the pet population. They might come up with a plan for dealing humanely with strays or for preventing animal waste in public places. Whatever topic they choose to address, students should come up with a clear goal, steps to accomplish the goal, a list of people who might contribute to the effort, and a clear understanding of how their project will impact the community.

"The Masque of the Red Death"
by Edgar Allan Poe

"The Garden of Stubborn Cats"
by Italo Calvino

Build Language Skills: Vocabulary, p. 171

A. Students' answers will vary based on the words they choose. Sample answer: word—predominant; synonym—superior; antonym; subordinate; sentence—The predominant mood in the classroom was one of dread as the teacher passed out the final exams.

B. Sample Answers

1. does make sense; *predominant* means "main" or "most noticeable," and the Marchesa's main feeling toward the cats is indeed resentment

2. does not make sense because *comprehend* means "to understand"; During his lunch break, Marcovaldo likes to follow cats along their pathways in an effort to comprehend their world.

3. does make sense because the two events happen at the same time

4. does not make sense because *infer* means to figure something out—the bloody costume and mask do not figure out that he is dressed as the Red Death; Based on his bloody costume and mask, the revelers infer that the uninvited guest is dressed as the Red Death.

Build Language Skills: Grammar, p. 172

A. 1. PV; 2. AV; 3. AV; 4. PV

B. Sample Answers

1. The Marchesa's neighbors told Marcovaldo that she never fed the cats.

2. The mischievous cats stop the construction.

3. Bleeding from the pores characterizes the Red Death.

4. The real Black Death of the 1300s is the basis for the fictitious disease, the Red Death.

"The Garden of Stubborn Cats" by Italo Calvino

Selection Test A, p. 173

Critical Reading

1. ANS: D	DIF: Easy	OBJ: Comprehension
2. ANS: A	DIF: Easy	OBJ: Comprehension
3. ANS: D	DIF: Easy	OBJ: Comprehension
4. ANS: C	DIF: Easy	OBJ: Comprehension
5. ANS: A	DIF: Easy	OBJ: Literary Analysis
6. ANS: D	DIF: Easy	OBJ: Reading
7. ANS: B	DIF: Easy	OBJ: Interpretation
8. ANS: D	DIF: Easy	OBJ: Reading
9. ANS: D	DIF: Easy	OBJ: Comprehension
10. ANS: A	DIF: Easy	OBJ: Interpretation
11. ANS: A	DIF: Easy	OBJ: Literary Analysis
12. ANS: A	DIF: Easy	OBJ: Literary Analysis

Vocabulary and Grammar

13. ANS: D	DIF: Easy	OBJ: Vocabulary
14. ANS: B	DIF: Easy	OBJ: Vocabulary
15. ANS: B	DIF: Easy	OBJ: Grammar

Essay

16. Students should explain that the story is an allegory because most or all of the characters, settings, and events can be considered symbolic. They might list major symbols such as the cats, which represent resistance to human development; the Marchesa, who symbolizes the conflict between the forces of nature and modernization; and the construction workers, who represent human development.

Difficulty: *Easy*

Objective: *Essay*

17. Students should explain that the Marchesa felt trapped because she thought the cats were preventing her from selling her house and the garden lot. She tells Marcovaldo that they tripped her and scratched her if she tried to leave. They leapt through her windows and tore up the papers when she tried to sell the property. She seems frightened of the cats, but she never seems to try very hard to free herself. Some students might say the Marchesa was simply crazy and imagined the cats' behavior. Others might say that since the cats later attacked the construction workers, the Marchesa was right and they were preventing her from selling.

Difficulty: *Easy*

Objective: *Essay*

Selection Test B, p. 176

Critical Reading

1. ANS: C	DIF: Average	OBJ: Comprehension
2. ANS: C	DIF: Average	OBJ: Interpretation
3. ANS: D	DIF: Average	OBJ: Comprehension
4. ANS: D	DIF: Challenging	OBJ: Reading
5. ANS: C	DIF: Average	OBJ: Comprehension
6. ANS: D	DIF: Average	OBJ: Interpretation
7. ANS: C	DIF: Average	OBJ: Reading
8. ANS: B	DIF: Challenging	OBJ: Literary Analysis
9. ANS: C	DIF: Challenging	OBJ: Interpretation
10. ANS: A	DIF: Challenging	OBJ: Reading
11. ANS: B	DIF: Challenging	OBJ: Interpretation
12. ANS: C	DIF: Average	OBJ: Literary Analysis

Vocabulary and Grammar

13. ANS: C DIF: Average OBJ: Vocabulary
14. ANS: A DIF: Average OBJ: Vocabulary
15. ANS: A DIF: Average OBJ: Grammar
16. ANS: D DIF: Average OBJ: Grammar

Essay

17. Students should explain that the story is an allegory because most or all of the characters, settings, and events can be considered symbolic. They might list major symbols such as the cats, which represent resistance to human development; the Marchesa, who symbolizes the conflict between the forces of nature and modernization; and the construction workers, who represent human development.

Difficulty: *Average*

Objective: *Essay*

18. Students' essays should clearly define their positions on the issue of what should happen to the Marchesa's garden. They might support their positions with details from the story, such as some neighbors' desire either to have a bit of nature in their neighborhood or to modernize the area with a new building. They might also support their positions with personal opinions or observations. Students might even mention modern alternative solutions to the problem of maintaining green areas in cities.

Difficulty: *Average*

Objective: *Essay*

19. Students might identify the two opposing forces as order and resistance to order, or nature and human development, or modernization and traditionalism. Accept any reasonable combination of ideas as long as students are able to justify them with symbols and details from the story. Most students will probably say that the cats (representing nature or resistance to order) prevail since it seems at the end of the story that the cats are successfully keeping the construction workers (representing modernization or order) from building over the garden. However, some students might say that order or modernization prevail because they believe the cats will not be able to keep the garden from being developed forever.

Difficulty: *Challenging*

Objective: *Essay*

"Like the Sun" by R. K. Narayan
"The Censors" by Luisa Valenzuela

Vocabulary Warm-up Exercises, p. 180

A. 1. sabotage
2. scheming
3. scrawled
4. distraction
5. frank
6. unique
7. absolute
8. critics

B. Sample Answers
1. True; If you *anticipated* the ending of a book, you expected it to end the way it ended.
2. False; There is very little *electronic* equipment old enough to be considered antique.
3. False; Magazine articles give information; they are not a form of *censorship*.
4. False; Although some writers produce their best work, or *masterpiece*, first, others write their finest work later.
5. True; One can feel *assailed*, or overwhelmed, by the loud noise at a rock concert.
6. False; A gossip cannot be trusted to keep information *confidential*, or secret.
7. False; An *attentive* listener is paying careful attention.
8. False. If you have *fulfilled* a goal, you have achieved it.

Reading Warm-up A, p. 181

Sample Answers
1. These machines do not test the truth of a statement; *Absolute* means "complete."
2. A polygraph test is usually given in a quiet room; Loud noise is a *distraction* when I study.
3. (dishonest); *Frank* means "honest."
4. on scrolling paper by a set of moving pens; *Scrawled* means "written hastily or sloppily."
5. to throw off the test results; Scheming means "plotting."
6. (bite their tongue or cheek), (place tacks inside their shoes); A jealous student might try to *sabotage* another student's science fair exhibit.
7. they do not provide clear proof that someone is lying; Critics might judge the effectiveness of lawyers in a trial.
8. the polygraph remains the most reliable tool we currently have; The microscope is a *unique* tool that helps us view very small objects.

Reading Warm-up B, p. 182

Sample Answers
1. (stunning success); *A Wrinkle in Time* is Madeleine L'Engle's *masterpiece*.
2. an endless repetition of three Party slogans; *Assailed* means "overwhelmed" or "attacked."
3. (secrets); People are curious, so it is hard to keep interesting information *confidential*.
4. watch other citizens; *Attentive* means "paying close attention to."
5. The computer is an *electronic* device that was invented after 1948.
6. (opposing ideas); *Censorship* means "removing materials considered to be offensive or dangerous."

7. how popular the name Big Brother would become; I *anticipated* who would be the winner in the swim meet.
8. (this aim); *Fulfilled* means "did what was needed."

"Like the Sun" by R. K. Narayan
"The Censors" by Luisa Valenzuela

Literary Analysis: Irony and Paradox, p. 183

A. 1. It is ironic because the headmaster expects Sekhar to praise his performance; situational irony.
   2. Possible answers: Both Juan and the reader expect Juan to let the letter pass, and neither expects him to die; situational irony. It is ironic because the word *naturally* makes the reader realize how unnatural Juan's actions are; verbal irony.
B. 1. In "Like the Sun," Sekhar tells the headmaster the cruel truth about his singing. This keeps the headmaster from embarrassing himself in the future.
   2. In "The Censors," Juan exposes himself as a traitor because he has become so loyal to the state in his role as censor.

Vocabulary Builder, p. 184

A. Sample Answers
   1. A person doing a kind deed might have the ulterior motive of wanting to impress someone else.
   2. Two children with water balloons might be conniving to throw them at someone.
   3. Tempering your tone might come in handy when disagreeing with a parent.
   4. An irreproachable person may make a poor leader because he or she may not be patient with other people's faults.
   5. Staidness would be appropriate at a funeral.
   6. A person's signature might be scrutinized if it is thought to be forged.
   7. Many people find ingratiating behavior annoying because it is fake.
B. 1. D; 2. A; 3. B; 4. C

Selection Test A, p. 186

Critical Reading

1. ANS: D	DIF: Easy	OBJ: Comprehension
2. ANS: C	DIF: Easy	OBJ: Comprehension
3. ANS: B	DIF: Easy	OBJ: Interpretation
4. ANS: D	DIF: Easy	OBJ: Interpretation
5. ANS: D	DIF: Easy	OBJ: Literary Analysis
6. ANS: A	DIF: Easy	OBJ: Comprehension
7. ANS: C	DIF: Easy	OBJ: Interpretation
8. ANS: B	DIF: Easy	OBJ: Comprehension
9. ANS: B	DIF: Easy	OBJ: Literary Analysis
10. ANS: C	DIF: Easy	OBJ: Interpretation

11. ANS: A	DIF: Easy	OBJ: Interpretation
12. ANS: A	DIF: Easy	OBJ: Literary Analysis
13. ANS: D	DIF: Easy	OBJ: Interpretation

Vocabulary

14. ANS: C	DIF: Easy	OBJ: Vocabulary
15. ANS: B	DIF: Easy	OBJ: Vocabulary

Essay

16. Students should respond that in "Like the Sun," Sekhar's mission is to tell the absolute truth for one entire day. Most will say the mission is a success, based on the headmaster's acceptance of Sekhar's honesty. Students should respond that in "The Censors," Juan's mission is to get a job as a censor in order to intercept his own letter and protect himself and Mariana from the government. Most students will say that the mission changed over the course of the story and therefore failed. By the end, Juan's mission is to be the best possible censor—which means that, once he finds his own letter, he has to turn himself in.

Difficulty: *Easy*
Objective: *Essay*

17. Ironic moments in "Like the Sun" include Sekhar's honest comment about his wife's cooking; Sekhar's honest assessment of the headmaster's singing; the headmaster's appreciation for Sekhar's honesty; and the headmaster's request for the one hundred graded papers the next day. These moments of irony help Narayan express the idea that the truth may hurt, but that it ultimately helps people. Ironic moments in "The Censors" include Juan's getting a job as a censor; his enjoyment of his work; his betrayal of his co-worker; his promotions; his increasing commitment to his work as a censor; his turning himself in; and his death. These moments of irony help Valenzuela express the idea that deception of others ultimately leads to self-deception; or that the total truth may lead to death.

Difficulty: *Easy*
Objective: *Essay*

Selection Test B, p. 189

Critical Reading

1. ANS: B	DIF: Average	OBJ: Comprehension
2. ANS: D	DIF: Average	OBJ: Literary Analysis
3. ANS: B	DIF: Average	OBJ: Comprehension
4. ANS: C	DIF: Average	OBJ: Literary Analysis
5. ANS: A	DIF: Average	OBJ: Interpretation
6. ANS: C	DIF: Challenging	OBJ: Interpretation
7. ANS: D	DIF: Challenging	OBJ: Comprehension
8. ANS: A	DIF: Average	OBJ: Interpretation
9. ANS: B	DIF: Average	OBJ: Interpretation

10. ANS: C   DIF: Average   OBJ: Literary Analysis
11. ANS: B   DIF: Average   OBJ: Comprehension
12. ANS: D   DIF: Challenging   OBJ: Literary Analysis
13. ANS: C   DIF: Average   OBJ: Interpretation
14. ANS: A   DIF: Challenging   OBJ: Interpretation
15. ANS: C   DIF: Average   OBJ: Literary Analysis
16. ANS: A   DIF: Challenging   OBJ: Interpretation
17. ANS: D   DIF: Challenging   OBJ: Interpretation

Vocabulary

18. ANS: B   DIF: Average   OBJ: Vocabulary
19. ANS: B   DIF: Average   OBJ: Vocabulary
20. ANS: C   DIF: Challenging   OBJ: Vocabulary

Essay

21. Ironic moments in "Like the Sun" include Sekhar's honest assessment of his wife's cooking, which she does not expect; Sekhar's honest assessment of the headmaster's singing, which the headmaster does not expect; the headmaster's appreciation for Sekhar's honesty, which neither the reader nor Sekhar expects; and the headmaster's request for the one hundred graded papers the next day, which neither the reader nor Sekhar expects. These moments of irony help Narayan express the idea that the truth may be painful but is ultimately helpful; or that the truth can have unpredictable consequences. Ironic moments in "The Censors" include Juan's enjoyment of his work, his betrayal of his co-worker, his promotions, his increasing zealousness as a censor, and his self-betrayal when he turns himself in. All of these moments surprise the reader, although Juan himself seems surprised only by the last one. These moments of irony, many of which are lost on Juan, help Valenzuela express the idea that censorship is dangerous because its effects are gradual; or that under censorship, the truth may lead to death. Accept other logical responses.
   Difficulty: *Average*
   Objective: *Essay*

22. Students should respond that in "Like the Sun," Sekhar challenges the social system of "polite dishonesty" by vowing to tell the absolute truth for one entire day. He does this because he believes that if a person cannot be totally honest at least *sometimes,* life is meaningless. Students should respond that in "The Censors," Juan challenges the system of censorship by getting a job as a censor. He does this in order to avoid censorship itself (or in order to protect himself and Mariana from the effects of censorship). Students' opinions regarding the more successful character will vary but should be logically supported. Most students will say that Sekhar enjoyed more success, as his actions ended up helping

the headmaster; they presumably convinced Sekhar himself that life has meaning; and they did *not* lead to self-betrayal or death.
   Difficulty: *Average*
   Objective: *Essay*

23. Students may say that in "Like the Sun," the truth is shown to be blinding like the light of the sun, but that unlike the sun, it casts a kind of paradoxical darkness over Sekhar's life during the course of his experiment. By hurting the feelings of others, the truth is shown to be chilling and hurtful rather than warm and healing. Students may say that at first the censors are the official state censors—that is, Juan's enemies—but that by the end of the story, "the censors" includes Juan himself. Juan has become his own worst enemy.
   Difficulty: *Challenging*
   Objective: *Essay*

Writing Workshop—Unit 2, Part 2

Problem-and-Solution Essay: Integrating Grammar Skills, p. 193

A. 1. stand; 2. are; 3. honors; 4. gives
B. 1. Donations to the library system buy new books and other media.
2. Most of the city's tax revenue pays for equipment and grounds maintenance.
3. correct
4. Each of the two children's librarians works just twenty-five hours a week.

Spelling Workshop—Unit 2

Unusual Vowel Combinations, p. 194

A 1. sergeant; 2. acquiesce; 3. pseudonym; 4. matinee; 5. distinguished; 6. bureaucracy; 7. surveillance; 8. sleuth
B. Sample Answers
1. The writer used a pseudonym to pen his mysteries. The stories featured a sleuth who, using surveillance, gathered information about his suspects.
2. The government is a large bureaucracy made up of different groups trying to serve the needs of the American people. The sergeant distinguished herself by displaying courage and intelligence in performing her duties.
3. I acquiesced and went with my friends to the matinee of their choice. Several distinguished musicians performed for the audience.

Unit 2, Part 2 Answers

Benchmark Test 4, p. 197

MULTIPLE CHOICE

1. ANS: B
2. ANS: A
3. ANS: B
4. ANS: B
5. ANS: D
6. ANS: A
7. ANS: B
8. ANS: D
9. ANS: A
10. ANS: A
11. ANS: D
12. ANS: C
13. ANS: B
14. ANS: C
15. ANS: C
16. ANS: A
17. ANS: B
18. ANS: D
19. ANS: C
20. ANS: B
21. ANS: A
22. ANS: B
23. ANS: D
24. ANS: C
25. ANS: A
26. ANS: B
27. ANS: D
28. ANS: B
29. ANS: C
30. ANS: D
31. ANS: D
32. ANS: B
33. ANS: A

ESSAY

34. Narratives should include symbolism.
35. Character analyses should include explanations of the character's importance to the plot and be supported by details from the text.
36. Essays should describe the problem clearly and suggest detailed and persuasive solutions.